The Way We Are:

How States of Mind Influence Our Identities, Personality, and Potential for Change

The Way We Are:

How States of Mind Influence Our Identities, Personality, and Potential for Change

Frank W. Putnam

International Psychoanalytic Books (IPBooks),
New York • http://www.IPBooks.net

Cover Photo:
Pablo Budassi, a South American artist and musician, used data and images from NASA to create a logarithmic-scaled image of the universe centered on our sun.

Logarithmic Radial Photo of the Universe by Pablo Budassi

Figure 3-4: William James, 1890, *The Stream of Thought,* This work is in the public domain in its country of origin and other countries and areas where the copyright term is the author's life plus 70 years or less.

Figure 8-1: A. Brouillet, 1887, *Une leçon clinique à la Salpêtrière.* This work is in the public domain in its country of origin and other countries and areas where the copyright term is the author's life plus 70 years or less.

Interior book design by Lawrence L. Schwartz

ISBN: 978-0-9980833-0-8

Dedication

This book is dedicated to all psychiatric patients
who have participated in scientific research
for the greater good of humankind.

Preface and Acknowledgements

As I neared the end of writing this book, I realized that it represents a distillation of my life's work. Although I have been working on the book for over a decade (well a lot of other things had to get done also), I've been thinking about states of being and their role in mental life for virtually my entire career (e.g., see discussions in my first book, *Diagnosis and Treatment of Multiple Personality Disorder,* 1989).

A fortunate result of this career-long gestation is that many people have contributed in countless ways to those thoughts and to this book. Regretfully, there is no way to thank them all—some are deceased— nor is it possible to properly acknowledge their numerous and diverse material, intellectual, and inspirational gifts over these many years. I can only humbly offer my deep gratitude to all who helped complete this volume.

I especially wish to thank David Rubinow and Richard Loewenstein, long-time friends, who critically simulated my thinking, believed in me, and supported my work across the good times and the bad. Over the years they were joined by Lisa Amaya-Jackson, Bill Harris, Bethany Brand, Alicia Lieberman, Carly Rubinow, Debbie Sharp, Lisa Connelly, Penny Trickett, Jennie Noll, Bob Ammerman, Judy van Ginkel, Barbara Boat, Erna Olafson, Robin Gurwitch, Michael Silver, and Jeff Orchard whose love, care and consideration means so much. Important career influences include Frank Walker, Francis Howland, Herbert Weingartner, Arthur Blank, Ira Levine, Richard Wyatt, Norman Garmezy, Hazel Rae, Judy Herman, Bessel van der Kolk, Julie Guroff, Pam Cole, Richard Kluft, Sherrill Mulhern, Cassandra and the Pod, Deni and the Flock.

Karen, my wife, and our sons, Philip and Will, are the center of my life. While no words suffice, the Epilogue conveys what they mean to me.

My thanks to Leslie Rubinkowski for her editing and instruction in the craft of creative nonfiction, to Lawrence L. Schwartz who made layout and typesetting a pleasure, and to Lisa DiMona for her suggestion.

The Way We Are:
How States of Mind Influence Our Identities, Personality, and Potential for Change

CONTENTS

The Sciences of States of Being

Chapter One—On States of Being   3

Chapter Two—Our First States   25

Chapter Three—Brain States   51

Chapter Four—Changing States   89

The Self and Its Proclivities

Chapter Five—Memory & Identity   125

Chapter Six—Secret Lives: Personality and Its Paradoxes   147

Trauma and Addiction

Chapter Seven—PTSD   193

Chapter Eight—Dissociation   217

Chapter Nine—Drugs & Addictions   251

Opportunities for Change

Chapter Ten—Exceptional States of Being   291

Chapter Eleven—Using What We Know   333

Epilogue   381

References   395

Index   409

The Sciences of States of Being

CHAPTER 1   ON STATES OF BEING

William James

As he shuts his eyes, he feels drawn into a sphere of brilliant illumination. Truth lies open—layer upon layer, depth upon depth. Instantly, he sees all of the relations of Being in their myriad subtleties. Mind and object, center and surround, are one. Difference and no difference merge into a torrential stream of examples flowing through his mind. Seeking to capture these revelations he writes furiously:

> *"What's mistake but a kind of take?"*
> *"What's nausea but a kind of –ausea?"*
> *"That sounds like nonsense, but it is pure onsense!"*
> (James, 1882)

There is an enormous sense of rapture. He is beholding a process that is infinite. But this insight rapidly changes into a feeling of dread, a sense of indifferent and inescapable fate. He is overcome by:

> *. . . a pessimistic fatalism, depth within depth of impotence and indifference, reason and silliness united, not in a higher synthesia, but in the fact that whichever you choose it is all one* (James, 1882).

And then this too fades, and is replaced by an almost overwhelming feeling of bewilderment.

William James was a young instructor teaching psychology and physiology at Harvard when he first encountered nitrous oxide in 1874. Discovered by the English chemist Joseph Priestley in 1772, nitrous oxide, a gaseous anesthetic, has been used medically and recreationally for over two hundred years. James was introduced to this drug by Benjamin Paul Blood, a minor philosopher and small-town critic, who sent copies of his self-published pamphlet on its ability to induce metaphysical "revelations" to Ralph Waldo Emerson, Grover Cleveland and other luminaries of his day (Tymoczko, 1996).

Intrigued by Blood's claims of metaphysical revelation, James wrote a favorable review in the *Atlantic Monthly.* His first report on nitrous oxide was published anonymously, perhaps to protect his reputation, as he was a junior faculty member. However, James was far from alone in his experimentations on the Harvard campus. In addition to nitrous oxide, sniffing ether was also popular among students and professors of the time, leading a contemporary observer to note that it had *"long been a toy of professors and students at Cambridge* [Harvard]" (quoted in, Tymoczko, 1996).

James went on to become famous, acclaimed both as the father of American psychology and as a major philosopher. His early experiences with nitrous oxide, however, remained central to his thinking about both psychology and religious experience throughout his life. In his final essay, penned shortly before his death in 1910, he indicated that these experiences had been pivotal to his understanding of the human mind and its ability to experience multiple realities (James, 1987). For James, these brief, drug-induced states of momentary euphoria, revelation, and despair encompassed *"the strongest emotion I have ever experienced"* (James, 1882).

James freely acknowledged that much of what he thought and wrote during the intoxicated state sounded like meaningless drivel when read later. As the glow of the nitrous oxide faded, he likened seeing what he had just written to staring at the charred ember of an extinguished match. What had been on fire with infinite meaning was now dark and lifeless. Yet James apparently returned to drug-induced states of mind on multiple occasions. How often he partook of nitrous oxide is not known but in his first openly acknowledged essay on the subject in 1882 he indicates that he had *"sheet after sheet"* of phrases, some of which he had dictated and some of which he had written, indicating multiple episodes in different settings.

What was James, by nature a cautious individual, seeking? His writing makes it clear that he did not mistake these experiences for an *"absolute truth."* Indeed, he was well aware that such drug-induced experiences could be misleading or false. In part, it is the very fact that they can be both overwhelmingly compelling and yet simultaneously false that attracts him. They are psychologically real experiences irrespective of whether or not they give rise to the real "truth." And as such they revealed for him the existence of other states of consciousness.

Many years later in his famous work, *The Varieties of Religious Experience* (1902), James reflects that his *"observations"* of nitrous oxide convinced him that *"our normal waking consciousness, rational consciousness as we call it, is but one special type of consciousness, whilst all about it, parted from it by the filmiest of screens, there lie potential forms of consciousness entirely different"* (p. 283).

Although he called his experiments with nitrous oxide an "*artificial mystic state of mind,*" he sought out these experiences because they opened the door to the religious and mystical altered states of consciousness that were at the center of his life's work. James was not the first psychologist or philosopher to invoke the concept of a state of mind as a discrete and transient organization of mental capacities allowing access to special experiences, but he was the first to systematically detail the many properties of states of consciousness and theorize about their roles in mental life.

In Western accounts, Plato is generally credited with the first classification of distinct states of consciousness. In *Phaedrus* (Plato, 1961), he identifies four distinct *manias* or states of being in which a person could experience a divine form of "madness." The prophetic state allowed a person to see into the future. The poetic state provided creative inspiration for music and the arts. The erotic state centered on love and the initiatory state on spiritual ritual and religious ecstasy. The concept of a "state of being" can also be traced to the Latin word, *status*, which has layers of meaning similar to the English word *state*. On one level, *status* may be translated as a person's condition of being, attitude, or physical position. On another level, it denotes the government or body politic, or the political condition of the government.

By the time a young Sir Humphrey Davy began the first recorded experiments with nitrous oxide in December 1799, the notion of a state of mind as a distinct, time-limited, but powerful, mental experience was already well established. Upon inhaling the gas, Davy reported:

> *I felt a sense of tangible extension, highly pleasurable in every limb; my visible impressions were dazzling, and apparently magnified. . . . I existed in a world of newly connected and newly modified ideas. I theorified; I imagined that I made discoveries* (Davy quotes from Elkes, 1977 p. 243).

As the effects wore off, Davy, like James, found that his discoveries lost their meaning:

> *As I recovered my former state of mind, I felt an inclination to communicate the discoveries I had made during the experiment.*

I endeavored to recall the ideas, they were feeble and indistinct; one collection of terms, however, presented itself: and, with the most intense belief and prophetic manner, I explained to Dr. Kinglake "Nothing exists but thoughts!—The universe is composed of impressions, ideas, pleasures and pains (Davy quotes from Elkes, 1977 pp. 243–244).

The coming nineteenth century was to see the concept of a state of mind further expanded and elaborated by the burgeoning science of psychology and the birth of psychodynamic psychiatry.

Authorities often date the beginnings of modern psychology and psychiatry to Franz Anton Mesmer (1734–1815) (Ellenberger, 1970). More a stage magician than a psychologist, Mesmer's theories of animal magnetism, nonetheless, contained the seeds of psychodynamic thinking. As a therapist, he cured his patients by artificially inducing public crises in them by projecting his "animal magnetism." Mesmer formulated some of the first theories about the powerful influence the relationship between a doctor and patient plays in curing the patient. Although now disparaged as a quack or charlatan, Mesmer bridged the gap between demonic exorcism and modern psychotherapy and, in many respects, initiated Western psychology's approach towards altered states of consciousness.

By the 1880s, psychiatry was deeply involved in the descriptive study of altered states of consciousness including hypnotism, somnambulism, catalepsy and multiple personality. Hypnotism, in particular, was regarded as the royal road to the inner workings of the mind. The differences observed between an individual in the waking state, regarded as the normal condition, and a hypnotic state, came to largely define the properties of an altered state of consciousness.

In particular, altered sensory perceptions, a changed sense of identity, susceptibility to suggestion, and post-hypnotic amnesia were viewed as markers for the presence of an altered state of consciousness. William James, Pierre Janet, Sigmund Freud, Morton Prince and many other authorities of the day described patients suffering from a variety of altered states of consciousness, from catatonia to psychic mediumship, seeking to identify the larger mental principles at work.

Some of their more astute observations and speculations are supported by recent work with brain imaging and other modern scientific tools. These early clinical observations also gave rise to a set of popular assumptions and beliefs about altered states of consciousness that were echoed and amplified by contemporary accounts in newspapers, magazines, and the theater. Indeed, a learned segment of the late-nineteenth-century public was fascinated with the subject and avidly attended lectures on hypnosis, somnambulism, possession, fugue and the like. Amnesia, somnambulism and double personality were common plot devices in popular fiction.

Artists were especially intrigued by the transcendental experiences reported in some altered states and experimented with both drugs and mystical states. Physicians wrote enthusiastic accounts of experiences with hashish, cocaine, cannabis, and morphine. Sigmund Freud, for example, first garnered international attention with his treatise on cocaine published in 1884, just a few years after James's report on nitrous oxide.

The dawn of the twentieth century saw a continuation of these psychological and popular explorations of altered states of consciousness. Pierre Jane, the great French psychiatrist, brought his understanding of hypnosis and dissociative states to the treatment of what was then referred to as "hysteria," and now would be diagnosed as dissociative and conversion disorders. His "Psychological Analysis" therapy, a descendant of Mesmer's animal magnetism-induced 'crises' and the immediate precursor of Freud's abreactions and later psychoanalysis, made use of hypnotic states to rework the traumatic experiences that Janet believed to underlie hysterical symptoms.

Freudian psychoanalysis, which soon came to dominate late nineteenth and the first half of twentieth century psychiatry, began with the case of *Fräulein Anna O*. The centerpiece of Freud's collaborative book with Josef Breuer, *Studies on Hysteria* (1895/1957), Anna experienced a bizarre emotional crisis after the death of her father during which she alternated among several distinct states of consciousness marked by dramatically changed demeanor and behavior. During these times, she claimed to be a different person and reported amnesia for events that occurred in her other identities. Her identities spoke in different languages, German, Spanish, French and English or various mixtures thereof. Freud attributed her dramatic shifts in personality to "hypnoid states" that alternatingly exchanged control over her behavior.

Today Anna's symptoms would be diagnosed as dissociative identity states, which are highly associated with early traumatic experiences, such as incest. We now know Anna O's real name and more about her extraordinary life including the raids that she led into the Near East to free sexually enslaved women.

Freud, however, soon rejected the notion of "hypnoid states" and publicly repudiated his incest theory of hysteria, replacing it instead with the psychosexual theories that would come to constitute the core of psychoanalysis. But both World Wars would force psychiatry to again, at least briefly, address dissociative states of consciousness in the form of traumatic abreactions, flashbacks, and hysterical conversion symptoms. Following each world war, psychoanalysis would re-emerge as the dominant mindset and the brutal lessons of combat psychiatry would be largely forgotten.

A few psychoanalysts and psychiatrists, nonetheless, continued to "see" semi-autonomous states that controlled or influenced their patients' problematic behaviors. These mental states, often referred to as "ego states," were central to psychological theories developed by David Rapaport, Heinz Hartman, John Watkins and others. Eric Berne, known for his bestseller, *Games People Play,* popularized a simplified form of ego state therapy he called Transactional Analysis. A more sophisticated version of ego state psychotherapy, Configurational Analysis, was developed by Mardi Horowitz, whose early work on stress and traumatic states was instrumental in the formulation of the diagnosis of post-traumatic stress disorder.

From the later 1960s forward the dominance of psychoanalysis was challenged by the emerging science of "biological psychiatry." Stimulated by the introduction of potent antipsychotic medications such as Thorazine and the tricyclic antidepressants, psychiatrists began to theorize about the nature of mental illness in terms of specific brain states characterized by "chemical imbalances." These chemical imbalances were thought to be due to excesses or deficits in the levels or ratios of certain neurotransmitters, the chemical messengers that allow one neuron to communicate with another.

Biological psychiatrists sought to measure these chemicals in the brain and body and to use medication to change their levels in hopes of curing certain conditions. Although a number of psychiatric disorders were intensively studied in this fashion, research on manic-depressive or bipolar illness in particular, with its rapid transitions or "switches" between manic and depressed states, led to a deeper understanding of the biological mechanisms underlying the transitions between two very different states of consciousness. A series of medications, collectively referred to as "mood stabilizers," were tested in efforts to reduce and smooth state transitions and corral wild mood swings.

As biological psychiatry increasingly displaced psychoanalysis during the late 1960s and 1970s, another source of data about altered states of consciousness was emerging from the use of psychedelic drugs. The reasons for the explosion in recreational psychedelic drug use during this brief period are complex, reflecting both the counterculture Zeitgeist and the surreptitious testing by organizations interested in their use in interrogation and non-violent incapacitation of soldiers and civilians.

While proselytizers such as Timothy Leary urged youth to "*tune-in, turn-on, and dropout,*" a few professionals were attempting to systematically explore psychedelic drugs as an avenue into higher states of consciousness. A loose network of psychiatrists and psychologists began using psychedelic drugs in treatment, taking the drugs together with their patients for extended therapy sessions. Chemists such as Alexander Shulgin were synthesizing an array of variations on the basic molecular structures of psychedelic drugs and assaying their mind-altering properties individually and in small group sessions with friends (Shulgin & Shulgin, 1991). During the brief period in which these drugs were technically legal (i.e., they had not yet been specifically outlawed), systematic studies were conducted yielding a small—but interesting—scientific literature on drug-induced altered states of consciousness. These research efforts, especially for the treatment of refractory PTSD, alcoholism, and end-of-life care, have been revived recently by MAPS (the Multidisciplinary Association for Psychedelic Studies). Preliminary research appears to replicate earlier claims of efficacy for difficult to treat cases as well as improved comfort for terminally ill patients.

Charles Tart, a psychologist then at the Stanford University drew on these drug studies and anecdotal reports, as well as on research on meditative states and hypnosis, to articulate a comprehensive model of normal and altered states of consciousness (Tart, 1983). In a series of articles and books during the 1970s and 1980s, Tart detailed a broad theory about the nature of states of consciousness and defined a set of dimensions that could be used to characterize normal and altered states of mind.

Tart was the first to articulate a systems approach to the study of states of consciousness. In addition, he called for the creation of "state-specific sciences," that is, the use of distinctly different altered states of consciousness to access knowledge that is uniquely contained within different states of consciousness. This seemingly radical idea echoes James's use of nitrous oxide-induced altered states of consciousness to plumb mystical religious experience and is in line with assertions by authorities from antiquity to the present that certain kinds of insight are accessible only through direct experience (Windt, 2011).

In the brief period when an interest in drug and mystical states of conscious was at least a quasi-acceptable academic pursuit, classic papers by Arthur Deikman, Joel Elkes, Karl Pribram, John Lilly, and Andrew Weil, among others, inspired a generation of budding psychiatrists, psychologists and neuroscientists. Many of those specialists would later participate in the biological psychiatry coup that displaced psychoanalysis as the dominant psychiatric paradigm. Some major neuroscientists confidentially credit college experiences with psychedelic drugs with their career choice. Indeed, a few scientists and many more artists admit to using drug- or meditation-induced altered states of consciousness in their search for insight and inspiration.

More recently, the growing precision and sophistication of powerful new brain-imaging technologies has opened fresh windows on our understanding of mental states. Brain scanners that measure metabolism by blood flow or oxygen consumption allow us to map which regions of the brain are active and which are quiescent in different states of consciousness. Scanners that measure electrical or magnetic fields allow us to see the rapid ebb and flow of brain activity as mental states form and dissipate.

These new tools, initially applied to pathological states such as depression and anxiety, are now being used to explore the 'higher' states of consciousness such as meditation. Taken together with other methodological breakthroughs in the neural and cognitive sciences, we now have powerful new ways to characterize and understand the roles that discrete states of being play in everyday life as well as appreciate their potential to access both the positive and negative capacity of the human mind.

But what exactly do we mean by "state"?

How do Anna O's hypnoid states relate to James's nitrous oxide mystical visions or the biological psychiatrists' brain states of chemical imbalance? What do those states have to do with everyday states such as sleep, dreaming, boredom or . . . sexual arousal? Is this concept of "state" too fuzzy to provide a meaningful perspective from which to view human behavior?

References to states of being—human and otherwise—are an essential part of everyday language. In fact, English has a set of verbs specifically known as the state of being verbs—*is, am, were, was, are, be, being,* and *been*. But this ubiquity with which we causally speak about the various states of mind and being in ourselves and others has obscured taking a deeper look at exactly what is meant when we talk about someone's "state of mind."

This book is about taking a longer, deeper look at the notions of a "state of being," "state of mind," and "state of consciousness." Not that these phrases have exactly the same meaning. The differences, however, will become clearer as we proceed. Nonetheless these and similar phrases are used more or less interchangeably every day to talk about transient conditions that influence how we and others think, feel, and act. Despite its ubiquity in causal conversation, the larger concept of a state of mind/consciousness/being is invisible in our everyday discourse. Yet we often use this notion of "state" to convey powerful global messages about human behavior.

One day, curious about how the notion of a state of mind or a state of being was used in that bible of psychiatry, the Diagnostic and Statistical Manual (DSM), I telephoned Dr. Robert Spitzer, who had shepherded both the DSM-III and IIIR from drafting through publication. I knew Bob had a copy of the DSM-IIIR on floppy disks (this was a long time ago) that I could search with my word processor.

"State! We don't mention state in the DSM," Bob protested. He was adamant. The DSM was not about states of mind. It was about objective descriptions for the diagnosis of criterion-based psychiatric disorders.

I had lent my copy to someone in the building and had to retrieve it in order to read Bob a couple of examples. When I got back, the phone was ringing, "I guess you caught me in the wrong state," Bob laughed. The disks were on their way.

I found over a hundred examples consistent with conventional uses of "mental state" in the DSM-IIIR. I have since searched all of the more recent versions of the DSM. The number of times that mental state is invoked to characterize or explain behavior has declined but remains common. What is interesting is how embedded and yet unquestioned this usage of 'state' is in the diagnostic system that literally defines who has a mental illness.

There is another way to interpret the pervasiveness, the invisibility, and the conceptual fuzziness of the notion of "state." It is that this unremarked ubiquity, this apparent imprecision, and the many-layered meanings, reflect the fact that as an explanatory concept, the idea of "state" works at multiple levels of analysis. So, to start with simple examples, we can theorize that a specific "brain state" of chemical imbalance could be the cause of the "mental state" of depression. Or that a nitrous oxide-induced change in the chemical state of William James's brain resulted in his experience of a mystical state of mind.

Should we find that specific brain states—chemical, electrical, metabolic—correspond to unique behavioral, emotional or mental states, then we will have found a way to link the brain and the mind together. Indeed, one of the threads that we will be following is the degree to which the multiplicity of ways in which we can invoke the concept of state is 'isomorphic' across many levels of analysis and domains of knowledge about the brain and mind.

But there are other questions to consider first. We have to figure out ways to operationally define the notion of state so that we can measure and describe it scientifically and use it therapeutically. When and how do different states of being originate? What role do they play in everyday life? How do we transition from one state of being to another? What role do states play in who we are—in our sense of self, in our personality? How are states related to unusual or abnormal behaviors? To mental illness? Can we become "addicted" to certain states of being? To what extent can we volitionally control our mental states? To what extent can we control the states of others? Can we access "higher" states of being that allow us to tap latent abilities or enhance our well-being?

The evidence and data that we will examine comes in a number of forms. There are plenty of scientific studies upon which we will draw. But a wealth of experiential knowledge, which should not be ignored or discounted, emerges from both everyday and unusual life experiences. There is also insight to be gained from introspection and self-awareness. Finally, there is theory and informed speculation, which offer interesting perspectives from which to view data, but also contain untested assumptions. I will seek to make these levels of evidence clear, so that the reader may weigh them accordingly.

Italics are used to alert readers to quotations from other authors as well as to my personal vignettes. In the case of quotations, a paragraph or more is often set off so that the reader may hear the author's words within their larger context. In the instance of personal anecdotes, *italics* alert the reader to the retrospective nature of the example.

The book is divided into four sections. **The Sciences of States of Being** surveys some of the many sciences that have been brought to bear on the notion of a state of mind/consciousness/being. The second section, **The Self and Its Proclivities**, focuses on the nature of the "self" examined at two levels of analysis: identity and personality. **Trauma and Addiction** scrutinizes aversive experiences that can leave a profound mark on an individual's sense of self and personality. The final section, **Opportunities for Change**, describes epiphanies, meditation, peak experiences and other exceptional mental states that may profoundly alter an individual's personality for the better.

THE SCIENCES OF STATES OF BEING

In the next chapter (Chapter Two: Our First States), we look at how it all begins. Healthy newborn infants come into this world with a basic set of states of being. This discovery by a small group of scientists known as the "Baby Watchers" served to identify a critical principle for understanding infant behavior. The Baby Watchers soon defined coding systems to classify infant states using combinations of biobehavioral markers such as heart rate and eye closure. Applications of these coding systems, in turn, revealed the existence of regular behavioral cycles among an infant's states. Adept mothers intuitively recognize these cycles and use them as they nurture and comfort their baby. These repeating cycles can be mapped into a multidimensional "state-space" that serves to define a baby's range of behavior.

The behavioral states composing the infant's repeating behavior cycles are linked to each other by brief transitions known as "switches" that form connecting pathways bridging different states. In normal infants, each and every state is time-limited eventually switching into another state. Caregiver interactions, positive or negative, can evoke or suppress certain states and shape the infant's behavior. As babies develop, their state-space expands as new states and pathways are added and/or replace earlier states and pathways. We recognize this process of increasing behavioral complexity as part of normal development.

Premature babies and infants with brain damage or severe developmental delays often have abnormal states and dysregulated state cycles. Simplified versions of the coding systems developed by the Baby

Watchers provide a way to help parents, nurses, and others recognize the opportunities for care that occur in different states. In some instances, we can help with regulation of the state cycles by structuring the environment and timing our interactions to help these difficult-to-care-for babies achieve and sustain the states necessary for adequate feeding, affection, and socialization.

The emotional and mental states of primary caretakers, usually mothers, have powerful effects on their infants and children. We refer to this mutual interplay of maternal and infant states as "attunement." Good attunement greatly facilitates healthy attachment, which is the most critical life task a baby faces. Abnormal maternal states such as depression, substance abuse, or anger, stress and fear can negatively impact the quality of mother-child attunement resulting in disturbed patterns of attachment.

Much of what we understand about the nature of human states of being is implicitly present in the behavioral states of a healthy newborn infant. These properties will be elaborated throughout the remainder of the book, but the basic principles manifested in infant states provides a framework for understanding complex human behavior, including higher states of consciousness.

In Chapter Three (Brain States), we explore the question of how mental states can be mapped on to neurobiological brain states. We begin with sleep research, which was the first and remains the most thoroughly developed area of scientific inquiry about a unique set of states of being. As is often the case, it is useful to start with an extreme example. Ramon's nocturnal rampages illustrate a nearly universal human state of mind, dreaming, running amok.

Sleep and dreaming were the first human states to receive systematic scientific attention. In many respects, the approaches pioneered to study these common—yet still mysterious—states of consciousness have shaped subsequent research on other states of consciousness. The sleep stage coding system and the physiological instrumentation developed by sleep researchers has proven to be the most durable methodology for categorizing a specific set of discrete states of consciousness (e.g., the normal sleep-dream cycle). More recent examples, such as studies of depression, hypnosis, and sexual arousal, reinforce the utility of this combined psychological-behavioral-physiological approach to investigating the interrelationships of the states of mind, body and brain.

The ability of increasingly sophisticated brain-imaging technologies to specify brain states in terms of their spatial and temporal patterns and intensity of activity allows us to ask questions such as "what is the most basic brain state that we can measure?" The answer appears to be microstates, a limited set of recurrent patterns of neural activity believed to represent the activation of specific networks of brain cells. Microstates have been called the *"atoms of thought"* and within a given individual can be used to discriminate among different kinds of thinking.

The dynamic ebb and flow of brain states fit remarkably well with non-linear dynamical system models, a mathematical approach referenced in future sections as a useful quantitative method for describing common properties of states of being mapped at different levels of analysis. Researchers coming from different disciplines and empirical perspectives independently converge on the discovery that non-linear dynamical stim-ulations most closely replicate the dynamics of the particular set of states of being that they are interested in.

Chapter Four (Changing State) takes a longer look at the transition phenomena, "switches," that link and sequence states of being into larger segments and cycles of behavior. We start with extreme examples from the research studies of the biological psychiatrists in the late 1970's and early 1980's. Bipolar disorder, panic attacks, periodic catatonia, and even multiple personalities provide examples of rapid switches in behavioral state that can be studied—even experimentally induced—in controlled research settings.

THE SELF AND ITS PROCLIVITIES

If immediately upon awakening in the morning you had five minutes to tell someone the most important things to know about you and the course of your life, what would you say? Would you have said the same things just before you fell asleep the night before? Would you tell them the same things about yourself and life tomorrow afternoon? Would you have said the same things five years ago? How about five years from now? What is it that influences the "who" and the "what" that we would say about ourselves at any given moment?

In this book, we divide the complex notion of "who we are" or the "self" into two basic levels—identity and personality. We each have a number of identities that we activate as called for by different life situations. The result of our efforts to integrate our various identities together into a more or less unified 'self' is experienced by other people as our 'personality'.

The focus of Chapter Five (Memory and Identity) is at the level of 'identity'. We examine a psychological mechanism called state-dependent learning and memory (SDLM), through which states of being influence the various identities that people cycle through in daily life. Clinical observations linking changes in memory to changes in identity and behavior date to the early nineteenth century. William James even sought to codify this clinical insight into a psychological law. Modern laboratory experiments continue to document the powerful influence that mental and emotional states have on which of the many possible memories people will recall when asked about certain periods of their lives. These memories, in turn, influence the associations, assumptions, and trains of logic that people draw upon in their current situation.

Researchers find that the recall of certain kinds of events and types of information is more strongly influenced by a person's emotional state than are other types of memories. This necessitates taking a brief look at the separate memory systems that exist side by side in our brain-mind. One type of memory strongly influenced by a person's state of being is autobiographical memory—the memories that people recall about their lives. When asked about a certain period of your life, what you recall is influenced by what you were feeling at the time the memory was created and how you are feeling at the time when you try to recall it. Emotionally charged autobiographical memories, such as memories associated with deep depression, high anxiety, or traumatic experiences, can be highly state-dependent and not easily recalled in what most people would consider "normal" states of consciousness.

The linkage between state-dependent memories and an individual's sense of identity is most apparent when the person's identities regard themselves as separate people, such as in the psychiatric condition known as Dissociative Identity Disorder (DID). In these cases, the different identity states report separate memories for the individual's life experiences.

Most of us, however, typically experience minor discontinuities in memory and identity and manage to "keep it together" for the most part. However, when a person's different identities destructively compete with each other, generate continuing conflict with significant others, or are grossly inappropriate for the situation, it may be time for outside help. A number of psychotherapies focus on identifying dysfunctional identity states, what triggers them, and how they influence the person's thoughts and actions.

Chapter Six (Secret Lives: Personality and Its Paradoxes) marks a shift of emphasis in our exploration of states of being as we apply principles gleaned in previous chapters to everyday human behavior. Beginning with that complicated and vaguely defined thing commonly called "personality," here the public expression of the self that others experience, we view personality through the lens of classic psychoanalytic theory and then modern developmental and dimensional theories.

One of the conundrums or "hard problems" for all theories of personality is hypocrisy. How is it that people can be so two-faced—and seemingly not be aware or troubled by their duplicity? What do conventional personality theories tell us about hypocrisy? Very little, it turns out, can be explained by current dynamic, developmental, or dimensional theories—all of which assume that an adult's personality is relatively fixed and immutable.

The state model of personality seeks to account for hypocrisy, as well as for a number of other perplexing phenomena such as sudden, profound and permanent changes in personality that cannot be explained by current theories. The state model conceptualizes personality as the collection of identity, emotional, and other states of being that are available to a person weighted by their probability of occurrence. These identity and emotional states are behaviorally present or psychologically activated in varying degrees depending on life experiences. They may be largely insulated from each other by SDLM, permitting people to behave in contradictory ways across different settings and not be troubled by their inconsistency.

The state model of personality can incorporate or account for many of the critical elements and observations underlying the psychodynamic, developmental and dimensional models of personality. It also fits with neurobiological mechanisms known to produce permanent changes in behavior. Thus, the state model of personality does not negate or supplant conventional theories and their supporting data, but rather, offers a complementary and integrative perspective.

The expression of an infant's personality is limited to a relatively small number of basic behavioral states (Chapter 2). As the growing child masters basic state-related developmental tasks, such as acquiring and improving self-regulation of strong emotional states; developing an ability to match and sustain a state that is appropriate to the situation; and the ability to restore an appropriate state after it has been unexpectedly disrupted, the child's abrupt transitions among different states begin to blur and behavior becomes more self-regulated. It is adolescence, with its classic "identity crisis", that again reveals the state structure underlying behavior and personality.

If our personality is merely a collection of identity and emotional states linked together by probabilistic transitional pathways (switches), how is it that we subjectively experience ourselves as a single person? Psychotherapists, cognitive psychologists and developmental psychologists have each identified the existence of superordinate mental mechanisms, referred to respectively as the *observing ego, metacognition,* and *executive functions,* that serve to bridge the gaps among our discrete states of being and provide the "conscious" leverage for us to exert some measure of mindful control over our various states of being. While conceptualized somewhat differently by these disciplines, the bridging mechanisms serve to unify our array of identity and emotional states into a more coherent sense of self that is overtly expressed as our "personality." Disturbances in these bridging mechanisms are associated with problems with self-control, instability of mood, impulsivity, and fragmentation in sense of self.

TRAUMA AND ADDICTION

Experiencing an extreme state such as the fear of imminent death, absolute horror, shocking grief, and the like leave their mark on a person for life. At one level, humankind has always known this. It is the stuff of legend and literature—and, tragically for some, of daily life. But until a few decades ago, it was largely outside the scope of science and medicine. The coining of the diagnosis of posttraumatic stress disorder (PTSD) in 1980 in the revolutionary DSM-III changed that. It provided a new way to see the effects of trauma on the human psyche.

In Chapter Seven (PTSD) we see that many of the symptoms that characterize PTSD can be understood as altered states of consciousness during which an individual behaves in ways that are responses to memories of traumatic experiences. Flashbacks are the most obvious example, but states of hyperarousal, paranoia, and depersonalization are also common. Sleep disturbances, emotional constriction, and explosive outbursts of anger reflect disturbances in the mechanisms that regulate and modulate the normal cyclic flow of states of being.

Towards the end of the nineteenth century, clinicians learned to induce "twilight states" as part of their treatment for "hysteria," a condition then closely associated with traumatic memories. Using hypnosis to induce a detached, relaxed mental state, therapists would help patients to relive and "abreact" their traumatic memories and then reframe the meaning of the experience to reduce its traumatic qualities. By the end of the First World War, abreactive therapy conducted during drug-induced "twilight states" of consciousness proved to be the most effective treatment for "shell shock." Both drug and hypnotic abreactions were widely used by the British and Americans during the Second World War, successfully returning large numbers of soldiers with "combat neurosis" back to the front lines within days.

Any experience that recurrently produces extreme states of being in a person can be expected to impact that person's sense of self. This is dramatically illustrated by another trauma-related psychiatric condition, dissociative identity disorder, commonly known as multiple personality (DID/MPD) (Chapter 8—Dissociation). The cardinal feature of dissociative identity disorder is the existence of two or more identity states that exchange control over a person's behavior.

Dissociative Identity Disorder is the result of massive early childhood trauma disrupting a child's normal developmental integration of identity and emotional states into a more unified and stable adult sense of self. Early childhood trauma and adversity, frequently perpetrated by parents and family, disrupts the formation of healthy attachments with long-term dire consequences for the development of a healthy sense of self. Seminal nineteenth-century "talking therapy" treatments of dissociative patients, such as Breuer and Freud's *Anna O*, laid the foundation for early psychodynamic theories and later psychoanalysis.

Today, we have a remarkably complete developmental story that traces how early childhood experiences lead to a disturbed form of attachment (Type D—disorganized disoriented attachment) that, in turn, increases an individual's propensity towards pathological dissociation as an adult. Pathological dissociation, in turn, increases a mother's risk of having a Type D child. And so it goes across generations.

As far as we are able to look backward in time, humans have used psychoactive (mind-altering) drugs. The evidence suggests that mind-altering drugs were used in ancient religious ceremonies and healing rituals (McNamara, 2009). They continue to be used in this way today usually as part of a larger context in an effort to induce an altered state of being in which to have a religious or life-changing experience. Psychoactive drugs may also be used to alter sensation or level of consciousness to reduce pain—physical or mental.

While many drugs can affect thinking and mood as an unintended side effect, psychoactive drugs are taken for the express purpose of altering mental processes. Understanding the action of mind-altering substances—both psychiatric medications and illicit drugs—from a states-of-being perspective provides insights on their utility and appeal as well as the nature of addiction and its pernicious effects on personality. Chapter Nine (Drugs and Addictions) surveys psychoactive drugs and effects on perception, cognition, mood, judgment and other critical dimensions of state-space. As a consequence of their broad impact on critical state variables, taking a potent psychoactive drug often results in a dramatic shift in the person's state of being.

If you think about it, the ability of a given medication to alter one's state of being for the better is the implicit selling point of many drug commercials. Consider, for a moment, the ubiquitous *"Ask your doctor"* (increasingly *"Talk to your doctor"* and soon I suppose *"Tell your doctor"*) television ads for the array of pharmaceuticals that sponsor news and entertainment. They usually consist of before and after visual vignettes in which we "see" a dramatic transformation in the person's state of being, such that the isolated and incapacitated sufferer can once again enjoy life to its fullest surrounded by loving family and lively friends. "Seeing" such a dramatic state change sends a powerful, largely subliminal, message that overrides the often-horrifying side effects hurriedly listed in a sotto, affectless monotone.

The drug addict is the poster child for the self-destructive physical and mental effects of addiction. Increasingly, however, we recognize that an addiction can occur with other state-altering behaviors such as gambling, video gaming, or sex. In the state model, addiction is conceptualized as the collection of states of being related to the addiction, whatever that might be. Thus addiction includes not only the intoxicated or altered states directly induced by the substance or behavior, but also the collection of non-intoxicated states in which the individual cheats, lies, hides, steals or does whatever else necessary to protect and support their habit. It is this global change in personality—not just the inebriated states—that we consider evidence of an addiction. Interestingly, effective treatments for addiction—be it drug or deviant behavior—often require the person to develop a new identity (e.g., that of a recovering addict) around which to organize their post-addiction sense of self.

OPPORTUNITIES FOR CHANGE

Psychedelic drugs are far from the only way to have a mystical experience. Some people get there through sex. Others have life-changing epiphanies out of the blue. And for still others it only happens after years of arduous practice under the tutelage of a wise master. This innate drive to have a peak experience, to transform oneself, to mingle with the divine, is the ultimate expression of that childhood drive to explore altered states of consciousness. Altered states first induced by spinning around till you are so dizzy that you can't walk straight, by hanging upside down, by holding your breath till you almost pass out, and by being tickled till you think that you are going to die—or at least wet your pants. Later you try the grown-up stuff—whatever that happens to be in your neighborhood.

Abraham Maslow coined the term "peak experience" in the 1960s to describe those mystical and metaphysical moments that lead to greater self-actualization. Drawing on a variety of sources, he synthesized a description that encompassed core elements including a sense of wholeness, perfection, justice, goodness, and beauty—although not every peak experience includes all elements. Chapter Ten (Exceptional States of Being) looks at unusual experiences—spontaneous and induced—that contain peak elements. While difficult to study scientifically for a number of reasons, sufficient empirical data exist to conclude that something unusual is happening in the brains and minds of people having mystical and spiritual experiences.

For many people, sex is high on their list of lifetime peak experiences or, at least, the desire for peak sexual experiences is high on the list. Sex can be a profoundly state-altering experience—for better or for worse. An enormous range of human behavior qualifies as sexual. For most people, sexual orientation is an important part of their personality.

Sex is one of the few areas where vivid fantasy continues to play an important role in adult mental life by creating contexts for state-altering sexual experiences. One of the key elements in adult sexual fantasy is an alteration in the individual's sense of identity. Given the powerful state altering and identity generating properties of sex, some people develop semi-autonomous sexual "personalities" that get them into trouble. In many respects, the dynamics of the identity and altered states of consciousness associated with sexual compulsions resemble those seen in drug addiction.

While still a socially sensitive—if no longer altogether taboo—topic of general conversation, sex is increasingly being investigated in the laboratory and in more natural settings. Sexology, the scientific study of sex, is fast becoming an important field of research, although it continues to occupy an ambiguous niche overlapping with sociology, psychology, public health, and medicine. Like sleep, sex offers an interesting window on the interface between brain and mind. While scientific instruments track the body and brain's responses, subjects rate their levels of arousal and desire as they watch pornographic or neutral videos. A physiological sequence of sexual states, typically culminating in orgasm, is followed by post-orgasmic states of relaxation and tranquility.

Life-transforming, peak spiritual experiences sometimes occur when least expected. In the midst of an overwhelming personal crisis, some people have a moment of divine ecstasy that provides guidance and relief from previously insurmountable travails. Epiphanies and spiritual awakenings fascinated William James, who identified their salient features more than a half century before Maslow formulated the notion of a peak experience. More recently, William Miller, a psychologist interested in how people make enduring changes in their lives, collected and analyzed personal stories of profound ("quantum") change with his colleague, Janet C'de Baca, at the University of New Mexico. Their work replicates and extends James's and Maslow's ideas.

They found two basic types of transformational experiences, which echo James's observations from a century earlier. The first is a profound flash of insight that changes everything going forward. It is an "Aha moment" that breaks through all previous denial and rationalization to starkly reveal the person to themselves. The second is a mystical moment, in which the person feels moved by an outside agent—and there is no question or choice about changing. Both types of life transforming experiences mark a profound change in the person's personality and often leave behind an enduring sense of inner peace and trust in a higher power.

Transcendental experiences can also be achieved through the rigorous practice of a bewildering variety of meditational exercises. Eastern and Western authorities lump these seemingly diverse practices into two or three categories depending on how they influence the meditator's attention. A state of "enlightenment," the end goal of most meditational practices, although "beyond description," is nonetheless often described in terms similar to epiphanies and ecstasies. The mind is silent. There is a complete awareness of self at the same time that the self dissolves merging with the universe. There is the reconciliation of opposites as the person now sees through superficial differences to the deeper meaning, beauty, and unity beneath. There is light, joy, universal truth, and eternal love.

Western science has approached this mystical realm of knowledge from two perspectives. The first is to apply data and theories derived from experiments manipulating attention and perception. The most common method is to manipulate sensory input with an extreme example being the sensory deprivation studies conducted during the 1960s and 1970s. The second, and more fruitful, approach is the scientific study of the brain and body changes that correlate with the ability of Yogis and Zen meditators to alter their attention and sensory perception. These experiments demonstrate that experienced meditators have an ability to alter their brain rhythms and bodily functions (more or less) at will. Measurable physical changes in brain structure correlate with the amount of daily meditation practice and are associated with the ability to increase tolerance to induced pain. Experiments such as this indicate that repeated induction of meditational states of mind alters both the physiological and physical structure of the brain.

Hypnosis is the final exceptional state of being considered in Chapter Ten. The therapeutic power of hypnosis has been known for centuries both as an anesthetic for major surgery and as a detached state of mind in which to psychotherapeutically process an overwhelming traumatic experience. Although not a peak state in the traditional terms of spiritual ecstasy or enlightenment, while under hypnosis some people can perform mental feats of sensory and attentional manipulation that rival those of the Zen meditators. Pioneering research conducted in Ernest Hilgard's laboratory at Stanford University was instrumental in demonstrating that in highly hypnotizable people, semi-independent streams of consciousness can simultaneously influence behavior. Hypnosis provides an important example of how an altered state of consciousness can be used to deliberately tap human capacities that are not readily available in everyday life.

Chapter Eleven (Using What We Know) examines the multitude of ways—deliberate or reflexive—that people use to manage their states of being. Reviewing the principles of "stateness" derived from our prior explorations; we broadly survey the range of tools and techniques available to self-manage one's states of being. From imagination and fantasy, ritual to celebration, yoga to the martial arts, physical exercise to virtual reality, most people have discovered ways in which they routinely visit special realms of their personal state space.

The state model holds implications for healing, health, and understanding human behavior. Conceptualizing certain psychiatric disorders in terms of their state properties and dynamics has implications for all forms of therapy: psychological, physiological, and pharmacological. A state perspective helps to understand how and why traumatic and aversive life experiences leave enduring marks on an individual. It also accounts for common, but little understood, phenomena such as hypocrisy and precipitous permanent changes in personality. The isomorphic qualities of the concept of state of being/consciousness/mind allow it to be operationalized at multiple levels of analysis bridging brain states with mental states.

This book is about a big idea: that our consciousness is chunked into basic units that we call states of being/consciousness/mind and that all of these states, despite their many apparent differences, share common principles. If there is any basis for this contention, as we progress the reader should discover examples of the role of states in his/her own life and those of others.

CHAPTER 2   OUR FIRST STATES

Jonathan

For more than two hours, the man has been waiting for just the right moment; hidden, but watchful. The object of his attention, three-and-a-half-month-old Jonathan, is lying on his back moving his hands in front of his eyes and wiggling his fingers slightly. Intermittently expressing a contented-sounding grunt, Jonathan seems pleased by the results of his efforts. It has been more than two hours since Jonathan was fed and he hasn't cried or fussed in the past hour.

The man switches on a tape recorder, playing a recording of Jonathan's hunger cries made a week earlier. Jonathan stops, stiffening his limbs and stares towards the source of the sound, a cry expression puckering his face as he begins to whimper. The man stops the tape and then plays a recording of Jonathan laughing and cooing. Immediately, Jonathan stops whimpering, relaxing his grimace and resumes playing with his hands, cooing occasionally. A minute later, the man plays the crying tape again. Within 30 seconds, Jonathan stiffens, grimaces, and starts to cry vigorously. When the tape is changed back to his cooing, Jonathan's crying trails off after a few residual sobs. He begins to contentedly play with his hands again.

The man is a "Baby Watcher"—in this case, a distinguished researcher, Peter Wolff, seeking to understand the miraculous complexity the first year of life. He is investigating the phenomenon of "infectious crying," that is, the apparent propensity of infants to start crying when they hear another infant crying. Nursery and child care workers are well-acquainted with this phenomenon, but skeptical scientists questioned whether this apparent simultaneity of crying reflected interactive responses among a group of infants or merely that they all have been fed at more or less the same time and have become hungry again at about the same time.

Simple counts of the number of crying babies in nurseries find a notable relationship to the time from the last feeding, with more infants crying within 15 minutes of the next meal compared with the 45 minutes after the prior meal. For an hour after feeding, there is no evidence that crying in one infant triggers crying in another. Thus, prior attempts to investigate a commonly reported and widely accepted observation that crying in one infant can trigger crying in other infants, did not find evidence that it actually occurred. Instead, the data seemed to suggest that it is merely the coincidence of their hunger pangs that drives the common crying.

What Wolff finds, however, is that infectious crying does occur, but that it is limited to certain infant states. When Jonathan and the other infants in the study were drowsy or awake, but lying quietly, the crying tape does not elicit crying responses from them. However, when they were alert and active—such as when Jonathan was playing with his hands—they are significantly more likely to become distressed and to cry in response to a recording of their own or another infant's cries. Wolff's study showed that infectious crying was a real phenomenon, but that it did not first appear until the infant was at least 6 weeks old and that it only occurred in certain behavioral states. At first it was most likely to occur when the infant was fussy, but by age two months it was more common in an alert active state.

William James's famous statement that for a baby the world at large was but "*one great blooming, buzzing confusion*" was one of the few instances in which he was in grave error. Nonetheless, James's description of the infant's "*dumb awakening to the consciousness of something there*" (James, 1950 p. 8) remained a powerful, if erroneous, notion that shaped generations of beliefs about what babies were capable of experiencing.

Beginning in the 1950s, researchers seeking to better understand infant behavior were confronted, in any given infant, with what appeared to be a multitude of random behaviors together with an enormous inconsistency in responses to repeated presentations of the same stimulus. Applying the behaviorists' theories popular at the time, which were largely derived from experiments with laboratory animals, developmental psychologists were hard pressed to fit this behavioral chaos into the stimulus-response and reflex arc models of that era. And if even "simple" infant behaviors could not be well accounted for by the scientific models of the day, what could we say about higher and more uniquely human functions such as language, logical thought, and social interaction?

What every adept mother knows

Yet adept mothers can and do make sense of their infant's behavior. No one can make perfect sense of anyone else's behavior—nor can we always understand our own behavior—but adept mothers do develop an instinctive feel for the rhythms and peculiarities of their baby's needs and moods. In the first days and months, their shared world revolves around feeding and sleeping. They know when their child is likely to be hungry, when they need to sleep, and how deeply they are sleeping. They sense a natural rhythm in their child's cycles of waking and sleeping and learn to take advantage of it, to protect it, and to compensate for the inevitable intrusions and disruptions that occur.

The mother's behavior, in turn, becomes shaped by her infant's cycles so that she learns to time personal activities to take advantage of lulls in her baby's need for her presence. When planning some potentially stressful activity, for example, taking her baby while running errands or visiting, mothers learn to arrange feedings and naps in order to put their child into the most desirable state for the activity. Of course, none of these interventions works all of the time and one may still be left with a fussy or inconsolable infant. But this intuitive attunement between mother and child is an essential feature of adept mothering and, as we shall see shortly, is manifest in both mother and infant not only behaviorally but also biologically.

An adept mother recognizes that her infant's behavior is evolving and becoming more complicated as the child grows. New behaviors and interests appear as the child takes in the world around her. The child spends more time awake and interacting. A mother needs to distinguish new changes in her baby's sleep-feeding-waking cycle from the fluctuating background of daily variation. Much of this increasing complexity is driven by the infant's need for stimulation and interaction with people and the environment. The infant's need for richer social interaction, such as playing games, is balanced by an increasing ability to self-amuse by interacting with objects in the environment—playing with toys in a crib or staring intently at a mobile. The child is becoming aware of the larger world.

By six months, the infant is highly attentive, responding to even subtle changes in the mother's facial expressions. Wolff labeled this "strangeness anxiety" as opposed to "stranger anxiety." A majority of mothers report that "strange" expressions such as frowning or disgust can elicit strong reactions of surprise, discomfort, and crying from their child. Laboratory experiments, in which the mother's face is distorted in some fashion, e.g., by wearing a clear mask, demonstrate that infants are extraordinarily sensitive to changes in their mother's face. Yet a stranger, even one wearing a ghoulish Frankenstein mask, only elicits neutral curiosity.

This exquisite attunement by the infant to the mother's emotional state cuts both ways. A mother may use her loving tenderness to sooth a distressed infant. But that infant is also exquisitely sensitive to dysfunctional maternal states such as depression, anger, grief, fear, or intoxication.

Adept mothers are instinctively able to make sense of their baby's behaviors because they are in tune with a larger cyclic pattern of needs, moods, and responses. They implicitly understand that while there may be consistency within a given state, there can be enormous differences to the same stimulus across states. They can look at their sleeping baby and know when they can carry their child someplace or change a diaper without waking him, and when even the slightest sound will elicit a startled response followed by fussiness and crying.

An adept mother recognizes on some level that she must adapt to her child's ever-growing cycle of needs, moods and reactions to the world. With time, an increasingly essential feature of adept mothering is an ability to recognize that her own states and moods, particularly as they are expressed on her face, strongly impact her infant. Adept mothering requires an ability to be aware of the infant's state of being and the likely responses of the infant in that state as well as the effects of her state on the infant.

THE "BABY WATCHERS"

At approximately the same time (1960–1970s) as Tart and others were investigating the altered states of consciousness induced by psychedelics, meditation, and hypnosis, another group of academic researchers, "The Baby Watchers," were peering into cribs and systematically recording their observations of the lives of infants. Standing outside the infant's field of view, they continuously recorded the baby's behaviors, using a stopwatch to time durations and various instruments to measure heart rate, brain waves, and other bodily functions. Typically two or more researchers would divide their 7 to 10 or so hours of daily observation into shifts. The researchers tried to overlap for 15–30 minutes at least once a day to compare observations of the same behaviors in order to standardize their infant state classification system. In some instances, such as Wolff's experiments with infectious crying described above, they would systematically stimulate the infant with objects, sounds, or images to see how the elicited response varied under different conditions.

Their intention was to understand the developing capacities that infants bring to that crucial first year of life and their critical interactions with their mothers. As Wolff notes in the introduction to his book on behavioral states in infancy, when the "Baby Watchers" began their studies, more was known about the social behavior of the herring gull and the three-spine stickleback (a small fish) than the human infant (Wolff, 1987).

To understand humans in the nursery, researchers began to study them as if they were animals in the wild. Adopting the methods of ethology, the scientific study of animal behavior in the natural world, the "Baby Watchers" emphasized non-intrusive observations in natural or near-natural conditions and rigorous field experiments that collect repeated data that could be replicated across different studies. The roots of ethology are traceable to Charles Darwin, whose book, *The Expression of Emotions in Animals and Men* (1872), is regarded as the first ethological study of behavior (Darwin, 1872).

Konrad Lorenz is considered to be the modern father of ethology. He is credited with the discovery of imprinting, the observation that newly hatched baby birds such as geese and chickens spontaneously followed their mothers from the first day of life. Lorenz, who received the Nobel Prize in 1973 for his discovery that during a time-limited *critical* or *sensitive period* shortly after hatching, a chick's imprinting response can be transferred to virtually any animate or inanimate object, including a human infant.

By the mid-1960s, several scientists using ethological methods proposed similar systems for understanding the natural sleep-wake-activity cycle in human infants. The developmental neurologist Heinz Prechtl and the psychoanalyst Peter H. Wolff both described behavioral state-based systems for coding infant behavior. Prechtl pointed out that:

> *. . . there may be rapid and large fluctuations in behaviour states, from deep sleep to full activity . . . (and that) as the baby's behavior is affected by the state he is in . . . some responses may be present in one state but not in another . . .* (quoted in Thoman, 1990 p. 94).

Prechtl and his colleagues defined a set of "state scales" that could be used to code a variety of infant states from deep sleep to alert wakefulness. Wolff, carrying out intensive observations of infants in their homes, conducted systematic experiments with his subjects, and, like Prechtl, documented that the specific response evoked by standard stimuli was a function of the infant's behavioral state. That is, responses to the same stimulus were state-dependent—the same noise or sight of a familiar object elicits distinctly different responses in different states.

Research by Prechtl, Wolff, Evelyn Thoman and others confirmed that behavioral states were the essential ordering principle for understanding infant behavior and infant health, whether one was conducting research or evaluating the child clinically. Indeed, the presence of abnormal states or the inability of an infant to change state appropriately are now considered signs of maladaptation or pathology. Eventually several similar state classification systems competed for adoption within the small community of infant researchers.

Perhaps the community of Baby Watchers was too small because they could never agree on a common coding system. The definition of *state* varied somewhat across these different systems and was typically expressed in academic jargon, such as Wolff's definition of infant behavioral states as:

> . . . *mutually exclusive organismic dispositions . . . that apparently had a causal relation to, or were at least correlated with, moment-to-moment fluctuations in the type and frequency of spontaneous-movement patterns as well as to variations of input-output relationships in response to environmental events.* (Wolff, 1987 p. 13)

There was a consensus among the Baby Watchers, however, that distinct infant states could be identified and classified using a multidimensional system of easily observable variables such as the infant's eyes, face, skin coloring, motility, muscle tone, vocalization, heart rate and breathing pattern. Most of the infant state classification systems use four or five key variables that consistently identify half dozen or more distinctly different behavioral states that are shared by most full-term, healthy infants of the same age. These variables may be continuous, such as heart rate, or dichotomous, such as eyes open or closed. Specific infant states are defined by unique patterns of these variables.

These variables are representative of the types of "dimensions" that can be used to define a multidimensional "state-space" in which the baby's specific states exist. Researchers looking at other kinds of states, e.g., mental states created by psychedelic drugs or hypnosis, will use other variables or dimensions to define the mental states of interest to them. The concept of state-space is elaborated later in this chapter and is central to the remainder of this book.

The number of distinct infant states defined by the competing classification systems varied from about five to ten because researchers disagreed about how finely to divide certain infant behaviors and which variables were key discriminators across states. These often minor disagreements about the specifics of various classification systems seriously thwarted progress in the field, leading Heinz Prechtl to despair:

> *The discrepancy between the appreciation of the importance of states for infant research and the reluctance to arrive at a conceptual underpinning of the state concept is striking.* (Prechtl & O'Brian, 1982 p. 54)

Because researchers failed to achieve consensus on exactly how to define infant states, it was difficult to directly compare results across studies, leading to fragmented research findings about specific states. But over a decade of research a number of principles emerged that proved pivotal in our understanding of infant behavior—and in our larger understanding of the role of states of consciousness in everyday life.

Indeed, infant states contain the seeds for all of the principles, elements, and dynamics found in adult states of being from the pathological to the profound. This is where we all begin.

Infant State Classification Systems

Peter Wolff's infant state classification system was derived in part from Prechtl's and often serves as a starting point for later researchers defining their own coding systems. Wolff described five basic states in newborns, with additional states appearing as the infant matured. Classification variables include: (1) motor activity including types of movements such as startles, postural changes, and active playing; (2) muscle tone ranging from flaccidity in deep sleep to rigidity during crying; (3) facial appearance including eyes open or closed, expressions such as smiles, grimaces or puckers, and mouth movements such as sucking; (4) skin perfusion (limited to Caucasians) ranging from pale to angry red; and (5) respiration including both the rhythm and rate.

This set of variables permits Wolff to distinguish five distinct behavioral states in full-term, normal newborns that vary in their response to life experiences and experimental tests. Thoman, starting with the same variables, further defined a classification system with ten distinct infant states, in part by making finer distinctions based on the quality of certain variables. She observed,

> . . . *it is of little use to note whether the infant's eyes are simply open or shut—when the eyes are open they can be fully or partially open, they can be very bright-eyed and scanning or they can have a dull vacant stare* (Thoman, 1990 p. 97).

Both infant state systems have proved to be reliable; two independent observers using a given system will agree a high percentage of the time on which state an infant is in.

State I, Regular Sleep, in Wolff's system is regular, quiet and synchronous non-REM sleep. REM stands for Rapid Eye Movements, which occur during a unique sleep state associated with dreaming. (REM sleep is described in further detail in Chapter 3). In State I, the infant is at rest and muscle tone is limp. The limbs offer little resistance when a researcher moves them. The baby rarely moves spontaneously except for an occasional startle in response to noise. Eyes are firmly closed and the face is relaxed and symmetrical, with an occasional burst of rhythmic sucking. In Caucasians, the skin is pale or light pink. Breathing is rhythmic and even, varying between 30 and 40 breaths per minute with an average rate of 36.

In contrast, **State II, Irregular Sleep**, is characterized by irregular sleep, including the appearance of rapid eye movements (REM). Muscle tone is higher than in State I and there is more spontaneous motor activity, including periodic stirring and shifting of the arms and legs. The eyes are closed and may be pinched shut at times. Intermittent eye movements, both horizontal and vertical, can be observed through the closed eyelids. A range of expressions may flit across the infant's face, from smiling to sneering to frowning, puckering, pouting or crying. The infant may randomly chomp or protrude her tongue, but the rhythmic sucking of State I is not seen. Respiration is irregular in terms of rate and amplitude and is much faster, averaging about 48 per minute. There may be brief spells in which the infant holds its breath. Caucasian skin is usually pale or pink but may flush during bursts of motor activity (Wolff, 1987).

These two sleep states (I & II) alternate back and forth while the infant is asleep. They differ in their susceptibility to disruption to noise and movement in the infant's environment—a familiar example of state-dependent responses to external stimuli.

While awake, newborn infants exhibit three distinct states, according to Wolff's system. In **State III, Alert Inactivity,** the infant is at rest except for occasional small movements or a brief shift in posture followed by a long period of stillness. The face is relaxed and eyes are open, scanning the environment. The eyes have a bright, shiny appearance, often leading observers to wonder what the infant is seeing or thinking. Respiration is generally even in rhythm but faster than in State I.

State IV, Waking Activity, is characterized by frequent bouts of movement involving the arms, legs and infant's head. Movement varies from brief squirms to longer episodes of more intense activity. Eyes are open but not well focused, although the infant may quickly scan the surroundings during quiet moments. The face alternates between being relaxed and wrinkling up into a crying-like expression. Although there may be whimpers or grunts from time to time, there is no sustained crying. The skin flushes as the infant moves. Respiration is irregular without rhythm and is interrupted by the frequent movement.

State V is **Crying**. The cry may vary from persistent whimpering to screams. When vigorous, crying is accompanied by forceful "angry" movements or by a rigid stiffening of the infant's limbs. Attempts to move the arms or legs are met with strong resistance. The face is contorted into a grimace and flushed bright red in Caucasians. Eyes may be squeezed tightly closed at times. When they are open, the gaze is unfocused. Within hours after birth, vigorously crying infants will shed tears. Crying and sobbing drive respiration making it irregular, with gasps and periods of held breath.

A few months after birth, a new state appears called **State VI, Alert Activity**. In State VI, the infant begins to display controlled movements that are rhythmic or appear directed at a goal. The baby's eyes are open and display the bright and shiny appearance seen in State III. The face is relaxed and the infant purposely scans the environment even while moving. The infant can now do more than one thing at a time.

As time goes on, additional distinct states appear, adding to the child's growing behavioral complexity. This increasing variety and complexity confound attempts to characterize discrete behavioral states using the original set of variables, and coupled with the growing independence and mobility of infants, complicates attempts to apply ethological methods to the study of infant behavior.

By the time that they are toddlers, it becomes extremely difficult to study children in a naturalistic fashion for prolonged periods as well as to define workable systems that can readily and reliably code the enormous range of behavior that an active toddler exhibits. Researchers move out of the nursery and mostly observe children—usually through one-way mirrors—in preschool settings. The focus now is more on the kinds and quality of social interactions they have with other children and adults.

STATE CHANGES OR "SWITCHES"

The application of infant-state classification systems soon revealed the existence of recurring cycles of states that formed organizing structures for more universal behaviors. By doing this, researchers confirmed what adept mothers instinctively recognize: there is a roughly predictable rhyme and reason to the seeming mercurial shifts of infant moods and responses. Identifying states that flow from one to another also revealed brief transitions that mark the shift from one state to another. These transitions from one state to another are called "switches."

Researchers have identified a number of kinds of switches that will be described in more detail in Chapter Four (Changing State). One important general observation about switches between any two discrete states, call them A & B, is that switches from State A to State B will differ in a number of ways from switches of State B into State A. This difference is particularly evident in the onsets and offsets of pathological states such as depression, mania, panic attacks and catatonia.

A normal example is the difference between falling asleep and waking up. Infants falling asleep or waking up typically pass through a period of drowsiness. (Whether drowsiness should be classified as a discreet infant state or considered a type of switch was one of the points of sharp disagreement among the Baby Watchers). Drowsiness just before falling asleep, however, differs from the drowsiness seen on waking up.

During the transition going from wake into sleep, the period of drowsiness, as coded by changes in the infant's motor activity, breathing pattern, and eye movements, is much longer than when waking up. Typically the baby's movements slow or cease, eyelids droop, the whites of the eyes become slightly reddened, and infant's gaze becomes dull and unfocused. As the infant's eyes close, they often roll abruptly upwards and there may be a spontaneous startle or jerking movement, which often wakes the child up again. These myoclonic jerks, as they are known, usually occur within five seconds of closing the eyes.

The baby may cycle through this process of falling asleep and being jerked awake by its own startle movements several times before sleep finally takes hold. Waking up, however, is rarely associated with these myoclonic jerks and usually occurs much more quickly than falling asleep. The eyes suddenly open wide and rapidly become focused while breathing changes in rate and regularity as the infant becomes more active.

There are even differences in the switches back and forth between the two classic infant sleep states, States I and II, in the Wolff and Prechtl classification systems (Shirataki & Prechtl, 1977). While the infant is asleep, States I and II periodically alternate back and forth. Typically an infant falling asleep first enters into State II, irregular sleep. In an undisturbed infant, this is followed later by a transition into State I, regular sleep. States I and II then periodically alternate back and forth until the infant is disturbed or is awakened by an internal process, such as hunger.

Although each infant has its own characteristic pattern, transitions from State II to State I, take longer, on average, in most infants. About two-thirds of the time, switches from State I into State II are accompanied by gross body and limb movements. In the opposite direction (II to I) movement is rare. Babies at risk for developmental disorders, such as Down syndrome, may show reversed transitional patterns or other abnormalities in addition to or instead of the patterns seen in healthy infants.

If left undisturbed, states in healthy infants are relatively stable over periods of tens of minutes to several hours. Points of transition—switches—typically only last seconds to a few minutes at most. On the Baby Watchers' instruments, switches were evident by brief episodes of dysregulation of heart rate, breathing, as well as changes in alertness and movement. This simple example illustrates the role of switches (and their directional properties) in changing state of being.

Understanding the switching processes by which specific states are entered or exited is important as we seek to understand the role of discrete states in certain mental disorders or search for the pathways to attaining special states of consciousness. The switching process provides points of leverage through which we may deliberately change our states or those of others. The observation that there are directional differences in the switching process when going from State A to State B compared to switching from B to A emerges as a fundamental principle.

CYCLES OF INFANT STATES

Another general principle that emerges from the systematic coding of infant behavior is the existence of larger patterns created by repeating cycles of smaller sets of states. Sleep is a simple example that consists of two states (I & II) that oscillate back and forth. Later more complicated behavioral structures emerge from other combinations of infant and toddler states.

Figure 2-1 is a plot (using averaged data) of the set or system of states in a one-month-old infant. The five states—as coded by Wolff's system—occupy distinct regions within a larger, multidimensional state-space. In this case, we can only represent three dimensions, which here are the dimensional variables of heart rate (X-axis), motor activity (Y-axis), and respiration (Z-axis). Other state coding variables, such as degree of skin perfusion, muscle tone, EEG, or facial expression, could be substituted for one or more of these three dimensions and should still define essentially the same unique set of infant behavioral states. In practice, it is messier than that, but the conceptual point is that discrete regions of multidimensional state-space can be mapped out by objectively coding a set of observable variables of infant behavior and appearance.

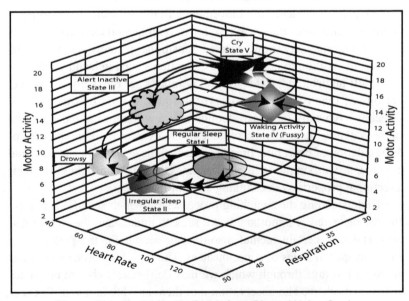

Figure 2-1: One-Month-Old Infant Sleep-Wake Cycle
in 3-Dimensional State-Space

At age one-month, these five states occupy distinct regions of a larger, multidimensional state-space. Transitional phenomena or switches (shown by arrows) connect the different states to each other. Some authorities conceptualize switches as a series of brief, unstable states that serve to progressively reorganize behavior and physiology as the infant transitions from one distinct state to another (Wolff, 1987).

In the first month of life, the five basic states (represented by colored shapes) are linked together so that each state predictably switches to the next. This directional sequence is not rigid, however. It can be interrupted or reset by environmental interruptions, such as a mother picking up and feeding her child. It is, however, sufficiently predictable that an attentive mother can usually anticipate her infant's needs.

The two infant sleep states, States I and II, form a mini subsystem of their own as they alternate back and forth over the course of a period of sleep. Following a brief interval of drowsiness, which serves as a switch out of State III (Alert Inactivity), sleep typically starts in State II (Irregular Sleep) and then transitions into the deeper, quieter sleep of State I, (Regular Sleep). The infant may spend several hours cycling back and forth between Sleep States I and II in this sleep-state subsystem.

If left undisturbed, the infant will eventually switch (through a brief period of drowsiness) from State II into State IV (Waking Active)—in other words, become fussy. Alternatively, the infant may switch directly from Irregular Sleep (State II) into a fussy state (wakes up crying), especially if she is disturbed in some fashion. If the child is not attended to, it is likely that shortly thereafter she will switch into State V and cry. If her mother is available and attuned to her baby's fussy state, her intervention—feeding, changing a wet diaper, holding her etc.—may short-circuit the normal transition to crying and instead switch the child directly into State III (Alert Inactive) instead.

The mutually shared contentment of the infant's State III is a powerful reinforcer for both mother and child. Eventually the infant becomes drowsy (researchers disagree about whether drowsiness is a discrete state or a type of switch) and switches into State II (Irregular sleep). In this, their first dance of states, we see both the organizational effects on behavior and the mutually powerful interactive social effects of shared states, which form a foundation for all subsequent social relationships.

Overall this recurrent cycle of states lasts about one to two hours at age one month. In the course of a typical cycle the infant spends about 20 minutes in Sleep State I and a variable amount of time in Sleep State II (ranging from 3–45 minutes). About half of the time, the infant is awake for about 20 minutes. Another third of the time waking states last up to 40 minutes with the remainder lasting 60 minutes or more. The amount of time spent in a given state varies by time of day, e.g., waking states last longer during the day than night.

STATE-SPACE

Figure 2-1 is also a depiction of a system of infant states recurrently cycling within a multidimensional state-space—which we can pictorially represent in only three dimensions. We first encounter this concept of a multidimensional state-space through the eyes of the Baby Watchers. But scientists working with other kinds of states and different types of data will independently invoke the idea of a multidimensional state-space within which the mental or physiological states of interest to them are located or "mapped." Throughout the rest of this book, we will repeatedly return to this concept of "mapping" states within a multidimensional state-space as we examine other states of being.

In the case of the Baby Watchers, the variables that define the dimensions of an infant's multidimensional state-space either can be observed and coded (skin color, eye closure) or are measurable with scientific instruments (heart rate, respiration, brain waves). The more dimensions we choose to include, the more tightly we can specify the location of a specific infant state in state-space. The trade-off, however, is that as more and more dimensions are required the coding system becomes increasingly complex and cumbersome to apply, especially in real-time. Furthermore we may begin to create false distinctions by over-specifying the preciseness of the state-space coordinates.

The variables that we are using as mapping coordinates in the infant's multidimensional state-space are "soft" measures. For example, the definition of State I (Regular Sleep) specifies that the mean rate of respiration is 36 breaths per minute. But the actual minute-by-minute count typically varies from 30 to 40 breaths. Many of the other dimensional variables, for example eye movements, skin perfusion, motor tone, movement patterns, and facial expressions are even less precise. As a consequence, states should be conceptualized as occupying a fuzzy region of multidimensional state-space as opposed to an exact point.

This constitutes another general principle, that a given state occupies a region of state-space that has blurry boundaries. These boundaries will vary dynamically over a time as the state initially forms and consolidates then later dissipates. Nonetheless, each state is confined within a larger, circumscribed volume of multidimensional state-space specified by unique ranges of the defining variables.

STABILITY AND TEMPORAL COURSE OF STATES OF BEING

Any given state has a finite life. If left alone, each and every state that composes the one-month-old infant's larger behavioral system will eventually dissipate and give way to yet another state. As the infant switches into the new state—for example, out of State II and into State III—there is a period during which the new state organizes and stabilizes itself.

Observing infant states form and dissipate, Wolff points out that infant states behave as self-organizing structures along the lines of the "strange attractors" found in non-linear dynamical systems. His observation is widely shared by scientists working with other kinds of states. Non-linear dynamical systems (commonly called "Chaos Theory") is a branch of mathematics that is proving useful in understanding how complex behavior emerges from apparently simple processes (See Chapter 3).

During this start-up process, every state is vulnerable to destabilizing environmental intrusions that may terminate it and thus switch the infant into another state depending on what is happening around the child. If undisturbed, the state will stabilize and sustain itself for a finite period during which it is relatively resistant to destabilization. Eventually, the state will weaken and become more vulnerable to outside disruption. Even if the infant is not disturbed, the state will eventually dissolve and a new one will appear following a brief switch.

Every state in the behavioral cycle has a life span that moves from an initial period of organization and self-stabilization to a more established and resistant period, followed by a weakening and eventual dissolution, to be replaced by another newly activated state. During the first month of life, this behavioral system of five states typically takes several hours to complete one cycle. Infants with developmental disorders or infants in disturbed or dysfunctional caretaker-infant relations may show abnormalities in their states, in the transitional switching processes, and in the regularity of their cycles.

Thus, in summary, during the first month of life, we see and can study many of the basic properties and principles of states of being.

Separate and distinct behavioral states can be located in a state-space coded by a multidimensional system of variables. The boundaries of these regions of state-space tend to be a bit fuzzy but are sufficiently distinct to differentiate states from each other. The baby moves from one state to another passing through brief 'switches', which differ somewhat depending on the pair of states and the direction of change. The infant's collection of individual states comprises a larger, repeating system of behavior that cycles in a generally predictable fashion, although it can be reset or redirected by caretakers or events.

In retrospect, it is not surprising that the "Baby Watchers" had difficulty in understanding infant behavior until they developed their state coding schemes. The prevailing stimulus-response and reflex arc theories of that era emphasized the hardwired nature of behavior. A given stimulus should always produce the same response. Yet the responses of infants to the same stimulus seemed enormously variable. The discovery that infant behavior was composed of distinct behavioral states that predictably influenced a baby's response to a given stimulus helped to restore a sense of order. This, in turn, led to the recognition of the existence of cycles of states orbiting within a multidimensional state-space that forms the foundation of an infant's rhythms and routines. This state-space expands as the infant matures—allowing for an ever-growing complexity of behavior.

ATTUNEMENT

Early in life, mothers and caretakers provide most of the stimulation and interactions that a baby experiences. The infant forms important bonds—technically called attachments—with these people. Child development researchers find that different types of attachment can have a lifetime effect on the child's personality. But the quality and sensitivity of a given mother with her baby actually varies from moment to moment.

This ongoing mother-infant interaction is a dynamic process called *attunement*. Although there may be some matching or mirroring of external behaviors between mother and child, Daniel Stern attributes the essence of attunement to a matching of their inner states (Field, 1985). Tiffany Field and other developmental researchers define attunement as the ability of the mother to match and gently guide her child's emotional state. She may do this in a number of ways, but primarily by matching the rhythms and intensity of the infants' behavioral states in ways that complement or turn them into mutually harmonious interactions.

Mothers instinctively use a number of cues to read their infant's emotional state. Prominent among these is whether the infant is looking into the mother's eyes or averting his gaze. When infants are stressed or overwhelmed by an interaction, they turn their gaze away from the source of their distress. Even happy interactions may eventually overwhelm an infant's tolerance of strong emotional experience and lead to breaking off the interaction by gaze-aversion. Mothers who adjust the intensity and rhythm of their interactions in response to their infant's gazing-toward and gazing-away cues help to structure and stabilize their child's emotional states.

The patterns are different, however, depending on the culture. For example, among the Gusii, an agricultural people in Western Kenya, it is the mothers who look away from their infants just as their infants become overly excited and emotionally aroused (Tronick & Weinberg, 1997).

Tiffany Field was among the first to call attention to the fact that the degree of mother-child attunement is reflected biologically in both the mother and infant (Field, 1985). By simultaneously measuring the mother and child's heart rates, cortisol levels, and other biological markers, researchers find that successful attunement is associated with a close biological matching of mother and child's rhythmic patterns. The absolute levels of the biological markers differ, of course, but their rising or falling curves will mirror each other.

Heart rate, in particular, is a telling measure of distress or harmony between mother and child. Stressful or disturbing interactions lead to increases in mother and baby's heart rates and greater gaze-aversion by the infant. Correspondingly, harmonious interactions are associated with more mutual gazing and lower heart rates in both. In the laboratory, scientists study the quality of attunement by tracking the levels and synchronicity of mother and child heart rates and other biological makers (Donovan & Leavitt, 1985). Natural and experimentally manipulated interactions find that disruptions in the synchronicity of maternal and infant states, e.g., by asking the mother to deliberately avoid her child's gaze, lead to greater emotional and physiological distress in both.

One of the most powerful demonstrations of the effect of a mother's state on the behavior of her infant is the "still-face paradigm" developed by Edward Tronick, T. Berry Brazelton, and colleagues at Harvard in 1978 (Tronick, Als, Adamson, Wise, & Brazelton, 1978). A number of variations now exist, but, in essence, the still-face paradigm involves a simple sequence in which—on command from the experimenter—the mother abruptly stops normally interacting with her child and freezes all movement, keeping her expression neutral and emotionless. She remains completely unresponsive to her child's protests for two minutes. And then, on command, she resumes normal interactions with her child.

During the two minutes in which mother is impassively frozen and unresponsive, her infant begins to emotionally crumble. Healthy, well-attached infants become acutely distressed and respond with one of the few coping responses available to them—looking away or sucking on something. Toddlers pull at mom's hair, poke at her face, and loudly protest. When that fails, they turn their back and collapse in abject resignation. When mom 'comes back' and resumes normal interactions, a well-attached child quickly recovers and rejoins her. In the quarter century since it was first described, this seemingly simple sequence of normal to still face and back again to normal maternal behavior has yielded rich scientific data about this most basic of all social interactions.

The still-face paradigm is an experimental example of the powerful interpersonal interactions that constitute our very earliest relationships. Central to this process is the effect of the mother's state of being—as perceived by an infant's extraordinary perceptual acuities—on her baby's state of being. We know from many different studies that a mother's emotional state impacts the ability of her child to regulate emotional states. We have ample evidence that life stresses that affect a mother are reflected, or even magnified, in her infant. For example, in some studies, biological measures of stress, such as levels of the hormone cortisol, show much greater rises in the infants of stressed mothers than in the mothers themselves. Tronick conceptualizes the still-faced mother as a short, experimentally produced form of neglect similar to that seen in cases of maternal depression (Tronick & Weinberg, 1997).

ATTACHMENT

The most critical process in all of child development primarily occurs during the first year of life. Attachment, that crucial psychological and biological bond between infant and mother, is shaped by the qualities of the mother-infant attunement. Healthy attachments result in a markedly greater capacity to self-regulate emotional states, to manage social interactions, and to withstand stress. Damaged or disrupted attachments predict more emotional problems, difficulties with relationships, mental and physical illness. Indeed a toddler's attachment classification status is the single best predictor of their degree of social and emotional success later in life.

First proposed by John Bowlby more than fifty years ago, attachment theory is now supported by an enormous body of scientific work which continues to provide new insights into the incredible power and complexity of mother-infant relationships. Numerous studies continue to identify the myriad ways in which mothers and children influence each other, literally altering each other's biology. Analogous relationship effects have been identified in many mammals, in which the underlying hormonal and brain mechanisms can be examined in detail.

Elegant animal studies from the laboratories of Michael Meaney and Paul Plotsky among others show that separation or other disruptions in maternal caretaking produce life-long changes in their offspring's stress resistance. Indeed, these changes can cross generations influencing the offspring's caretaking of its own young. Sometimes it takes remarkably little to cause profound life-long changes. For example, separations of about 15 minutes from the mother increase a young rat pup's lifetime stress resistance. But a separation of three hours or greater results in a profound, life-long impairment in resilience to subsequent stressors for that rat.

Thus trauma and adversity in one generation may affect subsequent generations. My colleagues Penelope Trickett, Jennie Noll and I prospectively demonstrated similar intergenerational effects in our 25-year study of sexually abused girls, as children and later as mothers (Noll, Trickett, Harris, & Putnam, 2009; Trickett, Noll, & Putnam, 2011).

The Strange Situation

A classification system developed by Mary Ainsworth in the 1960s and subsequently refined by others allows us to categorize an infant's attachment status in meaningful ways that are remarkably predictive of future behavior and coping capacity well into adulthood. The Strange Situation protocol is a research tool, not a diagnostic measure. It consists of eight 3-minute segments in which the child experiences a series of separations and reunions with the mother as well as being left alone and being with a stranger. The child's responses to this sequence of separations and reunions are observed and coded by researchers behind a one-way mirror.

On the basis of her research with the "Strange Situation," Ainsworth initially proposed three attachment categories. A secure attachment (known as type B) is characterized by the child's seeking proximity with the mother or greeting her with a smile, wave or other positive acknowledgement when she returns after a brief absence. An avoidant attachment (type A) occurs when the child avoids the parent or doesn't acknowledge the parent's return. Avoidant infants are usually not distressed by their mother's absence. A resistant or ambivalent attachment (type C) is manifest either by a passive resistance or a show of active hostility toward the returning parent. Resistant behaviors have an unmistakable angry quality that may be displayed towards the stranger also.

Not all infants, however, could be classified into one of these three categories. An important breakthrough came in 1990 when Mary Main, a former graduate student of Mary Ainsworth, proposed a fourth category, type D attachment. Type D attachment has proven to be powerfully predictive of serious lifetime mental health problems. It also predicts harsh parenting when the type D child becomes a parent (see Chapter 8).

Maternal Depression and Other Dysfunctional Parental States
The powerful disorganizing effects of the still-face paradigm typically occur within seconds to minutes after the mother breaks off interaction and becomes unresponsive. There is no evidence that this short (2 minute) experimental "mental separation" has any lasting effect on a healthy mother-child attachment. Indeed, all children inevitably face periods of mental and physical separation when a primary caretaker is either physically or emotionally unavailable. Within certain limits, there is no evidence that such experiences are damaging, and, indeed, they may even promote independence and self-reliance.

But what happens if that unavailability persists over an extended period? Perhaps, the best understood example is that of postpartum maternal depression. A variety of factors combine to increase the rate of depression in mothers, particularly during an infant's first year of life. In some instances, there appear to be biological factors related to hormonal changes occurring during pregnancy and/or following delivery. There are also many life-stress factors that come into play. Sleep deprivation, and the additional time, work, and expense of having a new baby can easily overwhelm mothers with few outside supports. Not uncommonly there are problems with spouses and partners related to the mother's unavailability to them. Job issues, child-care problems, and other worries contribute to feeling overwhelmed.

*Maternal Depression and the Failure to Form Dyadic States of
Consciousness*

About 15 to 20 percent of women experience significant depression
either during pregnancy or in the first year of the child's life. Among
women with fewer resources, rates of depression can be twice as high. A
history of childhood sexual abuse increases the risk of depression about
three-fold compared to mothers who were not abused in childhood. In a
program for young, first-time mothers with low income and few social
supports, Robert Ammerman and I found that 45 percent of women scored
in the clinical range on a standard measure of depression (BDI-II) at one
or more points during the first year of their child's life (Ammerman et al.,
2009). It is now well-established that even one episode of maternal depression lasting weeks to months can have an enduring effect on a child that
can still be measured many years later.

Depressed mothers and their infants are most often synchronous for
negative states and rarely match each other's positive states, particularly
when compared to non-depressed mothers and their infants. In one study,
infants of depressed mothers spent most of their interactions with their
mother in a protest state—grimacing, fussing, or crying. The second
greatest amount of time was spent in a look-away state with a negative
emotional expression and eyes averted from their mother (Field, Healy,
Goldstein, & Guthertz, 1990).

In contrast, non-depressed mothers and their infants spent most
of their interactive time in a play state, smiling, and making singsong
vocalizations. Non-depressed mothers and their infants also had
more synchronous heart rates. There was a "contagion" effect, in
that the emotional state of either the mother or the infant tended to
influence the emotional state of the other. For depressed mothers and
their infants this contagion was most evident for negative states;
whereas, non-depressed mothers and infants brought out positive
states in each other.

Tronick points out that there is no single, universal, optimal form of
mother-child interaction, deviations from which are considered pathological (Tronick & Weinberg, 1997). Rather, there are variations that will
have somewhat different meanings depending on the history of a given
mother-child pair as well as their culture. Regardless of these differences, however, a large percentage of both mothers' and infants' behaviors are powerfully influenced by the other's behavior. These mutually
influential interactions increase in frequency as the child matures.

It is not the absolute synchrony of their interactions that character-izes healthy mother-child state regulation, Tronick suggests, but rather an ability to make adjustments to one's own state to accommodate the other's state. In particular it is the infant/toddler's experience with rec-ognizing the mother's state and making adjustments or reparations to the mother's state that helps the infant to develop a sense of self that has the coherence, continuity and agency necessary to develop secure and stable relationships with others.

Depression compromises a mother's ability to interact with and thus regulate and stabilize her infant's emotional state. Depressed mothers typically interact with their infant in two dysfunctional ways that disrupt the infant's ability to move from one state to another. In the "intrusive" pattern, mothers handle their babies roughly and actively interfere with the child's activities, including self-soothing behaviors. Withdrawn mothers, in contrast, are uninvolved and emotionally flat with their infants, and they fail to support the infant's attempts to interact with his environment.

Infants react to these two patterns differently. Infants of intrusive mothers spend most of their time looking away from the mother and rarely look at or play with objects in their cribs. They tend to protest and cry less. Infants of withdrawn mothers are more likely to protest and to show more emotional distress. Boys seem more affected by these inter-actions than girls and are less able to self-regulate their emotional states during childhood. Some depressed mothers are mostly intrusive; others are more withdrawn, and some exhibit a mixture of both patterns.

Around one year of age, infants become directly aware of their mother's mental states and react to these more strongly than to what the mother is actually doing. This intersubjectivity, the ability to read and "understand" another's internal emotional state, is a critical step in the emergence of an individual's ability to empathize with others. Healthy intersubjectivity is fundamental to positive and functional human rela-tionships. It lies at the heart of successful friendships, marriages, and childrearing.

Investigations of early childhood friendships finds evidence of growing intersubjectivity together with regulatory effects as manifest by the same synchrony in heart rates and other biological measures as moth-er and child (Goldstein, Field, & Healy, 1989). Close friends, in particu-lar, show greater similarity in heart rates and cortisol levels. The presence of close friends helps decrease stress in a child indicating that these types of relationships also play an important role in normal development (Field et al., 1992).

It is believed that children who experience seriously dysfunctional mental states in their parents, such as major mental illnesses or drug and alcohol abuse, develop intersubjectivity with these parental states and thus are at greater risk for developing their own pathological states later in life (Tronick & Weinberg, 1997). Research indicates that children of substance abusing parents have lower levels of empathy, a greater lack of awareness of how their behavior is perceived by others, a lack of insight into personal relations, and difficulty showing empathy towards others (Johnson & Leff, 1999). These children are at greater risk for developing depression and anxiety disorders later in life. Similar problems are noted in abused and neglected children, who have great difficulty identifying and distinguishing among their own emotional states (Cicchetti & Barnett, 1991). It is likely that exposure to domestic violence or high-conflict divorce produces similar effects.

PRACTICAL USES OF INFANT STATES

Because the Baby Watchers could never agree, no infant state classification system has been universally adopted. The concept of infant states has nonetheless become an essential component of clinical practice. Nurses in neonatal intensive care units (NICUs) routinely monitor state variables such as heart rate, respiration, skin perfusion and movement, in order to optimally time their care and feeding with the infant's most receptive state. Babies born a month or more prematurely, for example, often have significant difficulty sustaining a state of alertness and motor control necessary to feed properly. When caring for these infants, NICU nurses use a variety of techniques to progressively arouse them to an appropriate state and to sustain this state throughout the feeding.

Many NICUs carefully arrange their lighting and activity schedules to help regularize the erratic state cycles of premature infants. Using measures of stress, such as heart rate, blood pressure, oxygen saturation and movement; researchers find that during enforced NICU quiet periods the infant's blood pressure and heart rate are lower and more stable (Slevin, 2000). They lie quietly, moving far less, and appear to be more peaceful and restful. Such studies also highlight the incredible intensity of activity, light and noise that characterize the typical newborn intensive care unit.

In addition to having difficulty sustaining an alert state, premature infants have significantly different patterns of sleeping and waking states compared with full-term babies (Davis & Thoman, 1987). Premature infants spend more time in alert and non-alert waking states and less time in total sleep. They have more difficulty transitioning in and out of sleep, spending substantially more time in the drowsy state. They also differ in terms of their state-specific responses to caretakers. Premature infants are most likely to fuss or cry while they are alone; whereas full-term infants fuss and cry more with their mothers. Thus, the larger pattern of specific states and switches that constitute the child's behavioral cycles may be markedly altered in premature or otherwise compromised newborns.

Infants born with mental disabilities or with brain injuries often show abnormal states and state cycles (Prechtl, Theorell, & Blair, 1973). Down's-syndrome infants spend more time awake than normal infants and considerably less time in State II sleep. When they do sleep, however, it will be for much longer periods than normal infants. Infants with brain injuries due to lack of oxygen or delivery complications resemble Down's syndrome infants in that they have significantly reduced amounts of State II sleep.

In some instances, such as severe brain injury, babies do not have a detectable state cycle, spending most of their time in a single comatose state that does not resemble either of the two normal infant sleep states. In such cases, the constellation of variables commonly used to define infant states no longer clusters together to sufficiently map to a specific region in state-space. For example, they may have a rigidly fixed heart rate at the same time that their breathing, limb and eye movement patterns vary markedly.

Some of the most seriously compromised newborns may spend months in a NICU. If they are lucky, their mother spends as much time as she possibly can with them. The nurses will help her learn how to identify and modulate her baby's states and allow her to guide them as to when and how they should interact with her infant.

One mother spent over a year in our hospital's (Cincinnati Children's) NICU monitoring her baby's states and helping nurses on the different shifts understand when and how to arouse him for care and feeding. The nurses, who were desperate to get this newborn to take nourishment through his feeding tube, credit her with saving her baby's life. They expressed amazement at her ability to recognize the optimum moments to interact with her child, who had only one functional lung and serious GI and heart problems. Follow-up when he started school revealed a remarkably normal child with only minor developmental delays despite his horrendous first year of life.

SYNTHESIS

Chapter Two (Our First States) sought to make four fundamental points. The first is that unique states can be scientifically defined and studied using combinations of behavioral and physiological measures or dimensions. By applying a state coding system we can map an infant's states within a larger multidimensional state-space. We find that healthy newborns exhibit a basic repertoire of distinct waking and sleeping states that switch from one to the next in a roughly orderly sequence that forms a recurring behavioral cycle—typically lasting a couple of hours in the first few months of life.

Second, despite differences in the behavior or emotional content of each state, e.g., crying versus quiet alertness, all of a normal newborn's states share a set of meta-principles and properties. They have unique "state-dependent" patterns of behavioral responses to the same stimulus. Each state has a finite life span waxing then waning until it is replaced by another state. Switches between pairs of states show directional properties. There may be cyclic subsystems, (e.g., sleeping infants switching back and forth between regular and irregular sleep) embedded within a larger behavioral cycle. As we proceed, examples of these meta-properties and principles will be identified for other states of being.

Third, we touch on a few of the ways in which states serve as the language of attunement and attachment. More powerful than words, this first dialogue of states, classically between mother and infant, crystalizes in the form of an attachment status that echoes across the individual's life. Healthy attachments are associated with greater self-control over one's emotional states. Unhealthy attachments are associated with lifelong states of anxiety, depression, anger and dissociation (more later). Thus chronically disturbed mental states in the mother and/or father (best documented for maternal depression) may leave lifelong marks on their children.

Finally, despite the failure of the Baby Watchers to agree on a common infant state coding system, their conceptual work led to important practical uses such as the care of premature babies. In many respects, the pragmatic application of knowledge gained from research is one of the strongest arguments in favor of a states approach to understanding others and ourselves.

Ramon

The growling woke Ramon's mother. It was a deep-throated, rumbling of a big jungle cat—it was growing louder. Watching from the doorway of his bedroom, she waited for what would happen next. Ramon rolled violently out of bed. Wrapped in tangled sheets, he struggled up onto his hands and knees. His clenched hands turned into tiger's paws, fingers spread with knuckles under and thumbs pointed backwards. He slipped out of the twisted sheets with feline grace and tensed, scanning the room. His dark eyes glinted with a soulless quality that chilled her. As if he really were a tiger—and not her son.

Then Ramon sprang, leaping over his bed and bounding out the bedroom door on all fours. She ran after him, shouting for her daughter to come help. For the next ten to fifteen minutes they would have to contain and protect him, while he roamed the apartment attacking furniture and eating raw meat from the refrigerator. At times he seemed to have superhuman strength. He was able to pick up and carry heavy objects in his mouth, dragging around mattresses or lifting tables and chairs. The furniture was scarred with his bite marks and their sheets, draperies, and towels were shredded. He moved on all fours, leaping and bounding with agility and climbing furniture, counters and shelves with curled fingers acting as claws.

Nothing they did would awaken him. Shouting, shaking him, splashing him with cold water, shining a light into his eyes—nothing could reach him. He averaged one or two of these nighttime episodes a week. Sometimes they lasted for as long as an hour. Usually they ended after about ten minutes—at which time he would suddenly collapse into a deep sleep from which he would shortly wake up. Invariably he would describe a recurrent dream in which he was a lion or a tiger following a woman carrying a piece of raw meat down a path. He was trying to get to the meat but was always disappointed. The dream would end when someone shot him with a tranquilizer gun and he would lose consciousness (Schenck, Milner, Hurwitz, Bundlie, & Mahowald, 1989).

Convinced that no one would believe them, Ramon's family videotaped some of the episodes to show doctors. After four years of almost twice-weekly episodes, Ramon was admitted to the Minnesota Sleep Disorders Center in Minneapolis. There Dr. Carlos Schenck and his team recorded two of these sleep episodes under controlled conditions.

On the first night in the sleep laboratory Ramon fell asleep for about an hour, progressing normally through stages 1 through 4 of non-REM sleep. Then he entered into behavioral sleep—a state in which he appeared to be asleep, but the pattern of his brain waves (EEG) was that of an awake brain. Almost immediately he began to growl intermittently for several minutes. Then he abruptly left the bed and crawled around the room on all fours, growling, grinding his teeth and biting and tugging at the mattress. He chewed and swallowed part of an instrument used to measure his breathing. After six minutes, he suddenly collapsed, his hands still contorted into the shape of paws. Two minutes later he was up again, crawling and growling for another five minutes before he collapsed and couldn't be awakened by staff. Shortly thereafter he awoke and related his recurrent dream of following a woman carrying a piece of raw meat. He had no memory of his behavior. He was rewired and after another hour of sleep had a second episode in which he crawled around the room, attacked a lamp, then chewed and swallowed parts of another breathing monitor. This lasted about nine minutes, at which point he again collapsed, could not be awakened, slept twenty minutes and awoke to relate essentially the same dream. On both occasions, his EEG again showed a brain wave pattern associated with an alert, waking brain.

Even as a small child, Ramon was an exceptionally restless sleeper. At first his parents placed fishnets around his bed to protect him. Later, they locked him in his bedroom with a screen door that allowed them to check on him. Born prematurely, Ramon was later diagnosed with major learning disabilities. Despite intensive special education, he did not graduate from high school. However, he was friendly and well behaved when awake. His family often referred to his good side during the day and his bad side at night. When shown videotapes of his nocturnal behavior, Ramon burst into tears, expressing disbelief. Multiple episodes were observed later when he was hospitalized for a month. Psychiatric medications appeared to increase his nocturnal rampages. Hypnotherapy seemed to have improved them, but he was lost to follow up and its long-term effectiveness is not known.

SLEEP

Ramon's case is an example of the strange behaviors that some people engage in while asleep. Normal sleep was one of the first mental states to be scientifically investigated. A 1913 book on sleep problems, *Le probleme physiologique du sommeil,* by French scientist Henri Pieron, is considered the forerunner of modern sleep medicine (Pieron, 1913).

In the 1920s Nathaniel Klietman (1895–1999) at the University of Chicago pioneered research on sleep characteristics and the effects of sleep deprivation. In order to study subjects deprived of all day-night cues, some of his studies were conducted in Mammoth Cave, KY. One of his students, Eugene Aserinsky (1921–1998), was the first to identify an important type of sleep known as rapid eye movement or REM sleep. Another of his students, William Dement described the cyclic nature of sleep stages and linked REM sleep to dreaming. Dement found that, in addition to humans, the sleep of many other species showed cyclic patterns of a number of distinctly different types of sleep states or stages.

In the beginning, scientists and physicians simply thought of sleep as one of two basic mental states—either you were asleep or awake. Klietman, Dement and others demonstrated, however, that during the course of a normal night's sleep, we repeatedly cycle through a series of distinct mental and bodily states. Modern sleep studies use an instrument, a polysomnograph, that measures brain and bodily functions to categorize the sleep states. The polysomnogram (PSG) includes brain electrical activity, eye movement, jaw and leg muscle movement, airflow, breathing effort, blood oxygen level and heart rate.

During normal sleep an adult passes through five sleep states, conventionally referred to as "sleep stages," which can be distinguished from each other on the sleeper's polysomnogram. Figure 3-1 (see next page) is an example of a hypnogram, which integrates the multiple forms of data from polysomnography into a chronological map of sleep stages. Figure 3-1 is a hypnogram of a typical adult's night of sleep. On the left is a sample of the EEG (brain waves) activity associated with each sleep stage. On the right is a tracing of sleep stages (states) by time. The shaded segments represent periods of REM, typically dream, sleep. Most adults have one or two brief awakenings during the night, usually associated with a REM episode.

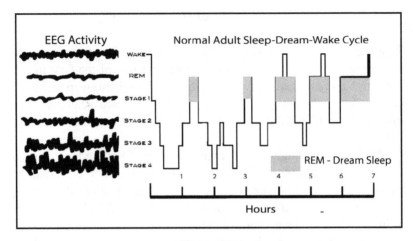

Figure 3-1
Typical Adult Sleep-Wake Hypnogram

Stage 1, or drowsiness, shows about a 50 percent decrease in PSG activity from wakefulness as the person closes his eyes and drifts towards sleep. The alpha brain waves that mark the waking state virtually disappear. The person may exhibit occasional sudden twitches, known as myoclonic jerks, as the muscles relax. If the person is aroused, however, they often feel that they have not actually fallen asleep.

In Stage 2 or light sleep, the PSG begins to show intermittent peaks and valleys of positive and negative waves that indicate changes in muscle tone. A unique brain wave pattern known as sleep spindles for their shape on the EEG begins to appear; the person loses awareness of his environment. The heart rate slows and the core temperature begins to drop by a couple of degrees Fahrenheit as the body prepares to enter deep sleep. Sleep stages 3 and 4 are known as deep sleep, with Stage 4 being a much "deeper" version of stage 3. Stages 3 and 4 are also known as slow wave or delta sleep, as the brain's activity shows a slowly oscillating pattern of large rhythmic waves. Stage 4 is the deepest of all sleep states. This is when people are hardest to wake up. It is also the sleep stage most associated with abnormal behavior such as night terrors, sleepwalking, sleep talking and bed-wetting.

These first four stages are called non-REM sleep, and they account for about 75 to 80 percent of a normal night's rest. Stage 5 or REM sleep is very different. On the PSG the brain suddenly appears to wake. The heart rate rises, and breathing becomes faster and more erratic. The eyes dart back and forth behind the closed eyelids, and the face, fingers, and legs may twitch—even though the sleeper's muscles from the neck on down are actually paralyzed. If awakened during a REM episode, the sleeping person may report a vivid dream. REM sleep occupies about 10 to 15 percent of total sleep time.

The first of several REM periods over the course of a night's sleep lasts about 10 minutes, and the final REM episode may last for as long as an hour.

A normal adult cycles through these five stages of sleep again and again. The first full cycle lasts about 100 minutes, ending with the first episode of REM sleep. Each cycle that follows lasts a bit longer, as the length of the REM stage gradually increases throughout the night. A normal night's sleep contains about five full cycles. Beyond the average, however, there is a wide range of normal differences, with some people needing far more sleep and others much less. Our need for sleep and the pattern of our sleep cycle also varies considerably with age.

In many respects, the variables used by sleep researchers to classify sleep stages are essentially the same as those used by the Baby Watchers to classify infant behavioral states. Sleep researchers, like the Baby Watchers, have conceptualized normal sleep as existing within a multi-dimensional physiological and mental state-space. And like the Baby Watchers, sleep researchers discovered that we cycle through a series of well-defined brain and behavioral states that, taken together, constitute larger patterns of behavior.

But the sleep researchers succeeded scientifically in a number ways that the Baby Watchers did not. As a group, sleep researchers are able to agree on the distinct sleep stages or states that constitute normal sleep and thus can directly compare data across most studies. Meanwhile, the Baby Watchers continued to debate whose classification system worked best—although nurses have largely agreed upon a state classification system for evaluating premature newborns.

Sleep researchers have also done more to scientifically connect brain and bodily states with mental and behavioral states such as dreaming and sleepwalking. They succeeded in large part because they started with normal adults who could tolerate the discomfort of wearing cumbersome scientific instruments while they slept and who could describe their mental experiences after being awakened in different stages of sleep.

Sleep Evolves with Age

My oldest son, Philip, was an active toddler. We used to put him in the playroom and listen on the baby monitor to his joyous babble as he played. All of a sudden it would cease. Checking, we often found Philip in a deep sleep slumped over the toys he was playing with only moments before. Almost as soon as they close their eyes, toddlers like Philip fall into a deep sleep, Stage 3 on the adult scale. The infant's two sleep states—quiet and restless—have evolved into four distinct stages by age 3. Their first REM episodes are short—only a few minutes—punctuated by multiple brief awakenings throughout the night. As children grow, they spend more and more time in Stage 4 or delta sleep.

Suddenly, in early adolescence, their sleep pattern changes radically. Stage 4 sleep decreases sharply with puberty, a shift that reflects a major reorganization of the adolescent brain marked by increased myelination and frontal maturation. This is the reason adolescents have greater difficulty falling asleep and waking up—just when they are supposed to wake up in the morning, they often sink into long bursts of REM or dream sleep. Eventually, these sleep state cycles morph into adult sleep patterns, which nonetheless continue to change over the ensuing decades.

Thus recurrent sets of states of being, such as the sleep-dream cycle, evolve over the course of a lifetime. They may also be profoundly altered by illness, drugs, and by life experiences such as stress and trauma.

Sleep Disorders

Once scientists had enough data on what constituted normal sleep in adults, it became possible to recognize and define disorders of sleep as well as to study the impact of disease, drugs, sleep deprivation, stress, and trauma. Among the most interesting sleep disorders are a group collectively called the parasomnias that involve a range of unusual behaviors—from common forms such as sleep walking to more bizarre behaviors such as sleep sex or Ramon's recurrent tiger dreams. Parasomnias occur at every age and are surprisingly common. About 4 percent of people have a history of sleepwalking, for example. The PSGs of people experiencing a parasomnia often show an abnormal sequence of sleep states or an unusual sleep state cycle that shuffles components from several normal sleep states.

For example, Ramon's cat-like nocturnal prowling occurred after he switched directly from Stage 1, a non-REM light sleep into an EEG REM state. He skipped over the normal passage through Stages 2 to 4 of the sleep cycle. In normal REM sleep, the body is paralyzed from the neck down, although the hands and legs may twitch occasionally when the person is dreaming of some vigorous physical activity. By skipping the normal deepening sequence of sleep stages, Ramon bypassed the progressive paralysis of his arms and legs that normally prevents people from physically acting out their dreams.

Because his body was not paralyzed, Ramon could crawl, leap, bite, and growl as he acted out his dream of being a tiger following a woman who carried a piece of raw meat. Interestingly, he never recognized the woman in his dream. He said that her face often changed but was never familiar. It is not known, however, why he had essentially the same dream over and over again.

Typical examples of dream-related behaviors during REM sleep include talking, laughing, shouting, and swearing. The person may gesture or reach and grab something. They can slap, kick or punch their partner. At times, they may leap out of bed, crawl around, or even run.

In 1825 the French author Anthelme Brillat Savarin described the case of a "somnabulistic monk" who attempted to kill the Prior of the Chartreuse convent (Eiser & Schenck, 2005; Schulz & Curtin, 2004). The monk was well known for his nocturnal wanderings and often was returned to his bed by his brother monks. All efforts to cure him had failed. The Prior reported that (translation by Schulz & Curtin, 2004) and quoted in (Eiser & Schenck, 2005):

One evening I had not gone to bed at the usual hour, but was in my office . . . when I saw this monk enter in a perfect state of somnambulism. His eyes were open but fixed and . . . he had a huge knife in his hand. He came at once to my bed, the position of which he was familiar with, and after having felt my hand, struck three blows which penetrated the mattress on which I lay . . . I saw an expression of extreme gratification pervaded his face. The light of two lamps on my desk made no impression, and he returned as he had come, opening the doors which led to his cell, and I soon became satisfied that he had quietly gone to bed . . .

The next day the Prior sent for the monk and asked him about his dream. The monk replied, "*Father, I had scarcely gone to sleep when I dreamed that you had killed my mother, and when her bloody shadow appeared to demand vengeance, I hurried into your cell, and as I thought stabbed you.*"

Schenck argues that the monk's case is a classic example of sleepwalking that occurs during non-REM sleep. It may appear within 15 minutes or so after falling asleep. Sleepwalking and the sleep terrors in children often occur during periods of a slow delta-wave sleep when they enter into a confusional state of arousal (Broughton, 1968). In such a state of arousal, people have walked or driven great distances. And the monk was not alone: about 20 somnambulistic murders have been reported with the defendant acquitted in about a third of cases (Siclari et al., 2010).

Many people who sleepwalk as adults also sleepwalked or had sleep terrors as children. In adults, episodes of sleepwalking are often associated with increased stress in the person's life. A number of factors, including a genetic predisposition, have been cited as possible contributors to sleepwalking and the other parasomnias. Certain medications reportedly increase sleepwalking, although some of the same drugs successfully treat it in others. Rare side effects of popular prescription sleeping pills include sleepwalking, sleep driving, and sleep sex. These episodes can place the sleepwalker at considerable risk and several deaths have occurred because of medication-induced sleepwalking. One survey found that about 2% of respondents reported injuring themselves or another person while asleep (Siclari et al., 2010).

Insomnia and Sleep Deprivation

Almost everyone experiences sleep problems at some point in their life. Surveys find that at any given time about 20 percent of people report difficulties—trouble falling asleep, staying asleep, or suffering a fitful night. When such problems last longer than a month and interfere with a person's daily functioning, we may diagnose them with insomnia. Symptoms of insomnia typically include problems concentrating, chronic tiredness, and irritable mood. Insomnias are often associated with psychiatric and medical conditions including depression, panic disorder, PTSD, diabetes, emphysema, and chronic pain. Several classes of drugs as well as a form of psychotherapy called Cognitive Behavior Therapy for Insomnia are used to treat insomnia with reasonable rates of success.

One rare but lethal genetic form called fatal familial insomnia usually strikes after age fifty, when the victim has already passed on their genes to the next generation. The first signs are an inability to nap. The person then gradually loses the ability to sleep until they are finally unable to go to sleep at all. Death is inevitable—there is no cure—and usually occurs within a year of the initial symptoms.

We need to sleep or we will die, though medical science still cannot explain exactly why. We do know sleep helps in a multitude of ways. Many studies show that getting enough sleep improves performance on all kinds of tasks. And numerous studies prove that sleep deprivation and disruption are associated with increased errors and accidents. The Institute of Medicine, for example, estimates that almost 20 percent of all traffic accidents happen because of fatigue (Max, 2010).

Sleep deprivation, when it occurs in certain occupations, is danger-ous not only for the person but also for others in his care, such as sleep-deprived airline pilots. Torturers use sleep deprivation to crush a prisoner's resistance. The cycle of states of being that constitutes the normal sleep cycle is absolutely essential to physical and mental health and well-being. Disruption results in dysfunction and deprivation in death.

Cross-species Similarities

Animals too need their sleep cycles or they go crazy and die just like us. As an undergraduate I worked in the psychology depart-ment's rat lab to earn a little cash and see if this kind of research appealed to me. It didn't, but I learned some useful skills. Mostly I ran Skinner box-type learning and memory experiments with rats that had their brains altered with drugs or surgery.

One professor, now deceased, studied the effects of selec-tively depriving rats of REM sleep. He did this by putting them in garbage cans filled with water except for a tiny island—the tip of a brick that stood on end and protruded just above the sur-face. Rats could perch on this miniscule dry patch, but as soon as they slipped into paralyzing REM sleep they would lose mus-cle tone and topple over into the water. Those normally docile little white rats became the meanest animals I have ever encoun-tered. When the professor lifted the lids off the garbage cans the rats would spring at him, trying to bite his face.

Sleep Research

In many respects, sleep researchers developed the current paradigm for the scientific study of brain, body and mental states. They brought their experimental subjects and patients into a controlled laboratory set-ting where an array of precision instruments collected data that were correlated with observations of the person's behavior and reports of their mental experiences. They made standard a number of tests and challenges to map normal sleep as well as to unmask sleep disorders and anomalies. The clinical application of their findings led to an important medical field; sleep medicine, which has saved numerous lives.

Besides normal sleep, modern sleep research focuses on many other areas relevant to medical and mental health, including the effects of stress, trauma, and illness, sleep disorders such as narcolepsy, the effects of sleep deprivation and shift work, and developmental changes from infancy to aging. The scientific study of normal and abnormal sleep states and sleep-state cycles shows why it is important to identify discrete brain and bodily states to understand and intervene in complex human behaviors.

NEUROIMAGING OF BRAIN STATES

During the same period that sleep research was developing into a science, neurosurgeons, neurologists, and radiologists investigated ways to directly observe brain activity and brain pathology. As early as 1918, the American neurosurgeon Walter Dandy injected sterile air into the ventricles, the brain's system of cerebrospinal fluid-filled cavities. Using a suspended chair that could rotate a patient in three dimensions, Dandy moved the air bubble around and silhouetted the shape of brain structures on an X-ray. (In my limited experience this test results in a patient with an absolutely terrific headache afterwards.)

A German physiologist named Hans Berger is often credited with having invented the electroencephalogram (EEG) in the 1920s, although earlier work demonstrated spontaneous electrical activity in the brains of rabbits and dogs that could be altered by shining a light into the animal's eye. The EEG measures the electrical activity of the brain using electrodes attached to the person's scalp. In neurosurgical cases, electrodes may be placed directly on the surface of the brain or even implanted deep inside.

Brainwaves—the fluctuating electrical signals picked up by the electrodes—represent differences in voltages between pairs of electrodes. These voltages are the product of tiny electrical currents ebbing and flowing among enormous numbers of nerve cells. The routine EEG only measures electrical currents at or very close to the surface of the brain. It cannot see what is happening deep in the brain's interior.

Berger described a set of rhythms or frequencies characteristic of most human brain waves. These include rhythmic alpha waves—also known as Berger's waves—that oscillate between 8 to 12 cycles per second and indicate an eyes-closed, resting-but-fully-awake mental state. Opening the eyes usually suppresses alpha waves and generates much faster beta waves. In the 1930s, researchers found that brain disorders such as epilepsy often produced specific EEG patterns that could be used to diagnose problems and to monitor treatment. The EEG continues to be a valuable medical and research tool.

Originally an EEG recording generated reams and reams of graph paper—an all-night sleep study might require half a mile. Powerful amplifiers boosted the tiny electrical signals from the brain to move a dozen or more ink pens that fluttered across the scrolling paper, tracing signals from the scalp electrodes. A bank of switchable filters selected which frequency bands of electrical signals to record and which to block out. It took extensive training and years of experience to mentally integrate these squiggly lines into a more global picture of the patient's brain wave activity.

As computing power increased in the late 1950s, scientists could process and view large amounts of EEG data as colored pictures overlaid on an outline of the human head. Dubbed EEG topography, these images were among the first images of brain states and the forerunner of modern brain imaging. Now EEGs are routinely digitized and displayed in such formats.

In the early 1970s the CAT scan—short for computerized axial tomography—was introduced by Allan McLeod Cormack and Godfrey Newbold Hounsfield, who shared the 1979 Nobel Prize in Medicine. In the 1980s the single photon emission computed tomogram or SPECT scan and the positron emission tomogram or PET scan were added to our tool set. About the same time, Peter Mansfield and Paul Lauterburg developed magnetic resonance imaging or MRI scanning, for which they received the 2003 Nobel Prize in Medicine.

Faster computer processing power during the 1990s led to ever more advancement in imaging technologies, especially the ability to see and record moment-by-moment differences in brain activity and responses to stimuli. Functional magnetic resonance imaging or fMRI, which measures changes in brain blood flow, has come to dominate much current brain imaging research because it is safe, non-invasive, and widely available. With a related technology, nuclear magnetic resonance spectroscopy or MRS, it is even possible to measure levels and changes of essential chemicals in the living brain.

An exciting brain imaging technique related to the EEG is magne-toencephalography or MEG, which measures the almost infinitesimal magnetic fields produced by brain activity. Using special sensors super-cooled by liquid helium that do not actually touch the person's head, the MEG can look deep within the brain. As fast as the EEG, the MEG can locate rapidly changing activity everywhere within the brain. It is being used to study fast sequences of brain activation—when a person hears a word spoken or considers the answer to a question.

Scientists now have a set of powerful brain imaging tools to investi-gate different states of consciousness. These different tools allow us to look deep inside the brain, to measure rapid changes in brain state, to identify regions of brain activity correlated with certain behaviors and mental experiences, and to link abnormalities in brain function to mental experiences and psychiatric disorders. However, no brain-imaging tool can do all of these things at once.

Each scientific technique for measuring brain activity and correlat-ing it with behavior and mental experiences has its advantages and limi-tations. Scientists typically describe these differences in terms of tempo-ral and spatial resolution and sensitivity. Temporal resolution refers to how fast or slow a change in brain activity the technique can measure. For example, the EEG and MEG can measure changes in brain activity happening as fast as 1000 times a second. The fMRI sees changes in brain activity happening over a 3 to 5 second period; whereas SPECT and PET scans measure brain changes occurring over periods of 45 seconds up to several hours.

Spatial resolution refers to how precisely we can locate the area of activity within the brain. An EEG has poor spatial resolution. It can only localize brain activity to within 10-15mm (approximately a ½ inch) of where it is occurring—and then, only on the surface of the brain. In con-trast, an fMRI can localize brain activity down to 1mm (4/100s of an inch) anywhere deep inside of the brain. PET and SPECT scans typically local-ized brain changes to within 5 mm (2/10s of an inch) anywhere in the brain. The spatial resolution of the MEG is good (~ 5 mm) near the sur-face of the brain but decreases as it looks deeper into the brain. Sensitivity refers to how small a change in brain activity the technique can measure. Sensitivity ranges over many orders of magnitude, with PET and SPECT scans able to detect changes a million times smaller than an fMRI can.

Until recently brain researchers had to choose whether they wanted good spatial resolution or good temporal resolution, as one generally precluded the other. To have the best of both, neuroscientists now couple two or more brain-imaging methods. Techniques are being developed to simultaneously measure the brain electrical activity with EEG or MEG and brain metabolic activity with fMRI. The first challenge is to understand how changes in the patterns of electrical and metabolic activity, which occur on different time scales (milliseconds v. several minutes), are related to each other. Eventually, the pairing of different brain imaging modalities has enormous potential to simultaneously examine mental states on multiple levels.

Scientists studying brain function seek mainly to identity patterns of brain activity that correlate with specific brain states and behaviors. The current challenge for neuroscientists is to integrate the enormous amount of spatial and temporal information generated by brain imaging tools into a comprehensive picture of brain activity then figure out how this relates to everything ranging from normal thought to abnormal mental experiences.

EXAMPLES OF BRAIN ACTIVITY STATES

Depression

Using all of the above techniques, scientists are searching for brain imaging markers of the depressive state. They are particularly interested in finding brain markers that will predict whether or not a depressed person will respond better to an antidepressant medication or to specific forms of psychotherapy such as cognitive behavioral therapy or interpersonal psychotherapy. Either medication or psychotherapy can be an effective treatment for many depressed people, but some patients respond better to one than the other—and some people seem to need both.

When a person becomes depressed, a substantial part of their brain is affected. Not only does their mood become deeply sad or even despairing, but their thinking also slows and their memory falters. Bodily functions such as eating, sleeping and energy level are profoundly disrupted. These changes reflect shifts in activity for different brain regions ranging from deep brain nuclei such as the amygdala, basal ganglia, and thalamus, to the frontal lobes, which govern reason, reflection, and judgment.

Indeed, scientists have found that the lower the level of brain's frontal lobe activity, the more severe the patient's depression. Changes in other brain regions have been associated with the slowing down of the patient's mental and physical abilities—what is known as psychomotor retardation—impairments in judgment, memory and reasoning, and higher blood levels of critical hormones such as cortisol (Mayberg, 2006).

As the person responds to treatment, these same brain regions show changes in activity. The best-replicated finding is that the frontal lobes resume normal activity, along with a lifting of depression symptoms. In many brain regions affected by depression the changes in brain activity vary with the type of treatment. Different treatments produce different patterns of change.

When serial brain images of depressed patients treated with antidepressant medications are compared with those treated with psychotherapy, different temporal patterns of brain activity patterns emerge as both groups of patients improve. Antidepressants seem to work by first increasing activity in deep-brain structures including the brain stem, the posterior cingulate, thalamus, and hippocampus. Then secondary changes occur in higher areas, including the frontal lobes.

Patients treated with antidepressant medications often first show signs of improvement in eating, sleeping and energy level, which are controlled by these deeper brain structures. In other words, what we now know about how antidepressant medications work is that they start by changing deep, older, and more "primitive" brain regions, which then influence the newer and more rational parts of the brain.

Psychotherapy seems to work in the opposite way, through a top-down approach. It treats depression by first changing the person's thinking about themselves and their world. For psychotherapy patients, the first signs of improvement often occur in quality of thinking and improvement in memory, which precede changes in bodily symptoms such as eating and sleeping.

Two proven effective psychotherapies, Cognitive Behavioral Therapy and Interpersonal Psychotherapy, produce somewhat different activity pattern changes in specific brain structures, suggesting even greater specificity in how treatments work on brain state (Mayberg, 2006). These results begin to tell us about the ways in which we can change brain and mental states for the better as well as something about how very different, but equally effective, forms of treatment work. Now we need better ways of predicting which treatment will work best for a particular person.

Perception of Pain and State of Mind
Perception of pain may be inhibited or augmented depending on a person's mental state.

Popular and scientific literature on human performance in war, disaster, and athletics is replete with accounts of individuals who were seriously injured, and yet in the heat of the moment felt no pain. Only later, after the crisis passed, did they become aware of their grave injuries. At the other extreme, are individuals suffering from what seem to be inconsequential injuries or minor discomforts, who nonetheless report immense suffering. In the former, the person is usually in a highly aroused state and totally focused on survival or accomplishing a critical task. In the latter, the person is often ruminating—thinking of little more than how they feel.

Perception of pain is influenced not just by an individual's physical state but their mental state as well. Pain specialists know that patients often feel worst when they are trying to fall asleep. Lying in the dark on the ragged edge of sleep, with little or no external stimulation to distract them, they can magnify even small pains or discomforts to the point where they seriously inhibit the switch into sleep.

Pain is complex and comes in many forms. Certain regions of the brain have been identified as critical to the perception of pain—or at least to the perception of pain as hurting. Scientists have methodically inflicted pain on voluntary subjects and then using a variety of brain imaging techniques observed the results (Peyron, et al., 2000). They may vary the type and intensity of the pain or try to block it with drugs, hypnosis, acupuncture or other methods to learn more about controlling pain and easing suffering.

A number of common elements have emerged across these brain-imaging studies. Two brain regions, the second somatic and insular cortical regions, almost always show increased brain activity when a painful or noxious stimulus is applied. These two areas help to process bodily sensations and differentiate among the many kinds of physical sensations—hot, cold, wet, rough, smooth, hard, or soft. In many studies, the thalamus, a major gateway between the body and the brain for sensory information, is also activated.

The anterior cingulate cortex is activated in most pain experiments. The anterior cingulate is interesting because it's involved in emotional responses to experiences and in making instantaneous—and sometimes impulsive—decisions about how to emotionally react to an event or stimulus. It is also an area that is exquisitely sensitive to prolonged stress and has been found to be abnormal in abused children suffering from PTSD. The anterior cingulate is hyperactive in individuals with a subtype of PTSD characterized by dissociative states of consciousness (see Chapter 7).

Because it is a part of the brain associated with emotional responses to experiences and events, the anterior cingulate responds to the situation and the meaning of the pain. Intense genital pain in childbirth, for example, has a very different emotional meaning than genital pain inflicted during a sexual assault. The anterior cingulate is also the region that most often shows changes in brain activity in response to different methods of blocking pain (Fulbright, Troche, Skudlarski, Gore, & Wexler, 2001).

If a given method is successful at blocking or altering the perception of pain, there will be increased brain activity in the anterior cingulate compared with a control condition. What is especially interesting is that this is just as true for hypnosis and placeboes as it is for potent pain medications such as morphine. To a certain extent, a person's responses to narcotic pain drugs predict their pain responses to placeboes.

Pain Perception in Hypnotic States

Among the most potent non-medication methods for blocking pain are the trance states of hypnosis. The ability of people in a hypnotic state to block out or significantly reduce their pain from injuries or medical procedures has been reported by Western physicians for at least 200 years—and, of course, even longer in some non-Western healing traditions. We now have ample scientific evidence showing that, though people differ in this capacity, hypnosis can effectively reduce pain.

Until recently, however, laboratory experiments investigating the effectiveness of hypnosis at blocking pain were restricted to demonstrating that subjects could tolerate a painful stimuli for a longer period of time in a hypnotic state than in a normal state. These data were often supplemented by the subjects' reports of an absence of pain or that the hypnosis had changed their sensation of the pain so that while still present it no longer "hurt."

Using an array of brain imaging tools, scientists can directly measure and compare brain activity in response to painful stimuli in normal and hypnotic states. Not surprisingly, hypnotic suggestions to block pain are associated with changes in brain activity in the anterior cingulate. For example, in one study, healthy volunteers had a heated probe attached to their right hand. The probe could be made comfortably warm or unpleasantly hot and painful. Subjects were compared across three mental states (hypnosis, a resting relaxed state, and a mental imagery state). Pain—as rated by the subjects—in the resting and imagery states was associated with an increase in activity in certain parts of the anterior cingulate that was roughly proportional to the temperature of the heated probe. In the hypnotic state, subjects reported significant decreases in both the intensity of pain and its unpleasantness that were associated with changes in anterior cingulate brain activity (primarily on the right side).

Similar experiments using other forms of brain imaging confirm that hypnosis changes the pattern of the anterior cingulate's response to pain—it somehow modulates or changes the meaning of the pain, so to speak, so that it no longer hurts. Brain imaging research with hypnosis offers convincing evidence that the way it alters mental state can affect how the mind-brain processes sensory information. A person's mental state can dramatically change how they experience an internal sensation or an external event by changing the neural processing of the sensation or emotional meaning of the event. So it is not surprising that people in a life-threatening situation or another extreme state of mind, may not register pain, even from grievous wounds.

Vegetative States

Horror stories periodically surface of fully conscious people trapped in paralyzed bodies who are mistakenly diagnosed as being in a permanent vegetative state. Some have suffered for decades before being recognized as an aware person—someone who saw, heard, felt, and remembers what went on around them. These cases highlight the difficulty that modern medicine faces in determining who is consciously aware of their surroundings and who is not. Recent advances in brain imaging research are now being applied to this situation, one of the most technically difficult and ethically challenging of all determinations of a person's state of being.

The medical diagnosis of a vegetative state is made when a patient appears awake, with eyes open, but does not respond to various tests and exhibits no apparent awareness of self or the environment (Childs & Mercer, 1996). Brain injury, generally due to accidents, is a frequent cause although drug overdoses, strokes, suffocation, and infections, can also produce a vegetative state. Most people who recover from a vegetative state do so within the first month. If a vegetative state lasts beyond a month it is considered to be persistent. If it continues longer than a year, it can be classified as permanent. A panel of doctors with expertise in this condition concluded that the likelihood of recovery after a year was close to zero (Laureys, 2007).

But reversal and at least partial recovery from so-called permanent vegetative states, even those lasting decades, have been reported in medical literature. And perhaps as many as forty percent of patients diagnosed as being in a vegetative state actually have some awareness of their environment and are in a minimally conscious state. Determining where on the spectrum a patient falls can have life-and-death implications as family and physicians struggle with difficult decisions about whether to continue life support.

Traditionally, clinical examination determined the diagnosis. Patients in a vegetative state continue to have a sleep-wake cycle in that they have periods with their eyes open and periods in which they close their eyes and appear to sleep. They may chew, grind their teeth, swallow and move their arms and legs in disorganized ways from time to time. They may occasionally smile or shed a few tears, utter grunts, groans, moan or even scream for no apparent reason. They respond to pain. They sometimes appear to follow something with their eyes, though they can't reproduce the action (Laureys et al., 2000).

Lower brain, brain stem function and basic reflexes could explain all of these behaviors. The examining physician makes a diagnosis of a vegetative state by determining that the patient does not communicate, does not respond to commands, shows only reflexive responses to stimulation, and does not exhibit intentional movement. Obviously some significant percentage of these clinical diagnoses may be in error.

Neuroimaging is increasingly being used to look for evidence of conscious mental activity in patients believed to suffer from a permanent vegetative state. In a seminal case, fMRI demonstrated that when an apparently vegetative patient was asked to imagine a tennis game, there was a significant increase in the activity in her supplementary motor cortex. When asked to imagine walking through her house, there were increases in the brain activity of her parahippocampal gyrus and other relevant brain regions (Owen et al., 2006). Her brain activity was indistinguishable from normal volunteers asked to imagine the same activities.

What we have learned from studying the brain function of patients in vegetative states is that, on average, their brain activity is only about 40 percent of normal individuals in an awake resting state. But a few patients in a vegetative state show essentially normal levels of brain activity.

What's more telling is that in a vegetative state certain brain regions that are normally joined are now functionally disconnected. Research shows that large-scale neural circuits and networks that cross major regions of the brain must be functionally intact for a person to be conscious. Functional disconnections of critical brain circuits are detected by stimulating the brain—say, playing a clicking sound in the ears—and following how brain regions activate in sequence.

In normal, alert subjects an auditory stimulus such as the clicking elicits a well-established sequence of brain activity that cascades through the brain's auditory circuits. In a person in a vegetative state, downstream brain regions normally spiked by sound show no evidence of "hearing" the clicking. Even though brain imaging shows the physical connections appear to be intact, they have become functionally disconnected from one another. In particular, the return response between the frontal and parietal cortices and the temporal cortex that completes a sensory processing feedback loop is interrupted (Boly et al., 2011).

Although islands of brain functioning may remain active in a vegetative state, they are disconnected from each other resulting in the splitting off of the dimension of wakefulness from that of awareness. In some respects, similar functional disconnections of brain regions can be seen in deep sleep or anesthesia, during which stimuli that normally elicit a complex cascading sequence of regional brain activity in the waking state fail to propagate. Waking, alert consciousness is associated with an integrative connectivity among brain regions. In normal sleep or with anesthesia, the process of waking up reconnects and restores the functioning of these circuits. Whether this waking up occurs at the level of specific brain structures or at the level of neuronal circuits or networks is subject to debate (Koch & Greenfield, 2007).

Figure 3-2 (adapted from Laureys, 2007) reveals that two general properties of states of being, the degree of conscious awareness and the physical level of wakefulness, that we often think of as being essentially the same thing, can actually become separated in certain states of consciousness. Individuals can be awake in a vegetative state in that their eyes are open and they appear to be looking at things, although their level of conscious awareness is low. Conversely a person having a lucid dream in which he is able to exert deliberate control over the content of the dream is nonetheless asleep by standard measures. Thus degree of wakefulness and level of consciousness are actually two independent dimensions of state-space. Mind and body are uncoupled.

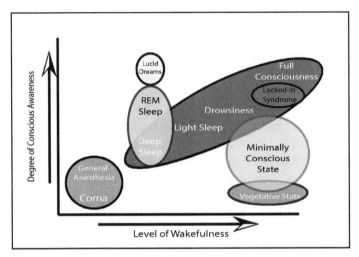

Figure 3-2
Separation of Wakefulness from Conscious Awareness
(Adapted from Laureys, 2007)

As chair of the Bioethics committee at a major children's hospital, I was consulted in decisions about whether to continue life support for children believed to be in a permanent vegetative state. It is daunting to confront our limitations in determining a person's degree of conscious awareness. In most instances we tried to respect the family's (when there was one) wishes within reason. In one extreme case, we were ordered by a judge to keep a brain dead child in the Intensive Care Unit (ICU) for three days until the family's religious leader stopped praying for a miracle and allowed us to turn off the respirator. Of course, that denied another child an ICU bed, and the hospital had to absorb the considerable costs as the insurance company stopped paying when the child first met criteria for brain death. Perhaps more telling was that it demoralized the ICU staff, who saw their job as caring for the desperately ill, not conducting a prolonged wake. There are no easy answers in such situations.

BRAIN MICROSTATES

Most of the scientists investigating different states of consciousness report brain and behavioral states as lasting for minutes to hours or even months in the case of conditions such as depression and mania. When specifying coordinates a given state occupies in multdimensional state-space they use values averaged over time. For example, the Baby Watchers use heart and respiratory rates averaged over periods of minutes. But what do you see if you repeatedly sample at a very, very, very fast rate? What if you could update your state-space plot a thousand times a second? Would you continue to see a repeating set of distinct brain states or would it just be random activity without pattern?

The EEG and MEG are the imaging tools best suited for looking at very rapid changes in the brain. They are capable of measuring changes in brain activity patterns occurring as frequently as one thousand times a second. When we use the EEG or MEG to investigate millisecond-by-millisecond whole-brain landscapes of electrical or magnetic activity we find a relatively small set of distinct and stable brain activity patterns called microstates.

A number of European researchers have most thoroughly studied microstates, especially members of a Swiss-based group called the Altered States of Consciousness Consortium. Dietrich Lehmann, Dieter Vaitl, Jiri Wakermann, and Thomas Koenig, in particular, have contributed to the detection and classification of microstates, their relationship with normal cognitive processes and their variations in mental disorders.

Microstates are defined as whole brain activity represented as a topographic map of the brain that is "segmented" (divided) into zones based on a measure of the strength of electrical activity (global field power) distributed across the individual's brain. These zones of brain activity are usually represented by different colors, typically ranging from red (high) activity to blue (low) activity, and displayed on an outline of the top of a schematized head—the "nose" and "ears" providing orientation (see Figure 3-3, next page). Individual microstates are differentiated from one another by mathematical comparisons (essentially subtracting one from another) to determine how similar or dissimilar they are according to predefined rules.

This is a technically complex process, but it reveals the existence of a relatively small number of distinct and stable brain activity states that repeat themselves in regular cycles. Microstates typically last between 90 to 160 milliseconds and switch from one after the other in predictable patterns. A given microstate may repeat several times in the course of one second. Figure 3-3 (Microstates) shows a simulated series of microstate electrical activity brain maps (see Koenig, 2002 for actual data).

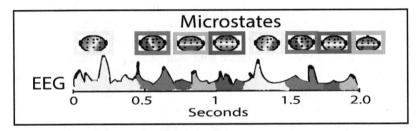

Figure 3-3 Microstates
(Adapted from Koenig, 2002)

When examined on a millisecond-by-millisecond time scale, it is evident that brainwave electrical rhythms—such as the alpha waves elicited by closing your eyes—are actually composed of a small number of microstates that repeat over and over. Specific classes of microstates can be defined based on their topography, the length of time they last, how often they occur, and the total percentage of time that they are present within a specific period of time. How long a microstate lasts appears to be a critical defining variable. Microstates are believed to represent the recurring activations of distinct neuronal networks that turn on and off as we look at things, recall past experiences, or make future plans.

Microstates have been called the "*atoms of thought*," as they appear to underlie much of our thinking and perceiving (Lehmann, Strik, Henggeler, Koenig, & Koukkou, 1998). Microstates associated with looking at an object can, for example, be reliably distinguished from those associated with abstract thinking. In the laboratory, scientists create mental tasks, such as solving a math problem or puzzle, and then examine the relationships of specific microstates to the individual's responses to the task. What we see and think appears to be a function of the microstate of our brain at the very instant of perception (Van De Ville, Britz, & Michel, 2010). While doing the same task, individuals often display unique personal patterns of microstates. But each person's types and sequences of microstates reliably repeat from trial to trial.

Types and patterns of microstates change with age (Koenig et al., 2002). Children have fewer distinct classes of microstates and, on average; their microstates last for longer periods of time. By early adolescence the number of microstate types increases—and, with few exceptions, those microstates last for shorter periods. In adulthood, and again after age 50, one can detect changes in the pattern of microstates that correlate with changes in information processing. Certain mental disorders such as schizophrenia, depression, and Alzheimer's disease as well as psychoactive drugs and hypnosis show significant differences in microstate topographies, frequency of occurrence, and duration when compared with normal individuals performing the same task. The major differences mainly occur in the time specific microstates last, rather than the appearance of abnormal or unusual microstates.

MOLECULAR BRAIN STATES

Brain states may also be studied at a molecular level. Scientists from an array of specialties have begun to probe the molecular biology of certain states of being. And, like the early sleep research pioneers, they are first trying to understand three basic states of being—waking, deep sleep, and dream sleep—at the molecular level. Primarily through studying animals, they apply the powerful genetic and microassay tools developed by the field of molecular biology over the past two decades. Their eventual goal: to understand the genetic, molecular, and cellular mechanisms underlying different sleep states. They hope that this level of analysis will help to develop better medications to treat sleep disorders.

Scientists seek evidence that certain genes turn on or off during specific sleep states. They also hope to learn whether some biological reactions are accelerated or inhibited, or whether exotic substances—referred to as "sleep molecules"—accumulate to induce sleep. They face the daunting task of collecting biological samples, often measuring tiny amounts of a chemical or RNA in brain tissue while at the same time trying to keep a living animal's sleep-wake cycles as natural as possible. Needless to say, besides the technical problems, they must grapple with thorny theoretical issues and vigorous disputes about the interpretation of experimental results. Nonetheless, exciting advances have been made that show that the molecular state of the brain varies with an organism's state of being (Lydic, 1998; Lydic & Baghdoyan, 1999).

"RESTING" BRAIN STATES

In the 1990s, researchers noticed by accident that brain activity actually decreased in certain regions when subjects were asked to perform a task. Further investigation, notably by Marcus Raichle and colleagues, led to

the identification of the Default Mode Network (DMN), which characterizes the brain at rest (Raichle, 2006). Although many scientists were
initially skeptical of Raichle's results, the brain activity patterns of the
mind in a state of rest, so-called stimulus independent thought, is now a
hot research topic.

The idling brain has characteristic patterns of activity that appear
when people report that they are daydreaming or thinking of nothing in
particular, just letting their mind wander aimlessly from thought to
thought. There is evidence that the neural circuitry for the default mode
network is present at birth in full-term babies, but must develop in
premature babies (Doria et al., 2010). Interestingly, in adults, the resting
or idle brain is characterized by only four microstates (Van De Ville et
al., 2010).

One of the amazing findings from studying the mind at rest is that it
accounts for the vast majority of the energy used by the brain. Giving a
subject a difficult mental task may only increase the brain's total energy
consumption by one percent or less (Raichle, 2006). Exactly what all of
the apparently idle brain activity is doing is an open question. The prevailing consensus is that it shows that most perceptual and cognitive
functions result from intrinsic brain processing of limited amounts of
sensory information—it is the mental activity of the brain-mind that
gives meaning to raw sensory input.

More than a century ago, William James observed:

Enough has now been said to prove the general law of percep-
tion, which is this, that whilst part of what we perceive comes
through our senses from the object before us, another (and it
may be the larger part) always comes (in Lazarus's phrase) out
of our own head. (James, 1890 p. 103)

Recent research suggests that the wandering mind is not a happy
mind, however (Killingsworth & Gilbert, 2010). Using an iPhone App,
scientists were able to study thousands of people answering questions
about their thoughts and moods that were put to them at random times.
They found that peoples' minds wandered frequently regardless of what
they are doing. When people were absorbed in their wandering thoughts,
they tended to be less happy than when their attention was focused on an
activity. What people were thinking was more predictive of how they felt
than what they were actually doing. Using time-lag analytic techniques,

they found that the mind's wandering was more often a cause of feeling unhappy than a consequence. They concluded that our ability to let our minds wander among memories of the past or to fantasize about possible future scenarios comes with an emotional cost.

MINDREADING

Until now, our wish to have some device that could accurately divine human thoughts and intentions was the stuff of myth and science fiction. Now, we are approaching the threshold of that possibility. Faster, more powerful computers permit whole new levels of brain imaging analysis to occur ever closer to real time. The most recent advance is an approach technically known as multi-voxel pattern analysis (MVPA) of fMRI data; the practice popularly known as "mindreading." The point of MVPA is to detect and classify unique patterns of brain activity that are associated with different states of consciousness. Once researchers recognized that this task was, in essence, a classic pattern classification problem similar to programing a computer to recognize faces or handwriting, great strides were made in adapting existing algorithms and experiments.

Conventional brain imaging research, the kind discussed earlier for depression, hypnotic analgesia, and vegetative states seeks to correlate the level of brain activity in specific brain regions, e.g., the anterior cingulate cortex, with a particular state of mind or mental task. The activity of the brain regions of interest is compared between the two states usually one region at a time. Brain state differences between two mental states can be detected this way, but they must be relatively large to be reliably distinguished.

MVPA greatly enhances our ability to distinguish between two brain states because it takes into account the pattern of activity in many brain regions. Because it simultaneously looks at many brain areas, MVPA extracts the maximum information available from fMRI data, increasing our ability to discriminate among certain mental states (Haynes and Rees, 2006).

A classic MVPA experiment involves demonstrating that a scientist looking only at the pattern of a subject's brain activity can (about 85 percent of the time) predict whether the person was looking at a picture of a face or a picture of a chair (Haynes & Rees, 2006). This good—but by far from perfect—degree of accuracy is greatly helped by the fact that a specific brain region, the fusiform face area, is dedicated to processing faces and activates a unique pattern when the subject sees a face. A picture of a chair, however, activates another brain area, the parahippocampal place area, or PPA. So comparing the brain activity patterns of the two conditions makes it relatively easy to differ between seeing a picture of a face from seeing a picture of a chair. MVPA, however, has a much harder time decoding what a person is seeing when looking at the natural world, with its profusion of unique objects and ever-changing conditions.

To detect covert or unconscious thoughts and attitudes, researchers exploit a number of strategies. They project different pictures separately into each eye, allowing them to watch patterns of brain activity change as the subject unconsciously switches back and forth between seeing the different images, a normal phenomenon called binocular rivalry. Other MVPA experiments follow more along the lines of a lie detector or scanner to detect prejudices, extremist, or criminal thinking. Studies purporting to find evidence of unique brain activity patterns for political or social values and racial bias have also made the rounds—consumer product companies are testing this technology to see if it can divine the secret desires of their customers. A few start-ups are attempting to market MVPA-based devices as a kind of lie or social deviance detector for law enforcement and security.

But many of the apparent differences between mental states or experimental conditions may actually reflect spontaneous and involuntary reactions to the artificial and somewhat sensory-deprived conditions of an fMRI experiment. One confounding factor rarely considered by scientists, entrepreneurs or the police: a lot of people space out in brain scanners. Lying in a narrow steel tube, partially restrained or forbidden to move lest it spoil the picture, eyes closed or staring at nothing or simple pictures and shapes, perhaps wearing head phones or earplugs, is definitely unnatural and sometimes anxiety-provoking. One survey of fMRI subjects participating in a variety of research studies found that two-thirds of them reported significant dissociative experiences, as measured by standard scales, while participating in an fMRI experiment (Michal, Roder, Mayer, Lengler, & Krakow, 2007).

Because of this, the current state of the science is nowhere near what would be required to create a true mind-reading machine that could be used outside of a controlled laboratory setting. The scientific challenges of creating a valid brain activity pattern analyzer for detecting nefarious intent or deliberate deception are daunting. However, the rapid growth of computing power, new algorithms, the coupling of two or more kinds of imaging, and the continuously increasing spatial and temporal resolution achieved during the last decade suggest that this possibility could be crudely realized in another decade or, at most, two.

If this happens a leading neuroscientist predicts that the real forensic use will be in probing an individual's overall pattern of honesty or dishonesty, rather than their truthfulness for a specific act (Gazzaniga, 2011). The obvious possibilities for misuse, intentional or accidental, are enormous. The ethical implications of an ability to penetrate an individual's mental privacy and read their thoughts or measure their degree of honesty are immense—conjuring up an Orwellian nightmare.

Peering into the Brain

In my scientific wanderings, I earned a master's degree studying the giant nerve fibers responsible for the escape reflex in the cockroach (i.e., large diameter nerves have faster rates of impulse conduction in invertebrates). You know, you flip on the kitchen light and the little buggers dart for cover in the blink of an eye. There is a longer story about how I got to this place, but the essence is that I was looking for simple examples in which to study the workings of a nervous system. By the time that conceptual journey ran dry, I was growing bits of nerve and muscle in Petri dishes. Anyway, I developed a humbling appreciation for the extraordinary complexity of the cockroach's nervous system and their survival, unchanged for hundreds of millions of years. That is Darwinian perfection.

My thesis required learning to use a variety of scientific instruments, including the electron microscope. Sitting in a darkened room in front of a starship console studded with knobs, dials, meters, and switches, all glowing with an eerie green light, I could see the magnified image of the tissue specimen on a glowing phosphorescent screen. I could change the magnification and move around, zooming in or out, focusing, and filtering the image. Amazing stuff. Remember, this was well before the microprocessor revolution. Now these kinds of image manipulations are so commonplace as to seem instinctive to the current generation.

I used this magic machine to look deeply into the cockroach's neuropil, a dense tangle of axons, dendrites, glial and nerve cells. At these levels of magnification, it became a vast serpentine jungle. To capture a single cubic millimeter of nerve tissue for more detailed study would require acres of 8 x 10 inch photographs. Once I did a back-of-the-envelope calculation to determine the number of square miles necessary to display an entire human brain on 8 x 10 electron micrographs taken at a high level of magnification. As I recall, it should be measured in Texas-sized units. When explored on this scale, the human brain is absolutely ginormous.

Zooming in on interesting-looking things in the cockroach nervous system—they don't really have a single "brain"—I had a reoccurring experience. There always seemed to be something interesting just beyond my ability to see it clearly. I would keep turning the rotary switch that increased the magnification in jumps, looking deeper (and therefore at a smaller and smaller part) trying to see what lay at the next level.

Studying the photographs later I would see things that I had missed while zooming around and wish that I had noticed them at the time and stopped to take a closer look. But in those days there was no going back: you only had ten 4-by-5, glass-plate negatives used for the sharpest possible plane of focus, and you had to make quick choices about what to photograph. Otherwise, the beam of electrons that made these levels of magnification possible burned up the specimen in front of your eyes.

Over the years I have witnessed a similar if-only-I-could-zoom-in-one-click-higher scenario play out with other scientific tools. The answer, it seems, always lurks a click or two higher than we can see. Despite the fact that we keep technologically increasing our resolution and thus seeing more and more details, the answer to that big question, "How does it all work?" always seems to lie just beyond the last click. Maybe it is time to take a couple of clicks backward and see if we can find a forest hidden in the trees.

NON-LINEAR DYNAMICAL SYSTEMS

As scientists from different disciplines learned more about states and studied cycles of states of interest to them, an important insight repeatedly emerged. The Baby Watchers, the psychiatrists, the sleep researchers, and the neurophysiologists independently converged on the discovery that states could be mathematically described and their interactions could be simulated on computers using a branch of mathematics known as dynamical systems.

William James anticipated a mathematical approach to states of consciousness by imagining a three-dimensional moving map tracing the flowing stream of thought (Figure 3-4). His imaginary mental mapping machine was constructed of a sheet of India rubber graph paper under which a moving ball traced-out a fluctuating, three-dimensional mental landscape over time. James intuitively understood that states of mind, especially identity states, exist within a multidimensional state-space.

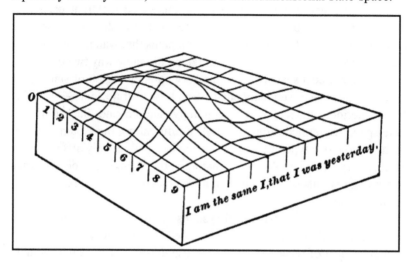

Figure 3-4
William James's Multi-Dimensional Stream of Consciousness
Figure from James's *Principles of Psychology—Vol 1,*
The stream of thought (James, 1950 p. 283)

Each and every dynamical system is specified by its unique set of mathematical equations that can be solved as a function of time. The behavior of many recurrent or cyclic phenomena can be closely modeled by dynamical systems—from the swinging pendulum of a clock to the increasing and decreasing numbers of interdependent animal populations such as a predator and its prey.

Mathematical models of dynamical systems are usually written in the form of difference equations or as differential equations. In computer simulations, once the state of a dynamical system is specified for a given starting point in state-space, all future states of that system can be calculated by repeatedly solving the set of equations while advancing the time variable in a series of small steps. This iterative process is referred to as solving the system or integrating the system. When we graph the series of solutions over time we see that they trace a pathway or trajectory.

Before we had powerful computers, solving a dynamical system and graphing its trajectory was a lot of work, and only simple examples were attempted. Now researchers and nonmathematicians alike can use readily available software to solve and plot a wide range of dynamical systems. The resulting explosion of interest has uncovered different classes of dynamical systems based on their trajectories. Some shift back and forth between two distinct states. Others exhibit paths that wander among multiple different states, seemingly never taking the same way twice in a row. In some dynamical systems, the trajectory enters a region of state-space in which the system suddenly changes its type of trajectory—say, going from a periodic trajectory to a seemingly random one. Such points in state-space are termed bifurcations. At a bifurcation, the system suddenly shifts from one type of trajectory to another qualitatively different type of trajectory. An example seen in nature is the change that occurs when something disrupts smoothly flowing water, causing it to break into roiling turbulence.

A special class of dynamical systems known as non-linear dynamical systems—what's more commonly called "chaos theory"—has attracted a great deal of recent attention because these systems can accurately model the complex behavior of many natural processes, ranging from molecular vibrations to celestial objects. Although chaos suggests total disorder and randomness, that's not true. Non-linear dynamical systems are deterministic—once the defining set of equations and initial conditions are specified, every future state of the system can be calculated forward in time.

Chaotic systems are sensitive to initial conditions, meaning that starting to solve the equations defining the system at two slightly different starting points in state-space can produce very different long-term patterns of behavior. This property, sometimes called the butterfly effect, was discovered by Edward Lorenz when, in order to save time, he restarted a computerized weather prediction program in the middle of a run rather than at the beginning. A tiny round-off error in the results from the prior run that Lorenz initially thought negligible, proved to produce large changes in outcome.

The name butterfly effect refers to the notion that even a tiny difference in initial starting conditions—metaphorically represented by the almost infinitesimal turbulence caused by a butterfly flapping its wings in the Amazon rainforest—could change the long-term weather patterns in Alaska. It also refers to the graphical trajectory in two dimensional state-space traced by classic solutions of Lorenz's set of equations (Figure 3-5). Known as the Lorenz attractor, with certain initial values this graph resembles the wings of a butterfly.

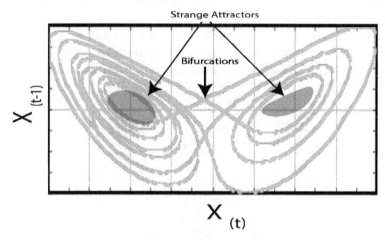

Figure 3-5 State-Space Plot of
the Lorenz "Butterfly" Equations

The graph (Figure 3-5) belongs to a larger class of mathematical objects known as strange attractors. Strange attractors are points or circle-like curves in state-space that appear to periodically capture the trajectory of a dynamical system exhibiting chaotic behavior. At bifurcation points, the trajectory suddenly jumps from one strange attractor to another, producing another circular trajectory in state-space.

It is thought-provoking that scientists studying different types of human or animal states, whether at a brain electrical microstate level or at a gross behavioral level, have independently observed that states of being behave as strange attractors within their respective multidimensional state-spaces. For example, sleep researchers have found certain sleep stages, notably Stage 2 and Stage 4, act as strange attractors on EEG state-space maps of sleep cycles (Babloyantz, Salazar, & Micolis, 1985). Bipolar researchers find evidence that the states of mania and depression act as strange attractors on state-space plots of mood swings over time (Gottschalk, Bauer, & Whybrow, 1995).

Figure 3-6 is a two dimensional (mood state) state-space plot of daily mood ratings for the "Christine" (described in Chapter 4) as she repeatedly and relentlessly swings between the extreme mood states of depression (blue) and mania (red), which act as strange attractors in her mood state-space. Christine spends the majority of her days in one of three global mood states: normal (approximately 40–65 on the daily mood rating scale), mania (90–100) and depression (10–25). Days (dots) lying outside of these three regions of state-space reflect switching among the three global mood states. Although Christine's switches were typically rapid, these are not well resolved temporally by (infrequent) daily ratings.

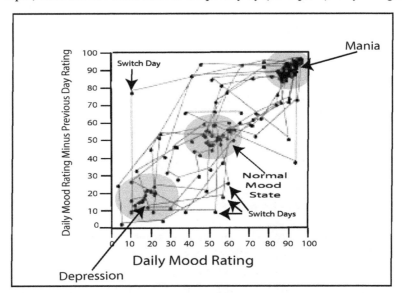

Figure 3-6
State-Space Plot of a Rapid Cycling Psychiatric Patient

Among the Baby Watchers, Peter Wolff and Ester Thelen drew attention to the goodness of fit between non-linear dynamical models and the pattern of infant states over their development. The pioneering team of Arnold Mandell and Karen Selz were the first to systematically pursue the mathematics of mood and personality using non-linear dynamical approaches. Others have since followed their example, correlating behavioral fluctuations with dynamical models (see Chapter 11).

Switches between and among states resemble the bifurcations characteristic of chaotic dynamical systems. While I have necessarily grossly simplified my discussion, the remarkable agreement between the mathematical models of non-linear dynamical systems and scientific data derived from research on many kinds of states of consciousness deserves further exploration. This approach may provide powerful new tools for understanding and predicting behavior—as well as define the limits of our ability to forecast human action (see Chapter 11).

THE MIND-BODY PROBLEM

Isomorphism

Professor Ira Levine (1937–2003) was a large, jovial man. Our lengthy conversations were frequently punctuated by laughter. But Ira understood seriously mentally ill patients better than any of my supervisors before or since. In the second year of my adult psychiatry training at Yale, Ira was one of my therapy supervisors.

We talked a lot about the mind as an idea. What is it? How can we understand it? One of the hard problems in brain science is integrating the many different levels of knowledge about the mind, the brain and behavior. There were so many ways to think about the brain-mind, from the membrane-ion channels fluxes and spiking neurons of my early neuroscience training to the psychodynamic meaning embedded within the auditory hallucinations of the paranoid schizophrenics served by Ira's clinic.

In these conversations, Ira introduced me to the concept of the isomorph: the idea that there was something that remains essentially the same across the many levels of understanding of our brain-mind.

Douglas Hofstadter popularized the term.

The word "isomorphism" applies when two complex structures can be mapped onto each other, in such a way that to each part of one structure there is a corresponding part in the other structure, where "corresponding" means that the two parts play similar roles in their respective structures (Hofstadter, 1979 p. 49).

My talks with Ira shaped my thinking as I began my scientific career. The idea of finding a brain-mind isomorph intrigued me. Years later I returned a long overdue book Ira loaned me as a resident. Attached was a note sheepishly confessing my guilt but also affirming that I was still looking for that isomorph.

Figure 3-7 is speculative. It depicts the way in which different state-space frameworks are isomorphically related by level of scientific analysis. In Figure 3-7 there are four levels of analysis: microstates, brain states, mood and identity states, and personality defined along three axes: duration, cognitive and behavioral complexity, and level of analysis.

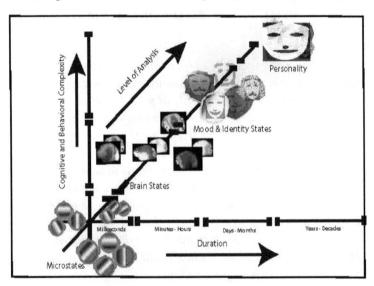

Figure 3-7
Isomorphism: From Microstates to Personality

Repeating combinations of certain microstates underlie specific brain states. For example, four basic microstates are consistently associated with the resting brain state seen in daydreaming (Van De Ville et al., 2010). Combinations of unique brain states compose larger mood and identity states (e.g., the sets of brain states associated with depression, hypnosis, and vegetative states discussed above). Mood and identity states, in turn, compose our global personalities (see Chapters 5 & 6).

Figure 3-7 offers a theoretical schema of how the concept of "state" may be defined at multiple levels of analysis. At each level of analysis the states differ in duration and cognitive and behavioral complexity. However, at each level of analysis, the concept of state defines a meaningful unit of analysis that maps onto state as defined above and below that level. We implicitly invoke something analogous to this fluidity across levels in every day conversation when we casually use the notion of state to describe both brief mental experiences like a moment of surprise and much longer lasting ones such as major depression.

We have preliminary evidence supporting this schema. Specific sets and probabilistic sequences of microstates are associated with moods (e.g., depression and anxiety) and cognitive states (e.g., focused attention and daydreaming). Studies tracking the same brain state on different times scales with EEG and fMRI find shared patterns that are time-scale independent (Van De Ville et al., 2010). The self-similarity of these patterns on different times scales has been advanced as evidence that states have fractal properties—i.e., that they show the same patterns at different scales of analysis in the way that a stream resembles a river or a branch resembles the tree it comes from.

Bridging Dualism

The fact that an individual's state of being can be specified at multiple levels of analysis makes it a candidate—indeed the leading candidate—to fulfill the role of an isomorph linking knowledge about the body, brain, and mind. In turn, the potential ability to map an individual's mental state as defined at one level of scientific analysis onto their biological state as defined by another level of analysis offers an approach to one of the enduring problems in Western philosophy and psychology—the mind-body problem. Debate about the nature of the relationship between the mind and brain has occupied Western philosophy since the time of Plato. Variations of the mind-body problem also appear in Eastern religions, such as the Yoga Sutra of Patnajali.

It is evident that the different levels at which we can scientifically examine the brain and behavior are interconnected. We believe, for example, that the biochemical processes in brain cells produce neural activity, which propagates through circuits and networks creating the electrical waves, rhythms, and patterns of brain activation that mark unique mental states. What we seek to understand is how these different levels and patterns of brain activiation generate conscious awareness and deliberate action. The enormous gaps in our understanding of the brain and our knowledge of the mind underscore the complexity of the mind-body problem.

In the seventeenth century, René Descartes celebrated both as the father of modern philosophy and the founder of modern mathematics, articulated the mind-body problem in its current form known as Dualism.

Descartes held that the mind was the source of consciousness and self-awareness; whereas the brain was the seat of intelligence. The mind was immaterial and unmeasurable while the brain was physical. These two entities, brain and mind, were therefore irreconcilable. It has been suggested that Descartes' formulation reflected an unconscious desire to reconcile his belief in the scientific method with his Catholic faith.

Many philosophers have offered alternate forms of the mind-body problem and various schools of dualism seek bridges between the brain and mind. The concept of state, which can be defined at multiple levels of analysis, from brain microstates to exceptional mental states, serves as a conceptual and empirical isomorph that spans the brain-mind discontinuities of the dualists. Understanding mind-brain-body interactions in terms of multilevel states of being may prove key to reconciling Descrates' dualism.

SYNTHESIS

Sleep, that rollercoaster of sleep stages that we must lap multiple times each night or suffer the consequences, is the most intensely investigated of all mind-body states. Sleep research and sleep medicine illustrate the advances possible when experts achieve a sufficient consensus in coding states to share common perspectives. But sleep, one of the most basic of all of our daily states of mind, remains a profound mystery. It is essential for our sanity—and ultimately for life itself. Yet, we still do not understand why?

Rapidly advancing technologies for measuring markers of brain activity—electrical, magnetic, and metabolic—allow us to "see" brain states. From idle daydreaming to PTSD flashbacks, we find unique patterns of brain activation and inhibition that track subjective experiences such as the remission of depression, response to a placebo, or the degree of awareness in an apparently comatose person. The future promises much more as we combine imaging technologies and develop software to overcome the spatial, temporal, and sensitivity limitations imposed by each method in isolation.

Coding systems such as those developed by the Baby Watchers and sleep researchers revealed that more complex behaviors (e.g., an adult's night's sleep or an infant's sleep-wake cycle) are composed of a limited set of distinct states flowing from one to another in a roughly predictable, repeating sequence. Brain imaging revealed that discrete states exist on multiple time and dimensional scales from microstates lasting fractions of a second reflecting activation in specific neural networks to global brain states such as depression lasting months.

By nature of this definability at different temporal and spatial scales, states offer an isomorphic construct that spans our many—largely unintegrated—domains of knowledge about the brain and the mind. States also fit well with a branch of mathematics, non-linear dynamical systems theory, which quantifies the operation of many complex natural phenomena that are impervious to more traditional mathematical approaches. Linking states of being at different levels of analysis suggests a way to bridge the mind-body chasm that has stymied Western science and philosophy for centuries.

CHAPTER 4   CHANGING STATE

Christine

Late one night, I found myself desperately struggling to stay awake. As part of a psychiatry research team it was my responsibility to keep the patient continuously awake until she switched out of her depression and hopefully into a more functional state. Christine, the subject of tonight's research, was sitting next to me on the couch in the dayroom. We were watching an old black-and-white gangster movie.

It was about nine months into my clinical research fellowship at the National Institute of Mental Health (NIMH) in Bethesda. My boss, Dr. Robert (Bob) Post, directed a unit that specialized in bipolar (aka manic-depressive) disorder. Much of our research focused on understanding and attempting to control transitions between depression and mania. I had just completed a residency in adult psychiatry at Yale in July 1979 and was interested in the newly emerging discipline known as "biological psychiatry" that was centered at the NIMH.

Desperately trying to stay awake myself, I fought against an almost overpowering feeling of slipping into sleep. It would be such bliss to just let go and sink into delicious sleep. I was so tired. Snatches of a dream started when my eyes momentarily fluttered closed. Forcing myself awake, I had to keep Christine from falling asleep—or our experiment could be ruined. Sometimes even a few seconds of sleep was sufficient to block the sleep-deprivation switching effect.

Tonight we were trying to trigger a switch out of her depression. Hopefully not into mania, but into one of Christine's calmer states, in which she came alive as a delightful and sensitive person. A bit of a poetess, she had an unfinished volume of delicate verse. The remnants of which were collected in a box in the nurses' safekeeping. She tried to burn it before falling back into another deep depression.

Nodding off, Christine slumping forward.

"Christine. No! Don't! Jean, come help me," I called the nurse sitting across the hall in the nursing station.

Shaking Christine, I pulled her to her feet. She was dead weight, collapsing against me as Jean and I dragged her up and down the hallway. Gradually she woke up. And with that awareness came biting sarcasm, accusing us of being sadistic torturers under the guise of science.

In some respects Christine was correct. We only had a vague idea of why keeping a person continuously awake—sometimes for several days—worked. She was a guinea pig—who we followed for well over a year trying to get a handle on her mood swings. (The State-Space mood plot, Figure 3-6, in Chapter 3 comes from Christine.) We were taking advantage of her illness to try to learn something. And that something, whatever it was, might never be of help to her. It seemed like a promising strategy—to switch her out of her depression and then to stabilize her in a new mood state with a combination of medications. But there were so many permutations of possible critical factors, mostly beyond our control, and precious little to guide us.

After about a half hour, we ended up back on the couch again. I tried to pick up the movie plot but had forgotten who did what, so it didn't make much sense. Seconds later, I jerked awake. Christine was doing jumping jacks in the middle of the dayroom—her unbuttoned shirt flopping open immodestly. Jean was trying to calm her down and button the shirt. But Christine was having nothing of it—pushing Jean away and throwing her elbows around wildly like a basketball player protecting a rebound. One caught Jean in the face. Blood spurted from her nose. I grabbed Christine from behind, pinning her arms across her naked breasts. Suddenly she was incredibly strong, twisting in my grip. She broke free and took off running for the ward door.

The door was locked against this possibility, but I wondered whether that would hold her. Drops of blood led to the nursing station. Jean was inside, head tilted back, pressing a wad of tissue to her face. I telephoned the hospital operator to call a code, which should bring staff from other wards to help us. It would take time for them to come. I had to let them on the ward while keeping Christine from bolting through the open door.

Fortunately, Christine ignored me, while she furiously tried to open the door. When the first face appeared in the small center window, I used my body to push Christine aside and unlocked the door. Jean was there also, clumsily blocking Christine, while still holding a bloody wad of tissue against her nose. Together we managed to keep her from the door while our backups slid in one by one.

The hospital policy was that the unit's most senior nurse took charge, so Jean directed the team on their roles, dispatching one to prepare our quiet room, a seclusion cell at the far end of the ward. It shared a wall with the on-call doctor's bedroom (probably not a coincidence). On command, the team rushed Christine, each firmly grabbing an arm or leg with both hands. We lifted her up waist high. Struggling wildly, there was little leverage for her manic strength to push against. Each of us tightly holding a limb, we carried her down the hall and laid her flat on her back on the stained linoleum floor in the bare seclusion room.

We fled, frantically locking the door behind us. But she didn't chase us. She just looked around—she had been there before. The research protocol called for me to draw her blood and collect her pee, but that obviously was not going to happen. We had switched her out of depression all right—into a full-blown psychotic mania. I hoped that when she came down that she would at least get a little time to work on her poetry before the next depression.

I could go to bed now. But, of course, I couldn't sleep. I lay there listening to her scream and cry and beat on the walls and door. Sometimes she half-sang, half-screamed a verse from the Rolling Stones.

> *Well this could be the last time.*
> *This could be the last time*
> *Maybe the last time*
> *I don't know. Oh no, oh no.*

Over the three years I worked on that research unit, I saw many other switches between depressed and manic states. I recall putting one of them back to bed after 48 exhausting hours of sleep-deprivation-induced mania. Watching her EEG tracing, we woke her up again as soon as she achieved Stage 2 sleep. She was as deeply depressed as I had ever seen her. There was a tragic look in her eyes. Once more she was being sentenced to an interminable period of anguish. No matter how exhausting or how badly she screwed up her life by the crazy things that she did and said while in a manic state, it was preferable to crushing depression.

We all have experienced abrupt shifts in mood and behavior such as Christine did in response to the sleep-deprivation experiment. In most people, these mood swings are not nearly as extreme as Christine's wild oscillations between depression and mania. But intense emotion can overtake any of us, seemingly out of nowhere—a burst of anger, a sudden overwhelming feeling of tearful sadness triggered by a chance remark or small memento, a sense of spiritual wonderment. At the time, we typically do not even notice the change. It is only later, as we reflect on what happened, that we appreciate the suddenness of the shift and—perhaps—identify the remark or event that triggered the switch.

ALL STATES ARE TRANSIENT BY NATURE

The chance to see the discrete nature of states of consciousness heightens at a moment of abrupt change between them. This moment of change, as one mental state transforms into another, is commonly called a switch. In Christine's case, by aggressively blocking her normal transition into sleep, we instead precipitated a switch into mania. One moment she was slipping into a state of exhausted sleep. The next moment, forced to stay awake, she was supercharged with manic energy and we struggled to contain her.

Although mental states such as depression can persist for prolonged periods, all mental states are transient—ultimately, any given state always switches to another. In normal daily life, these switches are relatively smooth and expected. Typically they are so embedded in our daily routines that they go unnoticed. It is only when a switch causes an extreme or unexpected change in mental state that we more clearly see how a given state of consciousness can impose a distinct structure and organization on mental and physical energy, attitude, and activity such as differences between depressed Christine and manic Christine.

In many respects, we consider psychological normality to be manifest by a flow of mental states that are appropriate to the situation and the culture. There are no extreme or inappropriate changes in mental state. Abnormality, in turn, is manifest by the absence of socially expectable mental states for a given situation, or by inappropriate changes in mental state that are extreme or incongruous, such as a fit of hilarity during a solemn funeral service.

TYPES OF SWITCHES

There are different kinds of switches. For example, the brief drowsy period of infants discussed in the preceding (Chapter 2–First States), is considered by some researchers to actually be a switch between sleep and wakefulness rather than a discrete state. The manifestation of drowsiness that leads from waking to sleep differs from that leading from sleeping to wakefulness. Similar directional differences can be observed in bipolar disorder, panic attacks, periodic catatonia and dissociative identity disorder among other conditions. The general principle is that switches between two recurrent states of being will differ depending on whether the direction of the switch is from state A to state B or the reverse of B to A.

Although we may be aware of becoming sleepy, in most instances we are not aware of either falling asleep or waking up at the moment that it happens. Rather it is only later that we realize that a switch has occurred. The familiar and natural nature of falling asleep and waking up makes these relatively extreme transitions in mental state 'normal' and unremarkable. No one says, "This morning I went from a recumbent, physically quiescent state of unconscious mental activity to an active, mobile, mentally alert state over the course of several minutes." Nonetheless—teenagers excepted—most of us more or less successfully finesse this extreme transition every day.

Neuroscientists, psychiatrists and psychologists have studied switches in a number of conditions. Besides the dramatic switches between depression and mania in bipolar patients, sudden and extreme changes in mental state occur in a number of other psychiatric disorders. A panic attack, for example, is an abrupt onset of a state of extreme anxiety that typically reaches a peak in around ten minutes and then subsides more slowly. Panic attacks may be triggered by situations or specific stimuli or they may occur unexpectedly. They can also be induced in several ways to be studied in a more scientific fashion.

Another dramatic psychiatric example is periodic catatonia, which is a mental state in which a person stays frozen in the same position, doesn't respond to questions or commands, won't talk, and often appears to be in a stupor. A catatonic person will allow his body to be rearranged into different positions, even when they are awkward or uncomfortable, and then will hold them unmoving for hours. This symptom, waxy flexibility, is a cardinal feature of the catatonic state.

Patients prone to catatonia may also exhibit another extreme state marked by agitation, incoherent shouting, and violent destructiveness. If untreated this agitated state can be fatal. Although catatonic states are often considered a form of schizophrenia, they are also common in other types of mental illness, especially bipolar and dissociative disorders. Switches in and out of catatonic states are usually rapid—and, like panic attacks, can be induced and studied.

THE SWITCH PROCESS

During the late 1960s, a group of young researchers at the National Institutes of Mental Health intramural research program in Bethesda, MD investigated the hypothesis that a neurobiological switch process causes rapid transitions from one extreme mental state to another. These pioneers included William Bunney, Dennis Murphy, Richard Wyatt, and Frederick Goodwin; they were part of a larger contingent of aggressive young scientists seeking to displace the then-dominant psychoanalytic model with a new approach to mental health research. Stimulated by the successes of early antipsychotic and antidepressant medications, this new approach became known as "biological psychiatry." Their protégés, notably Robert Post and Thomas Wehr, continued work on the switch process and served as mentors for my generation of research fellows arriving at the beginning of the 1980s.

When I arrived at the NIMH, there were many ongoing studies of rapid-cycling bipolar patients seeking to understand the mysterious switch process. By then, the psychoanalysts had vanished from the main research campus, although a few clung to old projects at distant satellite programs. For another year or so, evidence of their banishment lay piled in closets and storage rooms: shelves of audiocassettes, boxes of reel-to-reel videotapes, and stacks of process notes all testified to a premature and enforced end to years of psychodynamic research. Later, I would meet some of the psychoanalytic researchers who left the NIMH for private practice in the DC area. Their often angry stories of banishment served as cautionary tales as I watched the molecular psychiatrists, who view psychiatric disorders from a genetic perspective, displace the biological psychiatrists starting in the late 1990s.

Bunney, Murphy and Goodwin, together with colleagues and protégés, pursued the switch process by studying hospitalized bipolar disorder patients as they switched back and forth between depression and mania. Patterns emerged that differed for switches from depression into mania as opposed to switches from mania into depression (Bunney & Murphy, 1974). But in both cases, the individual makes a sudden transition from one extreme mood state to another in a brief time, compared to the time spent in their moods before and after the switch.

Exactly how long a switch from one state to another takes hinges on a number of factors including: what it is that you are measuring; how you define the switch's beginning and end; and how often you measure it. Bipolar researchers at the NIMH typically used mood and behavior scales administered by the nursing staff just a few times a day—usually at the change of a nursing shift. The nurses coming on duty and the nurses leaving for the day would meet in the nursing station and agree on mood- and behavior-ratings for each patient. As a result, these studies usually describe mood state changes as taking several hours to days to occur. Yet the baby watchers and other observers who did their studies on a minute-by-minute basis describe switches as occurring over a few minutes—or even seconds.

Information theory dictates that to detect the moment of change between two discrete states, we have to apply our measure of change at least twice as often as the switch takes to complete. So mood scales applied a few times a day can, at best, measure mood swings on time scales of hours to days; whereas virtually continuous measures such as EEG or heart rate can detect changes in state occurring over minutes or even seconds. Whatever time scale one chooses, it's important to remember that switches are brief events compared to the duration of the states that precede and follow them.

In the case of switches from depression into mania, the patient may have been depressed for weeks to months. During that depressed period, she would often sit unmoving for hours, seldom speaking. When asked how she was doing, the patient would express feelings of guilt, hopelessness and worthlessness. She would move slowly and seemingly with great effort—as if walking underwater. The patient would keep to herself and, if staff left her alone, would lie in bed for long periods, apparently sleeping.

Nursing notes quoted in a research paper capture the switch from depression to mania (Bunney, Murphy, Goodwin, & Borge, 1972):

> During the patient's depression the notes describe her behavior as *slow speech, retarded movement, seems to fade into the wallpaper. Mostly non-verbal. Guilt. Hopelessness.* She says, *I am no good to anyone. I am going to be dead soon.*

The day before a switch into mania the person often appears to be what most people would call normal, displaying a pleasant mood, making conversation and spending more time with other patients and staff. On the day before she switches into mania, the nursing notes remark on her *pleasant mood. Verbalizing more today. With other patients more.* In the evening she is reported to be *very pleasant* and *concentrating better.*

The shift from depression to mania is evident by a fast and furious increase in activity—incessant loud talking or shouting, agitated movements, demands for attention, preoccupation with sex, impaired judgment and sometimes anger and aggression.

At 4:15 a.m. on the day of the switch into mania she *came to lounge talking and moving rapidly. For the first time in months. Decorating ward. Manipulative. Angry and flighty. Trembling of hands. Laughing in old manic manner."* As the day progressed, she is reported as *"anxious, paranoid, blasting staff. Rambling. Provocative. Monopolized group therapy. Undressing.*

The final phase shows grandiose—sometimes paranoid— ideas about the self and her accomplishments, racing thoughts and flights of ideas, making rhymes and puns and talking gibberish. She is irritable and unable to accept advice or limits. The amount of sleep decreases, including the amount of time spent in REM, the stage associated with dreaming.

The following day she is *very angry, demanding, disruptive. Crying. Flight of ideas. Dancing. Laughing. Denying Illness. Stated, I am well. Psychotic, says, 25 men attacked me today* (Bunney et al., 1972 p. 296).

This mania could then last for days to a month or more.

Eventually the patient would switch out of mania and back into a profound depression. Typically there would be a short interval, often one to four days, marked by rapid spikes between symptoms of mania and symptoms of depression. Sudden tearfulness, paralyzing concerns about self-adequacy and fears of a lifetime of despair would alternate with manic grandiosity and delusional self-confidence. Speech and movement slows markedly and the patient visibly loses energy. Her sleep increases, REM sleep included, but she will still awake feeling exhausted and depressed.

Highly individual symptoms appear, too, (like the "trembling of hands") and unique behaviors ("old manic laughter") appear or disappear as her mood states changed. Transformed posture, movement, mannerisms and speech all heighten a sense of enormous personality change. The face would rearrange itself in ways much deeper than the typical differences between, say, a smile and a frown. The unit nurses came to use such individual state-dependent differences in demeanor and behavior to anchor the depressed and manic ends of their mood rating scales for each research patient.

The length of manic or depressive episodes and the frequency of shifts between the two extremes could be influenced by mood switches in other patients. Watching pairs of patients cycle in and out of depression and mania in virtual lockstep, researchers concluded that their synchrony seemed more than coincidence. It often appears that some event or situation that disturbs their routine triggers these bipolar switches.

Weekend passes home or planning for discharge from the hospital, in particular, seemed to bring on mania (Bunney et al., 1972). Using a number of experimental manipulations, we could switch patients out of depression into a range of mood states running from a normal mood to raging mania. Changing their day-night/sleep-wake cycles, pushing them to engage in continuous physical activity, or sleep depriving them such as Christine were all more-or-less successful in switching depressed patients out of a depressed state.

We did have one problem: we were unable to reliably switch those patients into a more normal or euthymic state and would often cause a burst of mania or hypomania instead. Even if we did achieve a switch into a desirable mood state, we could rarely sustain it, despite trials with numerous medications. In a few cases, however, a treatment seemed to succeed for one person but failed miserably with the next. Success at times hovered tantalizingly close, but we never achieved the reliability and safety we needed to make these approaches standard treatment. These techniques may nonetheless be warranted on occasion with patients who do not respond to conventional treatment.

By the mid-1970's, the NIMH group had identified another, even more powerful, trigger that could precipitate switches from depression into mania (Bunney & Murphy, 1974). Certain medications used to treat depression were also capable of inducing a precipitous and sometimes disastrous switch into mania. This is now recognized as a serious side effect of most antidepressant medications. How frequently it happens, and whether or not, some people are genetically predisposed to medication-induced switches, are matters of current research. But it is clear that at least 10%—and perhaps as many as 60%—of bipolar patients may be susceptible to medication-triggered switches from depression into mania (Papolos, 2003).

The fact that a number of different kinds of events and interventions, e.g., sleep-deprivation, antidepressant medication, or weekend passes, can elicit a switch between two extreme mood states such as depression and mania, illustrates that a variety of triggers can induce the same change between a given pair of states. The symptoms and time course of the switch induced by these different stimuli are sometimes similar and sometimes may differ, but the endpoints of depression or mania are remarkably constant in state space.

PANIC ATTACKS

At about the same time and in a similar fashion, another group of scientists at NIMH and elsewhere were discovering that panic attacks, those quick switches into a mental state of extreme anxiety, could also be triggered by a variety of stimuli and experimental techniques. These ranged from exposure of the individual to an emotionally charged object or situation to a wide range of medications that worked on different brain systems.

Three well-studied techniques for producing panic attacks are the use of carbon dioxide (CO_2) inhalation, hyperventilation, and the intravenous infusion of sodium lactate. These experimental procedures produce panic attacks that closely resemble spontaneous panic attacks (Nardi et al., 2004). For individuals not predisposed to panic attacks, these procedures do not significantly increase their anxiety nor produce much discomfort. For certain people, however, breathing high concentrations of CO_2, hyperventilating, or receiving an intravenous infusion of sodium lactate induces a panic attack. The majority of individuals susceptible to these procedures meet diagnostic criteria for a panic disorder.

Panic attacks are intensely unpleasant physical experiences. A pounding heart, a feeling of bursting or tightly squeezing chest pain, dizziness, shortness of breath, tingling and numbness, and feelings of almost paralyzing terror, may occur without warning. Suddenly the person feels as if he is suffering a heart attack, stroke or is going crazy. They believe that they are about to die or are losing their mind. Panic attacks can happen anytime and anywhere, even during sleep. Most last just a few minutes and rarely continue more than an hour or so.

An estimated 3 to 6 million Americans suffer panic attacks, which appear to be about twice as common in women as men. Certain situations can trigger them, leading the person to avoid places and activities that may trigger an attack. About a third of panic disorder patients curtail their activities to circumscribed settings, a response that interferes with their lives.

Although panic attacks can be exhausting, many who suffer them say the continuous worry about the next attack drains them even more. That worry also wears away at family and friends. Sufferers obsess over every possible sign, symptom or twinge that may signal an impending attack. Yet most panic attacks still catch an individual by surprise.

Cognitive Behavioral Therapy and a range of medications can help up to 70 percent of patients. Often these two approaches are combined. Some sufferers first discover that alcohol, certain medications or illegal drugs reduce their panic attacks and decrease their chronic anxiety. For this reason panic disorder patients are considered to be at higher risk for drug and alcohol abuse and long-term problems with addiction.

CATATONIA

The first time I witnessed a person switch into a catatonic state, I felt an enormous sense of relief. By suddenly becoming frozen and mute, my patient saved me from serious humiliation—in, of all places, a courtroom.

It happened when I rotated onto a psychiatric unit as an intern taking an elective. Reporting for duty, I was informed that I would be testifying in court within the hour. One of my patients was challenging her involuntary commitment that morning. As her newly assigned doctor, I was being dispatched to testify as to why she needed to remain hospitalized against her will. I hadn't met her (or, for that matter, my other patients). I didn't even have time to scan her voluminous chart.

And so I entered a courtroom for the first time in my life. While we waited for the proceedings to start, my patient's young lawyer approached and asked if I had read the three large psychiatric texts he held. I acknowledged being familiar with one of them, although I seriously doubt that anyone—except perhaps their editors—had read all 1,200-plus pages of each one. Belatedly, I realized that I was being set up. I became uncomfortably aware of how little I knew about my patient or about psychiatry in general. What a complete fool I was going to be on the witness stand!

There was something amiss with the paperwork, however, and the judge refused to begin until the patient completed and signed some document. After discussion at the bench, a form was brought for the patient to sign as she sat beside the judge in the witness stand. With a flourish her attorney handed her his pen and a clipboard, which she readily took preparing to sign. Suddenly she froze; the pen suspended an inch above the paper. A minute or so passed before it became apparent that she wasn't just carefully reading the document. She was immobile. In a now hesitant voice, her attorney urged her to sign so that we could begin. He called her name. She didn't respond. He touched her. She didn't move. He tried pulling her hand with the pen down to the paper.

The judge exploded. He castigated the young attorney in a manner that I have never again seen in the courtroom. I was ordered to return the patient to the hospital at once. She was equally unresponsive to me, but an elderly female nurse's aide who escorted her to court was able to gently talk her into coming back with us. In a zombie-like state, she numbly followed us out of the courtroom. With glazed over eyes and a frozen expression, she sat mute during the drive back to the hospital.

Yet, the next day when I spoke with her for the first time, I found an intelligent, albeit highly paranoid, woman, who remembered the events in court. She was nonetheless adamant that she would soon be going back to yet again challenge the legality of her involuntary commitment. She and I would replay this scenario several times, although we never again made it as far as a courtroom before she switched into a catatonic state.

The term catatonia covers a wide range of movement abnormalities. It is commonly associated with schizophrenia, but it also emerges in a variety of other disorders, including mania, depression, dissociative disorders, many neurological conditions, and toxic drug states. Clinical descriptions date to the 1500s, when it was called *Congelation* or *Taking*. In 1663 the English physician Robert Bayfield wrote:

A congelation, is a sudden surprizal of all the senses, the motion, and the minde, with which those that are seized upon, and invaded, remain and abide stiff, in the very same state and posture in which they were taken and surprised, with their eyes open and immovable. (cited on page 1, Fink & Taylor, 2003).

In the 1930s it was discovered that catatonic states could be reversed by an intravenous injection of sodium amobarbital, a medication used mainly as a sleeping pill or sedative. This discovery represented the beginning of the modern era of drug treatments for mental disorders. It would be more than thirty years before medication became standard psychiatric practice. Most clinicians of that era remained true to psychoanalytic interpretations of catatonia as a mental blocking process that suppressed unpleasant memories by silence and inappropriate actions by immobility. The famous psychoanalyst Frieda Fromm-Reichmann would sit for months in silence with her catatonic patients in a fruitless effort to wait them out (Fink & Taylor, 2003).

MULTIPLE PERSONALITY DISORDER

By the time that I arrived on Bob Post's NIMH research unit on the Bethesda, Maryland, campus of the National Institutes of Health, I had already seen numerous instances in which psychiatric patients demonstrated sudden changes in their mental states, often triggered by events in their immediate surroundings. These included switches from depression into mania, acute psychotic breakdowns, and posttraumatic flashbacks in the Vietnam veterans whom I worked with at the West Haven Veterans Hospital. There was even a patient on the neurology ward who had a complex partial seizure whenever he heard a Joni Mitchell song. This exceedingly rare phenomenon is known as musicogenic epilepsy. My subsequent experiences with rapid cycling bipolar patients at NIMH further amazed and educated me about the role that dramatic shifts in mental state play in some psychiatric conditions. Nothing, however, had prepared me for what I was to soon encounter.

Joan

I had been running a psychotherapy group for the rapid cycling patients on Post's bipolar disorder ward for about a year. It was challenging to maintain a sense of continuity from session to session while the patients cycled in and out of depressed and manic states, with an occasional—usually brief—stop at near normality. Sometimes these switches were spontaneous, sometimes they seemed to stem from personal events, and sometimes they were induced by one of our experimental trials. In hindsight I realize that it made little therapeutic sense to try to talk about this in a psychotherapy group. Beyond giving the patients a bitch session, I doubt that we accomplished much.

There was one patient, Joan, who was different from all of the others. She did not swing back and forth between depression and mania. In fact, she seemed bitterly and unrelentingly depressed. She went everywhere in a wheelchair. I did a neurological examination, probably her twentieth such exam, and found a classic hysterical paralysis. There was nothing wrong with her legs. Physically, she could walk. Psychologically, she was paralyzed.

Joan also paralyzed the unit. The staff, including the doctors, was afraid of making her angry or getting into an argument—her sarcastic wit could cut you to the quick with some dead-on remark. She had been hospitalized for almost four years and nothing seemed to help her. Indeed, she had made two near-fatal suicide attempts while on the unit and had to be watched around the clock to prevent another. Being so close to such an intimidating person took a toll on the staff's morale.

Yet, every once in a while when you least expected it, she would become animated and lively. Her humor was wickedly funny, as well as insightfully self-deprecating. There were also strange stories from the night staff about how they would find her curled up in a fetal position across the room from her wheelchair. She would be regressed, talking like a small, frightened child. Disoriented, as if she believed that she was somewhere else, she would mistake the night staff for other people. But then, who believes the night staffs' stories?

One day in the psychotherapy group, she said something that was hilarious and also fit exactly with the topic being discussed. She rarely spoke in the group, usually arriving last and sitting in stony silence with her wheelchair blocking the door, her demeanor making it perfectly clear that she was there against her will. After we stopped laughing, I turned to engage her. Her face was flushed; it almost glowed, and small tears of laughter trickled down her cheeks. She enjoyed her cleverness as much as the rest of us.

Yet as I followed up on her comment, she faded before my eyes, changing back into ice. When I pushed her on the meaning of her remark, she denied that she had ever said anything of the sort. I couldn't believe it. We all had just heard her say it, but now she was blatantly denying that any of it had ever happened. This was her pattern. In fact, when her young children came to visit, she angrily told them that she was not their mother—which broke the nurses' hearts.

Walking out to the parking lot that night, I described for my friend David Rubinow what happened. I couldn't figure it out. I had seen enough mood switches to know that whatever this was, it was not rapid cycling bipolar disorder. Without thinking about what I was saying, I wondered: could this be multiple personality disorder? I was not sure that I believed that multiple personality disorder existed. As a medical student I had met Dr. Cornelia Wilbur, Sybil's therapist, and heard her present three cases of multiple personality at grand rounds. Still, I remained skeptical. It seemed too fantastic to be real. Only later would I appreciate what a courageous pioneer Connie was.

I don't remember David's response—though he recalls asking if I also believed in witches—but I was sufficiently taken with the idea to visit the NIH library to read about multiple personality. Soon I was convinced enough to approach her primary psychiatrist, Edward Silberman.

Ed and I tell similar versions of this story, so there must be some truth to it. He was sitting at a computer terminal for the NIH Medical Information System, a very early experiment in computerized medical record keeping. Ed was struggling with the lightpen that was used to click off doctors' orders and which invariably checked a different box than the one you intended. In the midst of his frustration, I tactlessly suggested that he had misdiagnosed his patient and that she really suffered from multiple personality. The idea struck Ed as so preposterous that he literally fell off of his rolling desk chair laughing. Her real problem, he retorted, was that she didn't have a personality—much less more than one.

But Ed considered what I said and by that afternoon he asked Joan if there were more than one of her. She said yes and allowed him to meet some of her other (alter) personalities, including one who could walk normally. Ed was blown away by this revelation as were the rest of us. Suddenly many perplexing things made sense.

Alter personalities did not recognize her children. The near suicides were actually attempts at self-homicide, as some personalities tried to kill others. There were frightened young child alter personalities, whom we later learned were created in the context of incest and brutality by her father. There were calm analytical alter selves, who dispassionately described Joan's life history and the ongoing psychological mayhem inside of her mind.

These insights completely changed our approach to her treatment. Ultimately, she was successfully discharged into outpatient treatment. The last time I heard from her she was working, had achieved resolution with her husband and children, and was doing well. Bob Post told me that he had encountered her as a high-level executive (personal communication—2/2/13).

Seeing Joan switch among her different alter personality states opened my eyes to the presence of "multiples"—people with what was then called multiple personality disorder and is now termed Dissociative Identity Disorder, or DID for short. I prefer the informal term, "multiples" when speaking of them as a group. In turn, they often refer to the rest of us as "singles" and quip that we suffer from "single personality disorder."

In time I realized that I had seen multiples switching among alter personality states before, including at least two of my former patients. Back then my perception of what was happening at those moments was largely subliminal. I was vaguely aware that something had changed with the patient, but I couldn't identify what was different. I have since watched other psychiatrists interview multiple personality disorder patients and unconsciously react to alter personality switches without realizing what has just occurred.

While doing psychiatric consultations for other NIH institutes, we soon discovered two more MPD/DID cases. Amazed at this apparent coincidence, Ed Silberman, Richard Loewenstein and I published a paper attributing our finding three cases of this exceedingly rare condition to the fact that we were at a national research institution that studied rare disorders (Putnam, Loewenstein, Silberman, & Post, 1984). Our naïve paper soon led to numerous contacts with other psychiatrists and psychologists treating MPD/DID cases. Many said that they felt vindicated that the NIMH was finally recognizing the existence of this disorder (it was not) and that they rarely told colleagues about these patients because no one believed them. Soon I was shifting my research focus from rapid cycling bipolar patients to this mysterious condition.

At first, the kinds of things that I encountered appeared to defy rational belief. It seemed as if multiples indeed harbored many separate selves within one body. Later, as I studied this condition more, it became apparent that these alter personalities are not full-fledged people by any stretch. Indeed, a multiple's alter personalities are typically rigidly limited in many dimensions and their appearance is often restricted to specific situations or contexts that elicit their activation.

The alter personalities of a person with Dissociative Identity Disorder (aka multiple personality disorder) are best understood as "identity" states. The identity states are organized around distinct senses of self that usually include discrepancies in race, gender, age, or size from the individual's actual body. The alter personalities often have distinct patterns of speech, disagree with each other about certain events and people, and recall different memories from their collective past. These differences in the ways that they appear, act, and relate make them distinctive. Ultimately, I came to understand that the different alters are discrete states of being that share many elements in common with the manic, depressed, panicked and catatonic states that I had witnessed before.

It is now a well-established clinical principle that while one must interact with the alter identity states of a MPD/DID patient, a therapist should not relate to the different personalities as if they are separate people. Instead, collectively the different identity states comprise the person's global personality. The task of therapy is to help the different identities interact more harmoniously.

MPD/DID SWITCHING

One of the most amazing thing about multiples is their ability to switch alter personality states more or less on demand. This ability is particularly useful in the laboratory and allows us to study what changes as they switch into another alter personality state. With the aid of Theodore Zahn, Monte Buchsbaum, Herbert Weingartner and others, I began to research the neurophysiology and cognitive psychology of DID. This kind of research had been attempted as early as 1908 by Morton Prince. Thigpen and Cleckley, known for the famous case of *The*

Three Faces of Eve (1957), as well as Arnold Ludwig and Cornelia Wilbur, who reported the cases of Sybil and Jonah, also investigated physiological differences among alter personality states.

The degree of control a multiple has over her switching varies considerably with circumstances. A multiple who is comfortable with her multiplicity can often switch on demand among a subset of alter personality states in the research laboratory or during therapy sessions. During an emotional crisis, however, this voluntary control may be overridden by situational triggers that evoke unbidden alters over which the multiple has little control. Indeed, many of the alter personality states in DID are essentially powerful emotional states organized around overwhelming emotions such as anger, depression, or fear. These feelings have become personified over time and now have their own names, ages (usually dating to their first appearance), and other attributes to set them apart.

The hallmark of a DID alter personality switch is an abrupt discontinuity of behavior and demeanor. There may be a dramatic mood shift—say, a flash of anger for no apparent reason. The person may change the topic of conversation or contradict what they had just been saying without apparent awareness. They may suddenly stand up, aggressively change position, move around, or start doing something that is very different from what they were just doing. Their voice is different, their thinking and attitude are different, their posture and movement are different, and their behavior is different.

We see changes like this in people we know, and we may even retrospectively appreciate them in ourselves. What makes people with DID different is that they live their lives this way, in continuous discontinuity. In some respects, they are like the young infants we learned about in Chapter Two, abruptly moving from one discrete behavioral state to another—only the DID patients have a far greater number of behavioral states interconnected by more complicated pathways in state-space.

For infants, the repeated cycling of their limited set of states serves as a basic behavioral foundation that organizes their interactions with caregivers and the world at large. Abrupt shifts in emotion and behavior, as when a crying infant rapidly shifts to contently sucking on his mother's breast, don't present a problem. The more or less continuous discontinuity in an adult with MPD/DID is, however, a problem, as it complicates their efforts to lead productive lives.

Subjective Experiences of a Switch

Depending on the direction, switches between a pair of states of being are often asymmetrical in how long they last and how they affect behavior and the body. This is also true for subjective experiences on the part of an individual with DID switching among different identity states. Just as waking up and falling asleep are different experiences, moving back and forth between two alter personalities can feel very different.

In one alter personality the switch may be experienced as falling into a black hole of unconsciousness, only to wake up someplace else some time later, with no recollection of how this came to be. Another alter may report a sense of receding deep inside, seeing and hearing the outside world as if down a long dark tunnel. Others report being out of body, as if standing next to themselves, watching passively, unable to control their actions. And yet others may claim to see all and know all—and care not a whit about any of it.

Research on the subjective experience of a state change has been attempted with Zen meditators, marijuana smokers, and hypnotic subjects, among others (Putnam, 1994). In virtually all cases, it has been difficult for subjects to recall much detail about their mental experiences during the moment of transition between two distinct states of consciousness. Deikman calls this *"the problem of the missing center"* (Deikman, 1977).

It is theorized that because identity has strong state-dependent qualities, during a switch between two distinct states of being a sufficiently stabilized "self" isn't present to remember and report the experience. Research on the effects of drugs and alcohol on memory tends to support this hypothesis—the rate of change between a sober and intoxicated state is a more critical variable when it comes to predicting memory problems than the blood levels of the intoxicating substance.

The faster someone becomes drunk, stoned, or high, the greater the impairment of recall for the transition and the worse that they do on memory tests for information learned in the preceding state. Interestingly, the faster a drug or the mode of delivery—like smoking crack cocaine—gets you high, the more likely it is to become addicting.

Laboratory Studies

My experience in Bob Post's NIMH Psychobiology Section with rapid cycling bipolar patients was helpful, as I began to develop a research approach to MPD. Once I got past my initial amazement, one of the first steps was to look for similarities and differences between alter personality states using the same NIMH research laboratories that studied bipolar and panic disorder patients.

We used a common design for most of these experiments (Putnam, 1984b). There would be a group of MPD/DID subjects who, with input from their therapists, identified three or four alter personality states with distinctive attributes—age, gender, mood—that were able to sustain themselves "out" for the duration of the experiment. An age- and gender-matched group of normal control subjects were tested as themselves, so to speak, and in simulated alter personality states, that we referred to as "imaginary personalities."

Each control subject created and practiced two or three distinctive imaginary personalities. Controls created imaginary personalities with names and a defined set of attributes such as gender, age, race, height, weight, hair color, occupation, hobbies, interests—a variety of unique characteristics. They were encouraged to rehearse and elaborate their imaginary personalities outside of the laboratory. The analyses compared the imaginary personalities against the controls as "themselves" in their conventional or normal state of consciousness, as well as against the subject's other imaginary alter personalities. In some experiments we also allowed the controls to choose an altered state of consciousness, either hypnosis or deep relaxation, as one of their options.

Once in the laboratory, the MPD/DID alter personalities and the control subjects' simulated or imaginary personalities were addressed and handled in the same fashion. The alter personalities, both MPD/DID and simulated, were tested in random order across trials. For example, we might test each of three or four alter personalities of a subject (MPD or simulating control subject) on four separate days. On each day we would test those three or four alter personalities in a different order. Theoretically the research assistants administering the tests were "blinded" (i.e., deliberately kept unaware) as to which were the MPD/DID and which were the simulated alter personalities. But in practice it was pretty easy to tell. In most experiments, we measured each alter personality three or four times on different days to determine their degree of consistency.

Brain Imaging Studies

Working with Monte Buchsbaum's brain-mapping section, I learned about EEGs and evoked potentials as we used brain-imaging tools to examine patterns of brain activity across alter personality states. We found interesting differences among the alter personalities on measures of resting brain activity and brain activity evoked by standardized experimental tasks (Putnam, 1984a, 1984b). In general, the alter personality states of our MPD/DID subjects showed greater differences or conversely fewer similarities with each other on multiple measures of brain electrical activity than the control subjects pretending to be different personalities (Putnam, 1984a, 1984b).

Figure 4-1 (next page) shows composite statistical brain maps of intraclass correlation coefficients for the alter personalities of 10 MPD/DID subjects compared to the simulated alter personalities of 10 control subjects for the fast (gamma) EEG frequencies and total EEG power. An intraclass correlation coefficient is a statistical measure of how similar or different multiple measurements are—in this case patterns of brain activity across the 3 or 4 alter personalities of each subject tested on 3 or 4 different days.

The strength of the intraclass correlation coefficients is coded by colors superimposed on an outline of the left hemisphere of the brain. Correlation coefficients can range from -1 (perfect negative association) through 0 (no association) to 1 (perfect positive association). Note that the ranges of the colored intraclass correlation scales differ slightly on the two panels.

All of the conventional EEG frequencies were measured in this experiment, the brain state maps in Figure 4-1 show the intraclass correlation coefficients for Gamma waves, the fastest type of brain waves, and total power, a measure of the total energy across all of the brain wave frequencies as examples. The composite brain maps for the simulating control subjects (right side brain of each panel) consist primarily of strong positive intraclass correlations (i.e., 0.7 or higher) indicating that the controls are not changing their pattern or intensity of brain electrical activity when they pretend to be another person. Brain activity remains essentially the same across all of their imaginary personalities.

The composite brain maps for the MPD/DID subjects (left brain on each panel) shows low and even negative intraclass correlations for much of their cortex, indicating that the MPD/DID subjects generally showed statistically significantly different brain activity in the Gamma frequencies and total power across their different alter personalities. Simply said: the MPD/DID subjects are changing their brain electrical activity state when they switch alter personality states, whereas the controls are not. The higher frequency brainwaves, especially the 40 Hz gamma waves, are believed to organize or "bind" together the brain networks necessary to create conscious awareness.

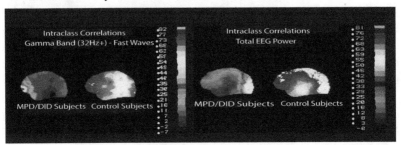

Figure 4-1
Intraclass Correlations of MPD/DID
Alter Personalities v. Simulating Controls

We found similar results at other EEG frequencies as well as for visual and auditory evoked potentials—unique brain waves elicited by repeatedly flashing a strobe light or loud tone. On a variety of measures of electrical brain activity, the alter personalities of the MPD/DID subjects showed significantly lower intraclass correlation coefficients than the matched simulating control subjects (Putnam, 1984a, 1984b). In basic terms, this means that the brain activation patterns of the alter personalities of the MPD/DID subjects were significantly more dissimilar, i.e., less like each other, than the imaginary personalities of the simulating control subjects.

Since our early brain mapping experiments in the 1980s, other researchers in the U.S., Europe, Turkey, and Canada have documented similar degrees of difference among MPD/DID alter identity states compared with simulating control subjects. Using a range of imaging technologies, studies by Ruth Lanius, Eric Vermetten, Vedet Sar, A.A. Reinders and their colleagues have demonstrated significant neurophysiological differences across alter personality states of MPD/DID subjects. These experiments document that when MPD/DID patients change their alter identity states, they are producing detectable changes in their brains and bodies. As yet, we really don't know a lot about what those detectable differences actually mean.

Bodily Differences

Ted (Theodore) Zahn ran a series of experiments looking at autonomic nervous system activity including heart rate and galvanic skin conductance (GSR) (Putnam, Zahn, & Post, 1989). We found that the MPD/DID alter personalities were able to consistently produce significant changes in physiological measures over multiple trials conducted on separate days. A few of our control subjects, using either hypnosis or deep relaxation, were also able to create equivalent degrees of physiological separation between "themselves" and an altered state of consciousness. The hypnotic and states of deep relaxation induced in the control subjects all had much lower levels of arousal compared to "themselves" or their imaginary personalities. Meanwhile, the MPD/DID alter personalities showed marked variations in their level of arousal, including much higher levels in certain alter personality states. This indicates that MPD/DID subjects and controls were producing their physiological changes through different mechanisms.

Memory Systems

Herbert Weingartner, a noted expert on memory, designed studies to test for the amnesias that multiples report among their alter personalities (Silberman, Putnam, Weingartner, & Post, 1985). Herb, in particular, helped me to see the state-dependent nature of their changes in memory performance (Weingartner, 1978). He also contextualized our learning and memory data as similar in type and degree to the differences found in the same individual who is cycling between depression and mania, or between someone in sober and intoxicated states.

Appearance and Demeanor

As I observed more and more alter personality switches in the laboratory and was able to relate what I saw with our physiological and cognitive measures, I increasingly focused my attention on the switch process itself. It was amazing to watch these changes. If I met many of the alter personalities in another context, I would have difficulty recognizing them as a person I knew.

> *I was having lunch with a multiple who was a research subject in the NIMH studies. When the waiter came to take our order, I was speaking with one of her personalities, a softly feminine alter with a lovely southern accent. After the waiter left, Harry came out to give me his views on the topic. Harry was a male protector alter personality who considered himself to be half Native American. According to Harry, he was always present, watching, and ready to emerge if*

"the body was in danger." He also protected the body against internal intrigues in which one alter might try to harm another. Harry had a deep, husky, masculine voice and imposing posture. He was speaking when the waiter arrived with our meals. Without hesitation, the waiter asked if the lady would be returning—and would the gentleman like a menu?

We filmed alter personality switches and studied them frame-by-frame. We took carefully lit photos of the alter personalities' faces and measured various distances, angles and right-left symmetries. Dr. Christie Ludlow dissected the differences in speech and voice so readily apparent across MPD/DID alters personalities. In the process we learned that when MPD/DID research subjects switched alter personalities, the position of the vocal cords changed in their throats, so much so we had to readjust the array of microphones and sensors strapped to their necks. As a result the fundamental resonances of their entire vocal structures changed, producing the distinctly different voices of the alter personalities. As Christie explained to me, *"Think of the voice as a pipe organ. When you change the length or diameter of the pipe, you change the pitch of the note* (undated videotaped experimental session)."

The facial changes occurring when MPD/DID alter personalities switched resulted from differential patterns of tension and relaxation in the facial muscles and shifts in the position of the lower jaw, in some cases to an extreme under- or overbite. Often facial appearance changed drastically, so that a smile or frown looked very different depending on which alter personality emerged. During the switch the eyes often rolled upwards and the eyelids fluttered, ranging from a brief quivering to prolonged rapid blinking. Distinct changes usually appeared in and around the eyes, which narrowed or widened as well as seeming to brighten, glaze, or flash in character with the emerging alter personality's persona.

It was more difficult to capture and quantify some of the postural and movement changes that accompany a switch, because the experimental setups usually required subjects to sit or lie quietly as possible during the procedure to reduce their movement as active muscles produce electrical noise that contaminates the data. One recurrent observation was that the young child alter personalities of the MPD/DID subjects usually exhibited a nervous fidgeting known as 'movement overflow', particularly when required to speak or interact with the research assistants. This nervous squirming, which was entirely absent in the controls' imaginary child personalities, is common in young children when they are nervous or stressed. When the small child alters were tested, the MPD/DID subjects also scrunched up, making themselves appear smaller and weaker.

PSYCHOPHYSIOLOGY OF SWITCHES

Rapid switches between MPD/DID alter personality states are characterized by an abrupt disruption in the pattern of variables such as heart rate, galvanic skin response (GSR), respiration, and EEG (especially the temporal leads). There would be a brief period of chaotic disorganization that usually quickly resolved into a new and stable pattern of the same physiological variables. Figure 4-2 consists of two examples of rapid switches between pairs of MPD/DID alter personality states. Panels A is an EEG (brain wave) record. Panel B shows autonomic physiology variables including skin temperature, heart rate, right and left arm galvanic skin responses and respiration. Rapid switches between two pre-designated alter personality states are marked by the ovals. These two examples come from different subjects.

In Panel A the EEG tracing shows higher voltage, slower waves rapidly transitioning to lower voltage faster waves after a brief moment of disorganization. Panel B shows the effect of switching alter personality state on bodily physiology. Note the marked change in heart rate, labeled "Finger pulse," most discernable near the middle of tracing B.

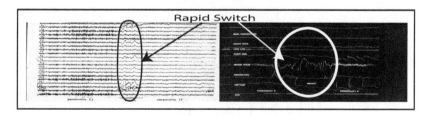

Figure 4-2
Rapid Switches between MPD/DID Alter Personality States

At the moment of the switch, it was as if our monitoring equipment briefly went haywire, the jumping pens splattering ink on the polygraph tracings that monitored the signals being digitized. Some of this was due to changes in muscle tension and posture as the body entered a new state, but even robust measures such as heart rate fluctuated wildly for a moment and before locking into a new rhythm. One DID subject reliably had premature ventricular contractions (PVCs) in one alter personality state, but not in her other alter personalities.

Switching Speed

Using a combination of physiological measures such as heart rate and respiration together with the consensus of two observers—myself and usually the MPD/DID subject's therapist—we sought to measure the time it takes to switch from one alter personality state to another. The observers had to agree that the personality switch had occurred and was complete (Putnam, 1994). Figure 4-3 shows the average time (the column is the mean and the bars are standard deviations—a statistic that measures the variability across trials) for either 6 or 8 (in parenthesis) switches in each of nine DID subjects. This provides a ballpark feel for the speed of a typical DID alter personality switch in a cooperative, non-stressed MPD/DID subject in a research laboratory. Subject 9 had great difficulty stabilizing in a new alter personality after a switch and often rapidly fluctuated back and forth between two or more alter personality states for several minutes accompanied by rapid blinking, eye rolls, and seizure-like trembling although no seizure was evident on the EEG. Most of her switches passed through a phase of unstable intermediate states (See Figure 4-4). Subjects

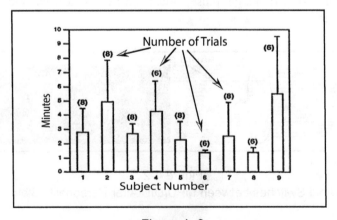

Figure 4 -3
Average Switch Time in Nine MPD/DID Subjects

6 and 8 (both males coincidentally?), however, were able to rapidly—and sometimes almost imperceptibly—switch among alter personalities.

These data overestimate the time a switch takes because we measured from one stable pattern of physiological variables to a new stable pattern of the same variables. In addition, we required that the newly present alter personality exhibit distinctive behavior characteristic of that particular alter. Often this required asking a question or evoking a prearranged response.

These studies also found that DID subjects could not always switch from one alter personality state to another on demand. Nor could a DID alter personality always sustain itself for the required time. After each experimental trial, we would debrief the alter personality, DID or imaginary, on whether he, she or it had been present during the entire procedure or at some point had switched out. We had several instances when a given DID alter personality just could not 'be there' or 'stay' long enough to complete the experimental procedure. Reports from the DID subjects about inadvertent or unplanned switching during the experiment usually coincided with events in the physiological record similar to planned switches. The controls, however, never once reported losing it during their trials.

One thing that these studies made clear to me was that the MPD/DID alter personalities—whatever they may be—are not separate people. Our experiments found evidence that information and experiences associated with a given alter personality were available to a greater or lesser extent in the other alter personalities. The memory experiments revealed certain information leaked across alter personalities although they often didn't seem aware of it. But the degree of leakage was typically asymmetrical—so that Alter Personality A might know significantly more of Alter Personality B's words than Alter B knew from Alter A's word list.

We also looked at "unconscious" processes such as tuning out an obnoxious noise. In my research with Ted Zahn for example, we periodically startled resting subjects with a loud noxious tone (Putnam et al., 1989). After two or three blasts, most people no longer startle because they have "habituated" to the tone. We found that all of our subjects' alter personalities—MPD/DID and simulators—show essentially similar patterns of habituation. This demonstrated that habituating one alter personality to a noxious stimulus transferred to all of the person's other alter personalities—at this level they are joined. So despite what the MPD/DID subjects report about their sense of separation, experimental evidence shows that the degree of separation is relative, but not absolute.

Types of Switches

Figure 4-4 is a simple categorical approach to the types of switches commonly witnessed in bipolar disorders, panic attacks, periodic catatonia and dissociative identity disorder. Christine's switch from depression to mania, my patient's switch into the catatonic state in the courtroom, and the EEG and physiological records of the MPD/DID alter personality switches in Figure 4-2 are all examples of what is known as a rapid switch (Fig 4-4A). Rapid switches usually take seconds to minutes. They are most apparent through abrupt shifts in demeanor and behavior and breaks in continuity of a person's thoughts and speech. Sometimes after a rapid switch the person is disorientated to time, place, and situation—confusion they may seek to disguise.

The categories of intermediate mixed state (Fig 4-4B) and unstable intermediate states (Fig 4-4C) may lie on a continuum that is difficult to quantify. In the former, it is as if the two states (like depression and mania, or Alter Personality A and Alter Personality B) are present at the same time, but neither is in full control of mood, thinking or behavior. In the latter, it is as if several states are alternately displacing each other, as if they were competing for control of the person's behavior.

Rather than the blurry mixed picture of co-present mixed states (Fig 4-4B), unstable intermediate states (Fig 4-4C) can look floridly psychotic, as the person switches among extreme versions of self, snapping back and forth between depression and mania or among alter personality states with different ages and agendas. This phenomenon, known among dissociative disorder specialists as the "revolving door," can occur in moments of extreme personal crisis.

Of course, we all experience a minor version of this with the tears-and-laughter or happy- and-sad mixed states that sometimes overtake us during milestone moments of life. In psychotherapy, mixed states of being, labeled "shimmering states" by Mardi Horowitz—more on this in chapters 5 and 6—are important markers of conflicted emotional experiences.

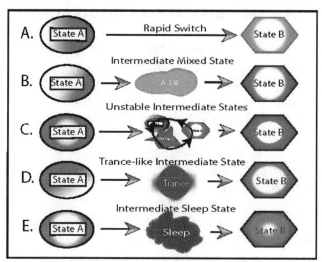

Figure 4-4
Types of Switches Among States of Consciousness

Switches that involve an intermediate trance or void-like trance state (Fig 4-4D) can be eerie to witness. As one multiple said, *"It's lights on— but nobody's home."* The person often sits immobile, staring blankly, not responding to voice or touch. This sometimes happens during therapy sessions and can unnerve inexperienced therapists. The trance state is self-limited, that is, it will end usually after 20 minutes or so, and another alter personality will eventually emerge to take control. The greatest problem is that this often occurs at the end of an intense session—and the therapist has another client waiting.

The category of intermediate sleep state (Fig 4-4E) is frequently seen in mood disorders in which the person goes to sleep in one state, for example, mania, and wakes up in another such as depression. Often this switch only requires a brief period of sleep. Sleep switches provide a new perspective on that old cliché about getting up on the wrong side of the bed. People may wake in mood states that are emotionally very different from the state that they were in when they went to bed. Sometimes they can trace it to an emotion that they were experiencing in a dream just before waking. These phenomena are, of course, almost impossible to study in the laboratory, so we must rely on common experiences for examples.

ISN'T THIS JUST REALLY GOOD ACTING?

The question is sometimes raised about whether or not a really, really—I mean *really* good actor—could produce the same degree of change in his brain activity when he assumes a role that he has played many times. I would love to know, but it turns out that really, really good actors and actresses are prohibitively expensive research subjects. I did have a friend whose ex-husband was the son of a famous soap opera actress who played the same character for literally decades. He complained that there were times as a child when his mother remained stuck in her TV character after she came home.

Once I got to see Harry Reasoner (1923–1991) snap into his 60 Minutes *television persona. It was an amazing transformation from the Harry Reasoner I had been talking with just a few minutes earlier. In fact, the Harry Reasoner I had lunch with before our interview did not look or sound at all like the Harry Reasoner I had seen many times on TV.*

Harry was interviewing me as part of a 60 Minutes *segment on the U.S. government's involvement in paranormal research. My purpose, or so I was led to believe, was simply to confirm that I had attended a particular meeting on paranormal research some of which was sponsored by the U.S. government—which I had. At least that was my understanding before we began. But as soon as Harry suddenly snapped into sharp focus as the familiar 60* Minutes *persona and the filming began, he started to grill me with unexpectedly tough questions about the meeting and attendees.*

My surmise about the chain of events that led to sitting in front of the 60 Minutes *camera is circumstantial.* Psychology Today *ran a story about my brain imaging work with multiple personality patients titled, "Traces of Eve's Faces" (Putnam, 1982). That short article, I believe, led to an invitation to give a public lecture in a series sponsored by the Smithsonian museum. Shortly after my lecture I received a mysterious phone call asking if I was interested in attending a meeting on "Anomalous Phenomena" held at a "secure facility". Of course I said yes. Who wouldn't jump at the chance to see that side of Washington?*

The meeting was held over two days (Nov 30–Dec 1, 1983) near Leesburg, VA. Members of congress, including at least one senator were in attendance. The audience glittered with gold braid, primarily senior Air Force and Navy officers. There were also civilians from defense contractors. It was a remarkable event that exposed me to research into paranormal phenomena conducted at major universities.

One memorable moment followed a presentation by researchers from the Man-Machine Interaction Laboratory at Cornell where they studied people whose mere presence appeared to adversely affect the functioning of machines. These are the people who reputedly stop watches and make computers go haywire when they walk into a room. The presenter concluded that these effects were real and that "low mass" devices such as computer chips that depend on tiny changes in electrical charge to represent information were particularly vulnerable to these people. An admiral stood up. Anxiously noting that a modern jet fighter is "wall-to-wall microprocessors," he said that if certain people negatively affected computers, we needed a way to identify them before they got too far in training.

At lunch on the first day, I was chatted up by two men who seemed to know who I was. They were especially interested in my multiple personality brainwave research. It turns out that in my Smithsonian lecture I mentioned that dissociation includes out-of-body experiences. That fact interested them the most, plus that I used a strobe light as part of our visual evoked potential studies. It eventually emerged that they were interested in using strobe lights to defend our national secrets against out-of-body spies.

You get a sense of the meeting from those two examples. Other than sporadic contact with one person who was interested in multiple personality for personal reasons, I had no further interactions. However, later I described the meeting to a friend, Ira Rosen, who was then a producer for 60 Minutes. Sometime after that, Ira approached me about appearing on 60 Minutes to confirm that such a meeting had taken place. He said that they had other sources that would discuss the substance of the government's paranormal research program. My role was merely to confirm that this meeting had taken place.

Before the interview, Harry, Ira and I had lunch in the NIH Building 10 cafeteria. Sitting there with "Harry Reasoner," who only looked vaguely like the Harry Reasoner I knew from 60 Minutes, I wondered if people would recognize him. A few took a quick second look as they walked past our table, but nobody seemed to recognize Harry as Harry. There was no buzz at the surrounding tables. No inquisitive trips for a second look. No requests for autographs.

Contrast this absence of recognition with the buzz created by Harry's famous partner on 60 Minutes, *Mike Wallace. Many years later I was in an airport waiting area—Terminal C at the Cincinnati-Kentucky airport—when Mike arrived waiting for another flight. Terminal C had a huge central waiting area with literally scores of small gates side-by-side for the now defunct commuter airline, Comair.*

Mike arrived at the diagonally far opposite end from me of this giant room and within 15 minutes or less, pretty much everyone at my end was aware of his presence through word of mouth. A steady stream of people—myself included—got up and causally wandered over to take a closer look. And he looked just like the Mike Wallace on TV—a bit older, grayer, and paunchier—but there was no doubt that he was The Mike Wallace.

When Harry sat down opposite me for our TV interview, he suddenly snapped into focus. Everything about him—his face, his eyes, his voice, his posture—became crisply etched and classically Harry Reasoner. He looked, moved and sounded like the TV version of himself. Fixing me with his skeptical gaze, he pointedly asked about things I had mentioned at lunch assuming (wrongly) that they were off the record because I was only there to "confirm" that such a meeting had taken place. Let that be a lesson to you should you ever appear on 60 Minutes*!*

The 60 Minutes *program segment never aired Ira told me, because the Reagan Whitehouse requested that CBS withhold it for national security reasons. A couple of years later an outraged editorial in the* Washington Post *mentioned the meeting while taking the government to task for spending on parapsychology. But, based on what I heard there, this has been going on for years. In response to my skepticism, an admiral beside me in the lunch line said, "Son, we've been using psychics to track Russian submarines for twenty years."*

Subsequently I have heard about similar examples, usually famous actors, who can snap in and out of their screen personas. In a Fresh Air radio interview with Terry Gross, the actor Jeff Daniels describes seeing Clint Eastwood transition in the blink of an eye from a laid back movie director into the flinty Clint Eastwood character of Dirty Harry fame. Daniels also recalled watching an elderly James Cagney struggle mightily to reprise his signature tough guy persona—then suddenly click into it.

We all are multiple to some degree or another. It is how well we can "keep it together," how harmoniously we can bridge, coordinate and even integrate the different parts of ourselves that determines how functional we are (see Chapters 5 & 6).

SYNTHESIS

We change our state of being many times during the course of a typical day as we change contexts and roles. For the most part, this is a natural process that occurs in the background as we traverse our daily routines. Indeed, "normality" and "abnormality" can be defined in terms of how well someone instinctively matches his state of being to the daily flow of changing social situations.

On occasion we may struggle against changing state (e.g., not falling asleep during a boring meeting) or conversely seek to trigger a state change (e.g., trying to fall asleep when experiencing insomnia). We also experience rapid and dramatic mood swings on occasion. But, for the most part, switching among our different states of being is like breathing: it occurs largely out of awareness.

Switches are best appreciated when the changes between two states are dramatic. Christine, suffering from bipolar disorder, goes from a weepy, exhausted depression to supercharged manic energy and strength in the blink of an eye. People with recurrent panic attacks, periodic cata-tonia, and dissociative disorders experience similar rapid shifts in their state of being.

In these disorders and conditions, switches in mental and emotional state can be experimentally induced and studied under controlled conditions. Changes between two highly disparate states of being are often marked by dramatic state-dependent changes in bodily and brain physiology, mood, memory, personal appearance and mannerisms as well as the individual's sense of self.

With a few exceptions such as research on the side effect of anti-depressant-medication-induced switches into mania, scientific investigation into the nature of the switch process has largely ceased. Another example is the research of Flavio Fröhlich and colleagues on the cellular mechanisms involved in switches between normal and pathological states (Fröhlich, Sejnowski, & Bazhenov, 2010). Clinically, the switch mechanism, however, remains an important, if largely underappreciated, point of therapeutic leverage. If we understood switching better, we should be able to rapidly switch people out of dysfunctional states of mind or prevent them from being sucked into others.

The Self and Its Proclivities

CHAPTER 5   MEMORY & IDENTITY

Polly

One day many years ago, I was in my office when I got a call from the police. The officer ordered me to meet him at a local emergency room where they were taking my patient, a woman whom they had just rescued walking down the fast lane of the George Washington Parkway heading toward DC. Baffled, I asked her name.

"Don't know," he snapped, as if this were my fault. "She says she doesn't know who she is."

"What does she look like?" His description didn't ring a bell. I couldn't imagine who she was.

"How do you know she's my patient?"

"We found your phone number on a piece of paper in her purse," he said. "It was the only thing in there." He made it clear that he thought I was grossly negligent about this poor woman's condition, and that I needed to do something immediately, if not sooner, to help her—and to get her off his hands.

It was clear that we were destined to meet, so I headed to the emergency room. I had never seen her before. Like everyone else caught up in the drama, I had no idea as to who she was.

A large (over 300 pounds) woman, she was simply dressed. A heelless shoe and general disarray suggested that she had walked a considerable distance. She was calm—serene almost—though the police said that she was agitated and had resisted their efforts to remove her out of the path of rush hour traffic. She said several times that her doctor—whose name she couldn't remember—had told her that she really needed to see me and not him. But she could not remember where she lived, any phone number, the names of family or friends, or anything else that might give us a clue as to who she was.

We transferred her to St. Elizabeth's Hospital, where I worked, and set about finding out who she was. I don't recall whether I used hypnosis or a sodium amytal interview to get the phone number and address that proved key to uncovering her identity. Over the years I have used both methods of inducing an altered state of consciousness to facilitate recall of identifying information in John and Jane Doe

*cases. In most instances, these approaches prove successful in elicit-
ing sufficient information to figure out who the person is.*

Polly's story proved to be long and complicated. She has Dissociative Identity Disorder with multiple alter personalities that emerged
over the course of years of treatment with trainees I supervised. Since
then Polly has done well, achieving an independent and productive life,
although never what it should have been given her intelligence.

Every year, a few similar cases bubble up for a couple of news cycles.
John and Jane Does found wandering in a confused state or who present
themselves to the police or an emergency room with absolutely no memory of who they are. Photos are broadcast in the hopes that someone will
recognize the person. When that happens, it is usually family or friends
who identify the person as having been missing for days to months. In
many instances, the missing person lived for a while in another state or
traveled a considerable distance before coming to attention.

Ansel Bourne

These kinds of cases, now diagnosed as dissociative disorders, are not
new. Indeed, they have been consistently reported since the beginnings
of modern psychology and psychiatry. The case of the Reverend Ansel
Bourne, examined by William James in his classic text, *The Principles of
Psychology* (1890), is an icon in American psychology (James, 1950).

Ansel Bourne had been a carpenter and an ardent atheist until a
spell of blindness and deafness around age 30 led him to convert to
Christianity. Thereafter he traveled as an itinerant preacher around
Rhode Island. On January 17, 1887, he withdrew a large sum of money
from a Providence bank to buy a parcel of land in Greene, Rhode
Island, boarded a Pawtucket horse-car, and disappeared. He was listed
as missing in the newspapers and police indicated that they suspected
foul play.

On March 14, 1887, a shop owner, known locally as A.J. Brown,
startled his Norristown, Pennsylvania neighbors by demanding that
people tell him where he was. Agitated and fearful, he said that he was
Ansel Bourne, refused to believe that two months had elapsed, and declared
that he knew nothing of shop keeping or of Norristown. Thought insane
by the local citizenry, he was pronounced so by Dr. Louis H. Read, who
examined him. His identity, however, was eventually confirmed after a
telegram to Providence brought his nephew, Andrew Harris, to the scene.

As Ansel Bourne, he maintained that he had no memory of his life as A.J. Brown and evinced such a horror of the episode that he refused to ever set foot in his Norristown shop again. James writes that his Norristown neighbors declared that although he was a taciturn fellow, he was orderly in his habits and "*in no way queer*" (James, 1950 p. 392). As a shopkeeper, he had tended to his trade, traveled to Philadelphia to buy new stock on several occasions, and been a regular churchgoer. On one occasion, he had addressed the congregation relating an incident that would have occurred while he was Ansel Bourne.

In June of 1890, William James saw Reverend Bourne and convinced him to submit to hypnosis to see if it was possible to recover memories of his time as A.J. Brown. He agreed, and it proved surprisingly easy to elicit the Brown identity state. As Brown, he said that he had heard of Ansel Bourne, but "*didn't know as he had ever met the man*" (James, 1950 p. 392). He denied any memory of his life as Ansel Bourne and when confronted with Mrs. Bourne declared that he had "*never seen that woman before*" (James, 1950 p. 392).

James observed that in the Brown state, he:

> *. . . looks old, the corners of his mouth are drawn down, his voice is slow and weak. "I'm all hedged in," he says: "I can't get out at either end. I don't know what set me down in the Pawtucket horse-car, and I don't know how I ever left that store, or what became of it."* (James, 1950 p. 392)

James hoped to ". . . *run the two personalities into one and to make the memories continuous.*" Unable to accomplish this, he concludes, "*Mr. Bourne's skull today still covers two distinct personal selves*" (James, 1950 p. 392).

ARE THESE PEOPLE FOR REAL?

So what is going on here? How did Polly lose her identity? Why did Ansel Bourne have two identities, each of which claimed to have no knowledge of the other? Is this for real or some sort of hoax? Or even, as some allege, the result of malpractice by a therapist? Such cases have incited fascination and recrimination in the fields of psychiatry, psychology and anthropology for as long as those disciplines have existed. Indeed, dramatic cases of dissociative amnesia, fugue and multiple personalities were central to the early beginnings of modern psychology and psychiatry (see Chapter 8).

By the time William James described the strange saga of Ansel Bourne, many similar cases had appeared in the medical journals of the day. In his chapter in *The Principles of Psychology* devoted to the "Consciousness of Self," James includes a series of seminal cases, including the earlier American example of Mary Reynolds, the famous French case of Félida X, and Pierre Janet's patients, Lucie and Léonie. All of who had alter identities that were responsible for perplexing and problematic behaviors. Indeed, until the late 1920s, reports of dissociative amnesia, fugue and multiple personality disorder outnumbered case reports of schizophrenia in the medical literature (Rosenbaum, 1980).

The existence of people who switch among alternate identities seems to be a universal human capacity. Comparing medical case reports across the past two centuries shows remarkable similarities in the clinical details. Evidence that this mental phenomenon—whatever it may be—is largely consistent over time. A comparison of modern cases across Western, Middle Eastern and Asian societies also demonstrates similar symptoms and behaviors across diverse cultures (Putnam, 1989).

But there are some differences across time and culture indicating that prevailing cultural and clinical beliefs do influence some elements of these cases. The greatest differences occur in terms of whether these phenomena are viewed through a clinical lens such as the DSM dissociative disorders or from a religious perspective, such as Shamanism or spirit possession. In both instances, however, the person exhibits a marked alteration in identity. In the West we consider this to be pathological. In other cultures, these individuals are regarded as having special access to the supernatural.

SO WHAT IS "IDENTITY" AND HOW CAN WE HAVE MORE THAN ONE?

How do you know that you are the same person who went to bed last night? Who ate breakfast this morning? Who married your spouse? Who graduated from high school? What proves to us that we still are the "who" that we were yesterday or last week or ten years ago? At one level this a nonsense question: of course you are the same person. Your DNA is the same. Your fingerprints haven't changed. But those physical features are not the proof that most of us use to convince ourselves of the unbroken continuity of our existence. We don't run a DNA test every morning to assure ourselves that we haven't changed identities overnight.

Instead, we rely on a sense of continuous memory as proof of our existence. We can remember graduating from high school, getting married, and perhaps, even what we ate for breakfast this morning. We feel and believe that we are the same person because we have a sense of our self that relies on our sense of the continuity of our memories over time.

But what if you can't remember anything at all about what you did yesterday? What if you have absolutely no memory for meeting, dating, and marrying your spouse, for graduating from high school, for serving in the military, or for other significant events in your life? How continuous would your sense of self be then?

James observed that "*Coupling* [Pierre] *Janet's law with* [John] *Locke's that changes of memory bring changes of personality, we should have an apparent explanation of some cases at least of alternate personality*" (James, 1950 p. 390).

This insight, repeated throughout James's subsequent writings, is that memory and identity are inextricably linked and that changes in one go together with changes in the other. In individuals such as Ansel Bourne, memory and identity are the most intertwined—when one changes, the other does, too. Through hypnosis, James was able to establish that Bourne's memories during the period when he was known as A.J. Brown were intact and could be reactivated to the exclusion of his memories for his life as Ansel Bourne.

In his masterwork, *The Varieties of Religious Experience* (1901–1912) published about a decade after *Principles,* James generalizes this insight to everyday life—or at least to less extreme examples than Ansel Bourne. He conjures up the image of then President Theodore Roosevelt on a camping trip in the wilderness. In this radically different context, Roosevelt will have forgotten, in a way, his presidential demeanor.

"The presidential anxieties," he wrote, *"have lapsed into the background entirely; the official habits are replaced by habits of a son of nature, and those who knew the man only as the strenuous magistrate would not 'know him for the same person' if they saw him as the camper"* (James, 1901–1902 p. 161).

What James was driving at here is that a person—even someone as sharply self-defined as Teddy Roosevelt—can think and act in very different ways depending on context.

STATE-DEPENDENT LEARNING AND MEMORY

William James was not the first and far from the last to propose that an abrupt shift in an individual's sets of memories causes the identity switches in individuals such as Ansel Bourne and Polly. In fact, most scientists studying these cases continue to hypothesize that a well-researched phenomenon, known as state-dependent learning and memory, (SDLM for short), underlies the joint shifts of memory and identity.

SDLM refers to the results of an array of experiments in both humans and animals. They show that information learned in a given state of consciousness is best remembered when that person or animal is again placed in the same state. Specific states of consciousness can be created in numerous ways. In animals, distinct behavioral states are created with drugs or by creating states of fear or rage through electric shocks. In humans, a range of techniques from drugs to hypnosis to inducing specific emotional states is used to investigate SDLM.

The basic SDLM experiment involves teaching subjects, human or animal, specific information—running a maze, solving a puzzle, or recalling a list of words—in a given state of consciousness. The subject's recall is then measured in the same state as it was learned in as well as in different states. Researchers often use a classic 2-by-2 experimental design. For example, a group of subjects memorizes a list of words while they are not under the influence of drugs, and then learns a second list of similar words after taking a drug such as alcohol, amphetamines or Valium. The subjects then try to remember as many words as they can in each state.

This 2-by-2 design leads to four conditions. (1) Information learned in the drug state and later recalled in the drug state (drug-drug). (2) Information learned in the drug state and recalled in the "normal" state (drug-normal). (3) Information learned in the normal state and recalled in the drug state (normal-drug), and (4) information learned in the normal state and recalled in the normal state (normal-normal). We can then examine the four conditions to see if certain pairs show greater recall and fewer errors.

Typically people best recall information when the state in which it is remembered is the most similar to the state in which it was learned. So subjects in the above experiment will perform best in the drug-drug and normal-normal conditions and worse in the drug-normal and normal-drug conditions. Usually, the normal-normal pairing produces better results than the drug-drug combination. Most subjects will be able to remember some words learned in the other state, but they will recall significantly more words when the learning and recall states are equivalent. The apocryphal story of the drunk who can't find his car keys when he is sober and must get drunk to remember where he left them is a folklore version of SDLM.

MEMORY SYSTEMS

But of course memory and the act of remembering are not as simple as we would like to believe. Indeed, most scientists accept the idea that there are many kinds of memory—often called memory systems—that are relatively independent of each other.

For example, severe alcoholics may develop a condition known as Korsakoff's syndrome that is caused by a lack of Vitamin B-1 in their diet. Named after the Russian psychiatrist Sergei Korsakoff, who published a series of cases around 1890, Korsakoff's syndrome makes people unable to form new memories. They also have trouble recalling old ones.

The syndrome includes two types of serious memory problems. In anterograde amnesia, the person cannot create new memories of what happens on a day-to-day basis—sometimes minute to minute. If the person is distracted by some new task or situation, he forgets what happened just moments before. With the second problem, retrograde amnesia, a person struggles to recall past events, such as childhood memories that happened before Korsakoff's syndrome occurred.

Yet Korsakoff patients can learn and remember how to solve a complex puzzle called the Tower of Hanoi just as quickly as normal individuals. Solving the Tower of Hanoi requires learning and recalling a complicated pattern of moves which are necessary to transfer a set of different-sized rings from one pole to another—using a third intermediate pole—so that a larger ring never overlays a smaller one. Yet each time the Korsakoff patient is presented with the puzzle, he denies having ever seen it or confabulates an impossible story about having seen it before.

Korsakoff patients learn to solve the puzzle at about the same speed as a normal person, and they remember the solution from session to session equally well. The memory system that records and remembers the complicated sequence of moves is intact. What is impaired is the memory system that records, stores, and retrieves memories of day-to-day life.

The question of just how many different memory systems exist—and just how separate and distinct they are—is a major area of scientific research. As with all active scientific fields, cutting-edge research generates strong opinions and contested theories. When these studies and data are brought into the courtroom, as in delayed-recall cases of childhood sexual abuse or amnesia for the commission of a crime, the tenor of the experts' discourse can become downright vituperative. The reader should be aware that there are strong disagreements among authorities on many details about what memory is and how it works.

What most authorities do agree upon is that there are a number of independent or quasi-independent memory systems that can be distinguished from each other by clever experiments or in neurological conditions such as Alzheimer's disease and Korsakoff's syndrome. Evidence shows that these different memory systems appear early in life but mature at different rates (Gerhardstein, Adler, & Rovee-Collier, 2000). These memory systems also age at different rates, so that negative emotional states have a greater impact on memory in the elderly than they do in younger people (Deptula, Singh, & Pomara, 1993).

Figure 5-1 represents one widely held categorization of these memory systems (Figure 5-1 adapted from Miyashita, 2004).

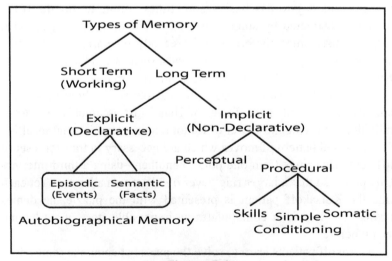

Figure 5-1
Types of Memory

Types of Memory Systems

In Figure 5-1, you see the first division of memory that most experts agree on, the distinction between short-term and long-term memory. Short-term memory, what some experts call working memory, helps you retain small amounts of information for a short period of time—like looking up and remembering a telephone number just long enough to dial it before forgetting it. Long-term memory covers a myriad of other things that you learn and remember in order to be able to use that information at some later time.

Long-term memory subdivides into explicit memory and implicit memory systems. This split is critical but involves a subtle distinction in what is being remembered. Explicit memory, also known as declarative memory, refers to memories of events and facts that a person can describe if asked—like recalling details of your first date with your partner or the name of the first president of the United States. Explicit memories can usually be put into words.

Autobiographical memory includes both the episodic (events) and semantic (facts) subdivisions of explicit memory. Episodic memories are the events and experiences that happened to us that constitute the memories of our past life. Sematic memories are facts that we learned along the way. Attached to many of these facts are memories of the source of the fact—where or how did we learn the given fact. Recall of the source of a fact is important because it strongly influences our confidence in the accuracy of the fact.

Implicit memory refers to all of those things that you can't easily express in words: all the things you know and use in your daily life, but don't remember when or where you learned them. Implicit memory includes how-to types of memory, such as riding a bicycle, simple arithmetic, touch typing, or memorizing long passages of prose, poetry or music.

In many respects, implicit memory operates below conscious awareness. Implicit memory involves different brain circuits than explicit memory and is generally resistant to disruption. Implicit memory is often preserved in individuals, such as Alzheimer's patients, who have essentially lost access to the explicit memories of their life. A subtype of implicit memory, procedural memory, is involved in solving the Tower of Hanoi puzzle described above. Procedural memory still functions in Korsakoff's patients, even though their explicit memory system has failed.

Explicit and implicit memory systems can be subdivided much further. When it comes to these subsystems of memory experts increasingly disagree. Researchers have also identified highly specialized subtypes of memory. For example, the ability to instantly identify a song based on the first few notes or an opening chord is an extraordinary feat of memory that we take largely for granted. Studies of musicians with severe strokes find that memory for music, especially rhythm, remains intact even when the musician has lost the ability to name common objects.

Spatial memory is another example of a memory subsystem. In one experiment, blindfolded subjects were seated in a robot vehicle and driven around at different speeds and distances (Berthoz, 1995 et al.). When tested later, they were able to reproduce highly accurate profiles of their travel with a remarkable degree of agreement from subject to subject. These results suggest that a relatively precise memory system exists that is dedicated to remembering speed, direction and turning angles, whether or not a person is moving on his own. Similar studies with animals indicate that memories of spatial movement require an intact vestibular system or sense of balance. Thus different sensory systems interact with various memory subsystems to encode, store and recall highly specific types of information, much of which is outside of our conscious awareness and thus difficult to express in words.

SO WHAT KINDS OF MEMORY ARE MOST LIKELY TO SHOW SDLM?

State-dependent learning and memory (SDLM) is responsible for some of the small—but vexing—memory problems we face in everyday life. Most people have had the experience: at work you think about something you need to do when you get home—but when you finally get home you forget it, remembering it again only after you are back at work. This frustrating process—remembering something in one context only to completely forget about it in another—continues until you do something to bridge your memory gap.

The apocryphal act of tying a string around one's finger as a way to remember to do something is a folklore example—reputedly dating to the Anglo Saxons—of a strategy to bridge the SDLM gap in the continuity of memory. Today we use literal, metaphoric, and virtual 'sticky notes' to span the SDLM chasms of memory that we negotiate every day.

Do different memory systems show greater or lesser degrees of state-dependent learning and memory? Scientific studies find that a number of factors influence just how profound state-dependent gaps in memory are. These include the degree of differences between the two states that are being compared. The type of information being learned and recalled also affects the degree of state-dependency. The greater the difference between two mental/physical states and/or social contexts, the more likely that there will be notable differences in the person's ability to recall and use the same information and memories.

Many species, from fish to birds to monkeys to humans, are capable of SDLM. In animals, drugs are often used to produce discrete internal states that the animal then uses to determine which one of two equivalent actions to perform—whether to press the red lever or the green one to find a reward. This kind of experiment is more properly called "drug discrimination" in that the animal senses drug-specific internal cues to determine which of two conditioned responses is the correct one. SDLM can also be created in animals using fearful states produced by unpleasant things such as electrical shocks or an ice water bath.

The effects of a variety of different states on SDLM have been studied in humans. Psychologists such as Gordon Bower have their subjects create distinct emotional states such as happiness or sadness in a variety of ways. In one approach they are told to think about happy or sad events in their lives or they will be told a happy or sad story. Or they may be hypnotized, which has the advantage of inducing many different emotions, e.g., feeling happy or sad, that can be maintained for several minutes at a certain level of intensity (Bower, 1981).

Herbert Weingartner, Eric Eich and others have studied the SDLM effects of extreme mood states in bipolar illness, epilepsy, steroid psychoses, dissociative disorders and other mind-altering conditions. An enormous range of drugs, from stimulants to sedatives, from hormones to psychedelics, is known to produce SDLM effects in humans. In addition, experimental manipulations such as sleep-deprivation or increased physical activity levels can be used to produce SDLM.

These different experiments reveal some fundamental principles. For one, SDLM is rather common, and it occurs in a variety of mental states. Its effects can be demonstrated in a wide variety of memory tasks and tests. In experiments in which SDLM is elicited with drugs, moderate doses appear to produce the strongest results. (In animals, very tiny doses of a drug may be all that is necessary to produce SDLM—a sign that relevant internal cues probably differ between rats and people.)

In SDLM the subject always knows the target information but in certain states is less able to recall it. Asymmetry often appears in the degree of SDLM between two different states. For example, someone who learns information in State A may recall it better in State B, compared to information he learned in State B and recalled (or tried to) in State A. Added up across all of the different kinds of human experiments, the effects of SDLM are moderate. But in extreme psychiatric conditions such as mania, depression, PTSD, and dissociation the degree of SDLM may be profound.

Only certain types of memory are likely to show strong SDLM effects. SDLM effects are especially strong for autobiographical memory—the recall of one's past experiences, behaviors, thoughts, feelings and related knowledge and facts. In the induced-mood studies, normal subjects recall significantly more happy experiences and fewer sad experiences when they are in a happy state and the reverse when in a sad state. These results are greatly magnified for bipolar patients cycling between extreme states of mania and depression.

Cognitive associations—the train of thoughts and/or images that occur in response to a given stimulus—are also likely to show significant SDLM effects. Psychologists often investigate this by having the subject generate word associations to stimulus words: "salt" may elicit the association "pepper" or "hot" elicits "cold." Research with bipolar patients, alcoholics both sober and intoxicated, and normal individuals with mood- or drug-induced states finds that self-generated word associations frequently depend on the person's state. So in two different states, a subject will generate different associations to the same word. And if an individual in one state is told their association to that same word given in another state, they often do not recognize or won't acknowledge it as theirs. In fact, they are likely to insist that the experimenter made up the word association, not them (Weingartner, Miller, & Murphy, 1977).

Recalling a correct sequence of information or action is another kind of information processing significantly disrupted when learning and remembering occur in different mental states (Weingartner, 1978). Executing a sequence of tasks in a specific order can go haywire if a subject is in a radically different mental state from the one in which the sequence was learned or is typically used. To avoid this situation, experts use checklists and other organizing systems to ensure a critical sequence of tasks is properly executed.

Such structure becomes crucial in emergencies and times of high emotion. That is why, as Captain Sully Sullenberger prepared to ditch his airliner in the Hudson River on January 15, 2009, his co-pilot was busy working through the checklist for an emergency restart of the engines. Sullenberger followed a checklist for ditching that he didn't quite finish before hitting the water. But he correctly accomplished enough steps to succeed despite experiencing the ". . . *worst sickening, pit-of-your-stomach, falling-through-the-floor feeling*" of his life (https://en.wikipedia.org/wiki/Chesley_Sullenberger). ("Worst moments of my life: pilot tells of ditching in Hudson." *Sydney Morning Herald.* AP. (Retrieved February 6, 2009 from the Wikipedia article: http://www.smh.com.au/news/world/audio-reveals-exactly-what-happened--a-hrefhttpmediasmhcomaurid45888blistenba/2009/02/06/1233423442580.html)

Clinical Examples of SDLM

The notion of SDLM was central to many of the psychological explanations of perplexing behavior offered by late nineteenth-century clinicians. The case of the Irish Workman reported by George Combe in 1830 is often regarded as the first description of SDLM phenomena. The workman in question could only recall certain events that occurred when he had been drinking when he was again drunk. This case, cited in many medical texts for decades after, is believed to have inspired the classic mystery *The Moonstone,* by Wilkie Collins in 1868 (Overton, 1984). Théodule Ribot (1839–1916), considered the founder of medical psychology, first theorized that differences in a person's psychological and physical states influenced what a person would be thinking about and what they could remember.

A dramatic example is the case of Sirhan Sirhan, who assassinated Robert (Bobby) Kennedy in the kitchen of the Ambassador Hotel in Los Angeles in 1968. Although numerous witnesses saw Sirhan shoot Kennedy multiple times, he denied all memory of the events. A forensic psychiatrist for the defense, Bernard Diamond, hypnotized Sirhan, who would then recount and relive his actions in increasing detail at the same time becoming progressively more agitated. At the moment of assassination, Sirhan would shout curses and "shoot" Kennedy and then start to gasp and choke as he relived the Secret Service agent grabbing and strangling him.

Despite a number of sessions, Sirhan never recalled the assassination when he was not under hypnosis. During the trial, he continued to insist that he was innocent, denied having met Diamond or that he had ever been hypnotized, and argued that it was not his voice when tape recordings of the hypnotic sessions were played (Bower, 1981).

Many other legal cases like Sirhan's exist, although few succeed in convincing an American jury that they should not be held accountable because of their mental state at the time of the crime. In France, however, there is the precedent of a Crime of Passion or *crime passionnel,* in which a husband driven to a state of jealous rage or heartbreak by the discovery of his wife's infidelity can, at least partially, mitigate his responsibility for her murder. In the US, this is known as the Texas law, because that state has a tradition of being exceptionally forgiving to murderous cuckolded husbands.

STATE-DEPENDENT IDENTITIES

Although SDLM occurs in minor forms throughout daily life, the vast majority of people never experience the profound inaccessibility of autobiographical memories seen in clinical cases. Nor do they manifest the dramatic shifts of identity that usually accompany these marked disturbances of memory. Many people do, however, experience variations in their sense of self and identity that—if examined closely—are associated with SDLM that disrupts the continuity and consistency of their behavior across different settings.

By virtue of the complex world that we live in and the many different roles that we are expected to fulfill, we must maintain a repertoire of identities that we activate as required by specific situations and circumstances—work, parenting, marriage and other intimate relationships, as well as in social, religious and civic settings, as athletes and artists, and in many other circumstances. When in those different life settings, we think, feel and behave in ways that are appropriate to the situation.

We reinforce these different identities in external ways, such as dressing and grooming differently for work, intimacy, social, religious, athletic and artistic activities. As we move from one setting to another, we use rituals or habitual behaviors that help make the adjustments necessary to assume our next identity. We may self-acknowledge this transformation metaphorically such as "Now I'm taking off my work hat and putting on my mommy hat," or speak of putting on our "game face."

The degree to which we think, feel, and act very differently across such settings and roles but do not become troubled by our inconsistencies depends in large measure on our ability to compartmentalize autobiographical memories, thoughts, and behaviors. SDLM helps to blur our awareness of our own inconsistencies but creates in turn some degree of discontinuity in our thoughts and actions. In extreme instances, we consider individuals who exhibit radical shifts in morals, behavior, and professed values across settings as examples of hypocrisy. Their do-as-I-say-not-as-I-do attitude is judged as evidence of either moral pretense or gross self-deception.

True hypocrisy does exist, no doubt. But it is also likely that many inconsistencies of character that we point to as evidence of moral failure actually represent examples of state-dependent identity, learning, and memory organized around conflicting roles and identities—so the individual behaves in contradictory ways but is not troubled by the discrepancy. What at first may seem like hypocrisy and duplicity may be more complicated and less calculated than they first appear—more on that later.

The fact that we respond or behave in apparently contradictory ways in different situations happens because of our different mental states across these settings. When someone points out our inconsistencies, we usually can rapidly and emphatically rationalize our behavior as consistent despite its differences. The fallacies in our argument may be transparent to others, but are usually self-convincing enough to allay any anxiety stirred by our apparent duplicity.

We are all prone to this process to a greater or lesser extent. It is the rare person who can achieve the psychological distance from which to carefully examine the contradictions in his or her behavior. Indeed, it is just such a dispassionate self-awareness and self-reflective equanimity that is sought in the quest to achieve a state of spiritual enlightenment.

So how would I know a state-dependent identity if I met one?

The scientific issues raised in documenting state-dependent alterations in sense of self and identity in adults are illustrated by the psychotherapy research of Mardi Horowitz and colleagues at the Langley Porter Institute of the University of California, San Francisco. Horowitz has made many contributions to psychiatric theory and practice, including a well-defined approach to psychotherapy, Configurational Analysis, that is based on working with the array of identity states that a patient reveals during a course of treatment.

Drawing on his pioneering work with traumatic states of consciousness in posttraumatic stress disorder, Horowitz extended his insights to some of the most difficult neurotic disorders psychotherapists encounter. He recognized that despite the fact that people may receive a single diagnostic label such as anxiety disorder or borderline personality disorder; many actually exhibit multiple mental states and hold divergent senses of self. The key to effective treatment is to identify and engage these multiple mental states in psychotherapy, ultimately helping the patient acquire insightful self-control over how they feel, think and act.

In a number of respects, the problems posed for Horowitz's research resembled those the Baby Watchers faced. Studying an infant lying in its crib had proven difficult enough for the Baby Watchers. How can we capture the essence of what is happening from moment to moment between a psychotherapist and a patient? And how do scientists organize and record the ever-shifting complexity of human interactions?

In both instances, the solution is to view that shifting behavior as being composed of a set of distinct states that can be identified by a coding system. The difference is that Horowitz needs to code and categorize a patient's mental and emotional content; the Baby Watchers restrict themselves to observable external variables such as level of activity and alertness, heart and respiratory rate.

In developing his system for coding a patient's mental states, Horowitz drew on an earlier line of psychoanalytic thinking known as ego psychology. Central to this theory is the observation that individuals entered into distinct ego states. The best-known example of a psychotherapy based on ego psychology is Transactional Analysis, developed by the psychiatrist Eric Berne and popularized in his 1964 best seller, *Games People Play* (Berne, 1964).

Berne characterized behavior in the form of three basic ego states that he labeled child, parent, and adult. When two people interact there are a half dozen possible combinations among their three ego states. Over time, such as in a marriage or work relationship, repeated transactions will occur among the various combinations of the three states that will define the "games" or repetitive transactional patterns among them.

The power of Transactional Analysis was its ability to reduce the complexity of ongoing human interactions into simple terms that many people could understand and relate to in their daily lives. The weakness is that it greatly oversimplified human behavior and failed to do justice to the psychological complexity of the people involved. And efforts to lump people into universal schemes such as Berne's three ego states of child, parent and adult utterly fail when examining the moment-to-moment flow of a patient and therapist grappling with the patient's thoughts, feelings, memories, and emotions.

Horowitz's seminal contribution was that he recognized the necessity of defining a unique set of identity states for each and every patient—no two patients have the same set of identity states. He also recognized that the application of each individual's set of states of mind was limited to that patient's therapy and may or may not characterize the patient's behavior in other settings. Part of the work a patient and therapist do together is to examine the degree to which the identity state dynamics that occur during therapy mirrors interactions in the patient's outside life.

Most people have many mental and identity states. A therapist must identify and work with the subset of these states that are most relevant to the patient's problems and symptoms. Therapy begins by drawing up a rudimentary list of potential identity states from the problems and complaints that led the patient to seek treatment. As the therapy progresses and the therapist comes to know the patient better, identifying and describing the patient's mental states becomes more refined. State descriptions are based on the patient's thoughts, feelings and behaviors. Labeling each state follows from what the patient tells the therapist about what they are feeling, along with what the therapist sees the patient actually do.

In his book *States of Mind* (1979), Horowitz uses the case of Janice as the central illustration of a state-based psychotherapy. Janice is a 24-year-old woman who experienced a catastrophic grief reaction after the unexpected death of her younger brother. At the start of therapy she is afraid that she will "*fall apart*" and was "*unable to get herself together again*" (Horowitz, 1979 p. 9). Her brother's funeral triggered family conflict around whether it was best to grieve or to celebrate his life. In particular, her mother criticized Janice for "*acting weird*" by not crying or outwardly mourning—for not showing the socially appropriate emotional states.

As therapy progressed, a series of discrete identity states emerges. Janice would periodically enter a mental state labeled by the therapist as "*Hurt and not working.*" When in the "*Hurt and not working*" state, Janice "*. . . felt dull and lonely, had bodily concerns, and tended to withdraw from social contacts and life tasks* (Horowitz, 1979 p. 36). When she entered this state, her voice would trail off into a mumble. In another state, labeled the "*Tra-la-la*" state, Janice was animated and cheerful but reported feeling that she was only pretending for the benefit of others.

With therapy, she came to recognize when she would enter or exit from these states and how they affected the ways in which she felt, thought and behaved (see Chapter 6 for further discussion of Janice).

The clinical organization imposed by categorizing a patient's behavior into an individualized set of states of mind clarifies the identification of transitions or switches from state to state. Horowitz notes that:

> *These* [switches in identity state] *are commonly recognized during a clinical interview because of changes in facial expression, intonation and inflection in speech, focus and content of verbal reports, degree of self reflective awareness, general arousal, shifts in degree and nature of empathy, and other communicative qualities* (Horowitz, 1979 p. 31).

In other words, the patient suddenly sounds and looks different and tells you different things about what they think and feel about some issue. The degree to which the patient changes is usually correlated with the degree to which her thinking, feeling and sense of self changes. In the *Tra-la-la* state, Janice is *"cheerful, lighthearted"* and *"entertaining"*; whereas in the *Hurt and not working* state, she is *"insulated,"* *"aloof"* and *"withdraws from contact with others"* (p. 37).

The therapist soon begins to see patterns and cycles among the patient's set of mental states that recur from session to session. The next step is to gain an understanding of these patterns and cycles and relate them to both the patient's moment-to-moment experiences in therapy and to larger life.

The insight achieved by applying Horowitz's coding system to a patient's behavior in therapy parallels what the Baby Watchers learned when they began coding infant states. Both discovered recurrent cycles in which the adult psychotherapy patient or infant orbits through an orderly series of distinct mental or behavioral states. If the patient or the infant is in a given state, there is a strong likelihood as to which state will appear next.

In the case of Janice, the *Tra-la-la* state often switched to the *Hurt and not working* state, which then tended to switch into a crying state. Whenever Janice felt herself slipping into a particularly painful mental state characterized by feelings of intense self-disgust, shame and despair, she would switch into the *"Tra-la-la"* state in which she appeared animated and cheerful but actually felt that she was only putting on an act for the benefit of others.

At times, however, the *Tra-la-la* state would switch into a state labeled, *Hurt but working*, marked by a head-down posture, sense of shame, and slow, soft speech. In this state Janice was able to reflect on her sense of self and behavior and to make progress in therapy. The result, however, was that this self-examination often triggered the painful state of *acute self-disgust*.

The major difference between Horowitz's therapy model and the Baby Watchers' coding systems is largely developmental. They are working at different ends of the life cycle. The Baby Watchers can specify a near universal set of normal newborn infant behavioral states because they are observing the basic behavioral repertoire that a healthy newborn brings into the world. As the child matures, many, many additional states are added, in large measure through seminal life experiences and powerful relationships. The web of pathways among these states also expands, leading to sequences and cycles of behavior shaped by the significant people and contexts in which the child lives.

At the other end of life's developmental continuum, Horowitz seeks to sort out and work with a subset of identity states that embody an adult patient's critical attitudes, problems, and responses to what were often painful early experiences and relationships. So he must identify mental states that are unique for each patient. Both models recognize, however, that the only way to make sense of the complex behavior being observed is to categorize it into a series of discrete recurrent states that switch from one to another in patterns that are both roughly cyclic and largely predictable.

Horowitz faces another problem: how to simplify his highly individualized mental state coding system to allow a psychotherapist to use it in actual practice. So he defined four categories of states of mind commonly shown by patients in psychotherapy (Horowitz, Milbrath, Ewert, Sonneborn, & Stinson, 1994). *Well-modulated states* display a smooth flow of expression and genuine emotion. In o*vermodulated states,* the individual seems stiff, rigid, walled off from their emotions, or feigning an emotion that they do not genuinely feel.

Undermodulated states feature sudden surges of emotion and the person under their influence appears to be impulsive and uncontrolled. In s*himmering states,* the patient switches back and forth between overmodulated and undermodulated states, appearing alternately coldly overcontrolled and emotionally impulsive.

Mixed Emotions: On Being Happy and Sad at the Same Time

Horowitz observes—as have many others from the Baby Watchers to the biological psychiatrists—that more than one mental state can be simultaneously or near-simultaneously present. In what he termed *shimmering states*, the person appears to rapidly shift back and forth between two very different ways of being:

> *Shimmering states are characterized by the individual shifting rapidly between undercontrolled emotions and overcontrolled emotion. The observer may recognize discordant signs of expression in verbal and nonverbal modes. The clashing symbols may occur simultaneously or within a brief period of time.* (Horowitz et al., 1994 p. 1767)

One of the major cues that psychotherapists use to identify psychological conflicts is observing a sudden switch in the patient's emotional state. In addition to a marked shift in the person's affect—say, from happy to tearful—the therapist will also see changes in facial expression, speech, posture, and content of thought. Other shifts may be more subtle but still exert power in self-awareness, thoughtful reflection, empathy and other communicative qualities (Horowitz, 1979). These kinds of switches signal that conflicting ideas, senses of self, values, and emotions are headed for a psychological collision.

In psychotherapy a shimmering state signals that a patient is venturing into emotionally conflicted territory. Simmering states mark mental hot spots for the patient. When one appears, the therapist's task is to slow the patient down to explore the emotions and memories that are driving the process (Nijdam, Baas, Olff, & Gerson, 2013).

Horowitz's concept captures an important feature for understanding the role of states of being in everyday life. The notion that two or more distinct and very different mental states can alternatingly exchange control over a person's behavior and subjective experience is an insight into how—at certain moments in our lives—we find ourselves caught in the grip of powerful but conflicting emotions.

A common example is the experience of feeling both happy and sad at the same time. Often such bittersweet experiences occur at a symbolic moment in the context of a momentous change in one's life. Packing up your house or office to move to a desirable new situation, sending a child off to college or marriage, are typical situations in which people often feel the rapidly alternating tug of polar emotions.

Another example of uncontrolled rapid switching occurs when we see young children flip back and forth between tears and laughter as an adult tries to distract them from crying by acting silly. A more dramatic shimmering comes with the abrupt mood swings between mania and depression that some rapid cycling bipolar patients exhibit as they transition from a manic state into a fully depressed one (See Chapter 3). The revolving door phenomena described in Chapter 4 in MPD/DID cases is yet another example of rapidly alternating mental states.

SYNTHESIS

Memory and identity are inextricably linked. We see this most clearly in people such as Polly and Ansel Bourne, who lose both. But, we all share a propensity to selectively remember learned information and life experiences depending on the context, role or identity state that we are in at a given moment. The cognitive mechanism underlying this process, state-dependent learning and memory (SDLM), has been well studied in man and mouse and boils down to a few basic principles. Information learned in a given state is best recalled in the same state and more poorly recalled in disparate states. The likelihood of retrieving a given memory across two states is a function of how dissimilar the two states are (certain state dimensions likely contribute to the disparity more than others) and the type of information to be recalled. There are different kinds of memory and certain types show stronger SDLM effects than others.

Autobiographical memories, a critical component of identity, are often strongly state-dependent. What people say about themselves and their lives depends on their immediate state of mind. In the modern world, people typically shift identities multiple times daily as they traverse roles and routines as spouses, parents, workers, and friends as well as numerous other identities with corresponding senses of self elicited by personal contexts and relationships. While this has always been true, modern life—and most recently the Internet—has dramatically expanded our degrees of freedom to create new identities.

The enormous range of unique identities available to every individual makes it difficult to develop a universal system to capture and code them. In highly circumscribed settings, such as psychotherapy, in which a person experiences strong emotional swings and recalls salient life events, it is possible to identify and track a recurring subset of an individual's identity states. Horowitz's Configurational Analysis is an example of this therapeutic approach. In his descriptions of Janice, we again see the general principles of stateness expressed in terms of transitivity, state-dependency of memory, demeanor, sense of self, and sequential directionality. Now, however, the cycle of states is highly individualized compared to infants.

Tracking a patient's recurrent states of mind within and across therapy sessions provides a therapist with meta-level information about the individual's psychodynamics. In particular, struggles between two disparate states of mind—anger and fear, happiness and sadness, joy and grief etc.—expressed as "shimmering states" mark points of psychological conflict.

CHAPTER 6   SECRET LIVES: PERSONALITY AND ITS PARADOXES

Bruce Ivins

Following within weeks of the 9/11/2001 attack on the World Trade Center, the anthrax-laden letters mailed to Senators Patrick Leahy and Tom Daschle, as well as NBC news anchor Tom Brokaw and the editor of the *New York Post,* set off an intensive hunt for a domestic terrorist. Although the crude letters contained the statements: "Death to America," "Death to Israel," and "Allah is Great," the FBI profilers believed that the source was most likely a domestic terrorist—one with both the microbiological expertise and ready access to the deadly but rare Ames strain of anthrax.

Although hundreds of scientists potentially had the skills necessary to create the finely-powered or "weaponized" form of anthrax spores that sickened 22 and murdered five, the FBI's investigation primarily focused on Dr. Steven J. Hatfill as a person of interest. Hatfill had both the necessary skills and unrestricted access to the Ames strain from 1997 to 1999. Colleagues reported that he repeatedly asked them about weaponizing anthrax. In fact to some, Hatfill seem obsessed with the topic, stopping them in the hallways to warn about the dangers of an anthrax weapon.

A search of his apartment found documents matching U.S. Army manuals on the production of anthrax weapons. Hatfill was writing a novel in which a Palestinian terrorist attacks Washington, DC with biological weapons. Pharmacy records showed that starting in January before the anthrax attacks, he filled five prescriptions for large amounts of the antibiotic Cipro®, the only drug approved for inhalational anthrax. Ultimately these medications proved to be for his chronic sinus infections. While the circumstantial evidence appeared suspicious, it was ultimately another arm of the FBI's investigation that cleared Hatfill's name. He received a $5.8-million-dollar settlement of his lawsuit.

In 2001, the FBI lacked the expertise to investigate biological weapons such as anthrax. Seeking government-affiliated expertise, they turned to the U.S. Army Medical Research Institute of Infectious Diseases based at Fort Detrick near Frederick, MD. In a paradox emblematic of the entire investigation, the FBI considered the scientists at Ft. Detrick to be both essential expert consultants and potential terrorists. Jeffrey Adamovicz, the deputy chief of the Bacteriology Division recalled the first meeting with the FBI, "*We were heroes in the morning and suspects in the afternoon*" (http://www.pbs.org/wgbh/pages/frontline/criminal-justice/anthrax-files/transcript-10).

Among the first Ft. Detrick scientists to become closely involved with the FBI was Bruce Ivins. Dr. Ivins was a senior microbiologist in the Bacteriological Division and had worked at Ft. Detrick for twenty-seven years. With over twenty years experience with anthrax, he was considered among the foremost experts in the country. Indeed, it appears that it was Ivins who suggested to the FBI the very strategy that would ultimately prove his undoing.

By November 2001 it was known that the strain of anthrax used in the attacks contained several genetically distinct subgroups of the bacteria known as morphs. On January 23, 2002, Ivins provided the FBI with a tutorial on how to use the existence of morphs to identify the source of the spores used in the attacks. A subsequent genetic analysis identified 4 distinctive morphs that could be used as a fingerprint for the version of the anthrax used in the attacks. As an example intended for colleagues, Ivins provided the FBI with a sample from his laboratory. One that appeared free of the telltale morphs. Indeed, Hatfill was exonerated because the anthrax cultures that he had access to did not contain the signature morphs.

With the collapse of the Hatfill investigation, the FBI turned to identifying the source of anthrax using the morph strategy suggested by Dr. Ivins. Reasoning that if they could find the source of the murder weapon that should give them a clue as to the identity of the murderer. It took several years of experimentation and testing before, in 2007, they were able to pinpoint the source of anthrax as originating from a single-spore batch of the Ames strain called "RMR-1029." This immediately narrowed the field of potential suspects from hundreds to just a few people who had access to this unique strain that was only housed at Ft. Detrick.

In the meantime, conventional background investigation was turning up evidence of unusual behaviors on the part of Dr. Ivins. While his colleagues at Ft. Detrick considered him to be among the most mild-mannered and innocuous of people, the FBI discovered that he had a longstanding secret obsession with the women's college sorority Kappa Kappa Gamma. In 1970, he compiled a list of all of the KKG chapters in the U.S. By his own admission, he took long nocturnal trips to stand outside of KKG chapters at universities in surrounding states. In the 1980's, he burglarized several KKG sorority houses stealing books containing secret sorority rituals involving the blindfolding of initiates. He attempted to sell these on the Internet and through ads in Rolling Stone magazine. A later search of his home computer revealed hundreds of pornographic photos of blindfolded women.

Dr. Ivins sent numerous emails and letters to colleagues, strangers, members of Congress and to the editors of publications and news organizations. In many of these instances he used a pseudonym—often transparently false ones such as Mia Hamm or Derek Jeter—mailing the letter or package from another city, frequently from mailboxes near a Kappa Kappa Gamma sorority house. At times he used a pseudonym that was a female derivative of a man's name. In interviews with the FBI he acknowledged being obsessed with a female colleague who was a KKG graduate, including sending her stalking emails as well as spray painting KKG on her sidewalk and car. Learning that he was a major suspect in the FBI's investigation, Dr. Ivins took steps to cover his tracks. At some point prosecutors contend that he realized that his strategy of using unique morphs to fingerprint the source of anthrax would ultimately point back at him. In particular, he secretly decontaminated his lab and office on several occasions. These unauthorized samplings and decontaminations violated official policy. When confronted with evidence of these activities plus his unprecedented late nights in the laboratory just prior to the mailing of each anthrax letter, Ivins had no coherent explanations according to the FBI final report (United States Department of Justice, 2010).

Furthermore, he gave conflicting statements about his actions, tried to point a finger at colleagues, and attempted to submit additional samples from his cultures that appeared to be manipulated to remove the tattletale morphs. A re-analysis of the very first anthrax sample that Ivins submitted as an example to his colleagues, however, now proved to contain the signature morphs. Additional, previously undisclosed, vials of the killer's anthrax were also discovered hidden in his laboratory.

Most revealing were emails Ivins sent to two colleagues whom he regarded as close confidantes. These show a man struggling against another part of himself that occasionally takes control. Ivins sounds mortified that perhaps he could be responsible for these heinous crimes, but admits,

> "*I may be heading towards becoming that kind of person that is the exact antithesis of who I want to be. I can't begin to tell you how much it hurts and scares me*" (United States Department of Justice, 2010 p. 45).

At times he refers to himself in the third person. Shortly after the anthrax mailing to Senator Daschle, he writes of himself in an email, *"Bruce has been a basket case these last few days"* (United States Department of Justice, 2010 p. 46). Even more revealing is a poem emailed on December 15, 2001:

> *I made up some poems about having two people in one*
> *(me + the person in my dreams): . . .*
>> *I'm a little dream-self, short and stout.*
>> *I'm the other half of Bruce—when he lets me out*
>> *When I get all steamed up, I don't pout*
>> *I push Bruce aside, then I'm Free to run about!*
>> *Hickory dickory Doc—Doc Bruce ran up the clock*
>> *But something happened in very strange rhythm.*
>> *His other self went and exchanged places with him.*
>>
>> *So now, please guess who*
>> *Is conversing with you.*
>> *Hickory dickory Doc!*
>> *Bruce and this other guy, sitting by some trees*
>> *Exchanging personalities.*
>> *It's like having two in one.*
>> *Actually it's rather fun!*
>
> (United States Department of Justice, 2010 pp. 46–47)

In a conversation (presumably taped because of the inclusions of hesitations and asides) with someone only identified as a witness, Ivins says,

> *And a lot of times with e-mails, I don't know that I sent an e-mail until I see it in the sent box. And it worries me when I wake up in the mornings and I've got all my clothes and shoes on, and my car keys are right beside there . . . And I don't have it in my, in my, I, I can tell you I don't have it in my heart to kill anybody."*
> *"The only reason I remember some of this stuff, it's because there's like a clue the next day. Like there's an e-mail or, or, you know, where you're, when you're in bed and you're like, you're like this, you know, that's, that's not real fun. It's like "oh shit, did I drive somewhere last night?"*

When the witness suggests that he considered being hypnotized to see if he can recall more of his missing memories, Ivins says,

> *What happens if I find something that, that is like buried deep, deep, deep and you know, like from, from my past or I mean . . . like when I was a kid or stuff like that you know*? (United States Department of Justice, 2010 p. 70).

Closing in, the FBI executed a search warrant of Ivin's home and office, finding guns, a bulletproof vest, homemade body armor and a shooting range in his basement. There was no evidence, however, of anthrax. Under the care of a psychiatrist for years and treated with heavy doses of antidepressant and antipsychotic medications, Ivins begins to visibly come apart under the strain of being the focus of the FBI investigation. On July 9, 2008 he tells his therapy group that he is a subject in the anthrax investigation. Revealing a plan to "*take out*" coworkers and others who he believes have wronged him, Ivins says that he is going to "*go out in a blaze of glory*" (United States Department of Justice, 2010 p. 50).

On the basis of these statements and with the recommendation of his psychiatrist, Ivins is taken into custody and committed to Sheppard Pratt Hospital in Towson, MD. Believed to no longer be a danger to himself or others he is discharged about two weeks later over the objections of his therapist. Forty-eight hours later he is dead from an overdose of medications.

Following Ivins's suicide, a psychological autopsy authorized by Chief Judge Royce C. Lamberth of the U.S. District Court in Washington, DC was conducted by a panel of psychiatrists, reviewing his medical and psychiatric records. Although colleagues, coworkers, and close friends still strongly believe in his innocence, the panel found evidence of multiple episodes of bizarre and sometimes criminal behavior. The panel chair, University of Virginia psychiatrist Gregory Saathoff, observed, "*The panel was quite struck by Ivins's ability to lead a parallel life*" (Shane, 2011).

> "*To most of his colleagues and acquaintances, Dr. Ivins was an eccentric, socially awkward, harmless figure, an esteemed bacteriologist who juggled at parties, played the keyboard at church and wrote clever poems for departing colleagues,*" the report said,

"That is precisely how Dr. Ivins wanted them to see him. He cultivated a persona of benign eccentricity that masked his obsessions and criminal thoughts."

The report describes Dr. Ivins's *"strange and traumatic childhood during which his mother assaulted and abused her husband—stabbing him, beating him, and threatening to kill him with a loaded gun."* (Shane, 2011).

Whether or not Dr. Bruce Ivins was or was not the murderer behind the anthrax attacks is a matter of contention that is beyond the scope of this book. The FBI investigation has been faulted on the validity of its genetic science and on the intense psychological pressure that it applied to a man, whom some believe was the ultimate milquetoast. Proponents of Ivins's innocence often portray him as a deeply troubled person, one who ultimately turned on himself, but who would have never harmed others.

What is important here, is that this extraordinarily intensive investigation—that was ultimately focused full bore on Dr. Ivins—revealed the existence of another and secret part of Ivins engaged in seriously deviant behavior, sometimes criminal activities. There was at least one other Bruce Ivins, who drove long distances to spy on Kappa Kappa Gamma sororities and mailed letters and packages under false identities from distant cities. Indeed, Ivins had a number of identities including female pseudonyms under which he blogged.

SECRET LIVES

The homophobic politician caught soliciting sex in a men's room. The hellfire-and-damnation minister embezzling the church's poor fund. The reputed financial counselor running a Ponzi scheme. The prudish librarian who moonlights as a stripper. The beloved priest who is a child molester. The nationally honored family comedy television father who is a serial rapist, and the courageous fireman who is an arsonist. We read or hear about someone like this from time to time. Pillars of the community. Respected and influential people in positions of public trust, who have cultivated an image of rectitude and loudly condemn any behavior or belief that deviates from the straight and narrow. Yet, we discover that all the while they have been secretly engaging in deviant, immoral or illegal behavior.

When such cases come to light, friends, colleagues and family express surprise and disbelief. At first, many refuse to accept the shocking revelations because it doesn't fit the person they know. How could he do this? Why didn't anyone notice? How can such a hypocrite live with himself? People are baffled by the extreme differences between the person's public behavior and their secret life. These cases are often treated as hypocrisy at its worst. Moralistic commentators hold them out as object lessons—until the next breaking scandal sucks away the public's attention.

What is going on here? How can people seem to be one way and yet also be someone else so totally different? How could such heinous behavior lurk deep within seemingly virtuous personalities? Some of us can think of people we know who exhibit marked contradictions in the ways that they behave in different settings. We may have also witnessed that certain triggers or circumstances can set off completely unexpected reactions in people whom we believe that we know well. What accounts for these apparently uncharacteristic changes of personality?

PERSONALITY

But first, what is "personality" anyway? Personality is usually defined as a set of stable and enduring aspects—behavioral, temperamental, emotional and mental traits and qualities—that both emphasize a person's uniqueness and yet allow us to compare him with other people. We expect those aspects will predict a person's behavior and responses to stress, to reward, to temptation. And we understand that personality is complex, that life events, family traits, and culture make strong contributions to the mix.

We also recognize that personality can be pathology. People can be prisoners of their personalities. People can inflict their personalities upon others, intentionally or not. Chronic, irresolvable conflicts between individuals are often attributed to the similarities or differences in their personalities.

In every society there are labels (e.g., Type A) that serve as a cultural shorthand for different types of personalities. From a scientific perspective, there are several ways to think about types of personality. One is to take three broad perspectives: traditional psychodynamic, and modern developmental and dimensional models of personality. Each has something to contribute, but all fail to explain a common yet startling phenomenon: some people just aren't who they seem to be.

Psychodynamic Models of Personality

The classic psychodynamic model of personality is Freudian theory. Freud thought of personality as the end result of a developmental process that passed through an epic series of psychosexual life stages. Experiences or events that disrupted development as a child passed through a given psychosexual stage could lead to what Freud called a fixation at that stage. In time that fixation would be strongly expressed in that child's adult personality.

Freud's oral stage, lasting from birth to about 18 months, focused on the gratification of oral or sucking pleasures. Too little or two much gratification would result in an oral fixation manifest as a tendency to overeat, drink alcohol, smoke or suck or chew on objects. The anal stage, from 18 months to 3 years, concentrated on eliminating and retaining stool. During this phase, the child first encounters social pressure to conform and to control urges and impulses. At one extreme, such as anal retentiveness, fixation appeared as an obsession with cleanliness, order, and perfection. With anal expulsion, the other extreme, the individual is messy and disorganized.

During the phallic stage, from ages three to six, the pleasure zone switches to the genitals. Freud believed that during this stage boys developed an oedipal complex in which they sexually desired their mothers and became rivals with their father for her affection. Later psychoanalysts added an Electra complex, in which girls experienced a similar sexual attraction to their fathers. Fixations at the phallic stage resulted in sexual deviations or a weak and confused sexual identity.

During the latency stage (ages six to puberty) sexual feelings were repressed and pleasure was derived from playing with same sex peers. The culmination of Freudian psychosexual development was the genital stage (from puberty onward) in which the sexual urges of the earlier oral, anal and phallic stages were re-activated and focused on genital pleasures.

Freud is rightly ranked among the great Western thinkers of modern times. His ideas and influence have thoroughly permeated our culture. In addition to his many original observations and theories, he collated and refined the then emerging contemporary knowledge about human behavior into a set of more sharply articulated and psychologically framed theories and models of the mind. This, in turn, led to the core principle of psychotherapy as we know it today—that self-reflection and talking about one's behavior with a trained professional can promote positive change.

One result of Freud's psychoanalytic formulation was to provide an understanding of how children become the adults they are. Perhaps his most compelling refinement of the ideas of the time was his elaboration of specific developmental stages that could be differentially impacted by adverse childhood events leading to specific expressions of neurotic pathology in the adult personality. Despite the limitations of Freud's theory of psychosexual stages of child development (and there are many), he firmly instantiated the idea that what happens in childhood matters! This tenet remains central to most psychodynamic formulations and treatments of the personality and its disorders. It is also proving true for the neurobiological development of the brain.

MODERN MODELS OF PERSONALITY

Modern psychologists seek more quantitative approaches to understanding the development and complexity of personality. Nonetheless, differing interpretations of the data give rise to an array of theories. Most of these sort into two basic types: developmental or dimensional theories of personality. Developmental models tend to categorize people; they focus mostly on how you came to be the way you are. Dimensional models view people along continuums—they describe how you are now without regard to your history. And, of course, there are the inevitable blends of these two camps.

Developmental Models of Personality

Developmental models are generally organized around the quality of the attachment between an individual and her primary caretaker, the classic dyad being the mother and her infant. We first talked about attachment in Chapter two in the context of the degree of attunement between a mother and her infant. Researchers use various methods to classify the security and organization of this relationship depending on the person's age. Categorical differences (such as the A, B and C attachment types described in Chapter 2) in the quality of early attachments have been found to both predict and contribute to certain enduring personality traits. Life experiences and caretaking influence the quality of what's known as an attachment relationship, which in turn shapes the individual's personality. Serious chaos in the child's primary attachment relationship increases the risk of psychiatric disorders, sub-stance abuse, and personality problems.

To measure attachments, researchers may observe their subjects—coding an infant or toddler's responses to mother's return after a brief separation (see Chapter 2). Older children and young adolescents may be asked to report their own responses, maybe completing a series of stories about family interactions or answering questions about their family. In older teens and adults the current gold standard is the Adult Attachment Interview, a fifteen-question semi-clinical interview that focuses on a person's early attachment experiences and her current thoughts about them. Questionnaires and scales seek to categorize these relation-ships, often referred to as *attachment styles*.

Most measures, from toddler to adult, seek to classify a person's attachment style into one of several broad categories. The original infant-toddler categories were anxious-avoidant attachment, secure attachment, and anxious-ambivalent also known as types A, B, and C respectively (see Chapter 2). Adult measures also seek to classify individuals into between three to five attachment styles. Most authorities agree that there is not a direct one-to-one correspondence between the secure, ambiva-lent and avoidant toddler classifications and those same labels in the adult measures.

Behavioral and developmental scientists can classify individuals of all ages into a predefined set of attachment categories that predict or cor-relate with psychological and social adjustment or maladjustment. Indeed, if you want to measure just one thing in a toddler that is the most pre-dictive of much later social adjustment, it is attachment.

The research is conclusive that it is better to be attached to a primary caretaker than not to be attached. Secure attachments (Type B) are the best and most predictive of 'ego resiliency' or the ability to be flexible and adaptive in response to environmental stressors. But a secure attach-ment does not, in and of itself, guarantee a successful social and psycho-logical outcome. Children may have more than one attachment and two secure attachments appear to be much better than one. Insecure attach-ments (Types A & C) predict more problems and are often associated with personality disorders. Type D (Disorganized) attachment predicts signif-icantly worse outcomes than the insecure attachments (see Chapter 8).

The long-term power of attachment to shape an individual's life has naturally led to many attempts to repair insecure or disorganized attach-ments. Most of these putative treatments are ineffective and a few, such as holding therapy in which aggressive children are swaddled and bound until they become passive, are dangerous and responsible for great harm and even the death of children. Scientifically evaluated treatments do exist, but—to date—permanently changing a child's attachment status for the better is very difficult (Berlin, Ziv, Amaya-Jackson, & Greenberg, 2005).

Dimensional Models of Personality

In the dimensional approach, it's hypothesized that personality is a set of measurable factors along a continuum from normality to pathology. Dimensional models can be traced to the Minnesota Multiphasic Personality Inventory, better known as the MMPI, the first empirically validated dimensional personality measure to achieve widespread acceptance.

Originally published in 1942, the MMPI was developed using the then-revolutionary approach known as empirical keying, which identified questions that reliably differentiated so-called normal individuals from psychiatric patients. For the record, however, the original 'normal' subjects were the relatives of the 'abnormal' subjects. After several revisions the current version, the MMPI-II, includes 567 true-false questions and takes about one to two hours to complete. It is complicated to score and interpret, but the MMPI-II is still widely used to evaluate psychiatric patients as well as to screen applicants for sensitive occupations such as nuclear plant workers, pilots, law enforcement and certain military roles.

The idea that dimensions of personality can be reliably measured and that different types of personality are defined by unique patterns of dimensional scores, evolved into what are known as factor models of personality. Factor models with as many as eighty dimensions have been proposed, but most studies converge on five to nine basic personality factors or dimensions. The generally accepted Big Five Factors are extroversion (also known as surgency), agreeableness, conscientiousness, neuroticism and openness to experience.

Each of the Big Five factors contains subdimensions. For example, extroversion includes energy level and the tendency to seek social stimulation. Openness to experience includes imagination, curiosity, an interest in the arts, and openness to new or novel ideas and experiences. Someone's personality profile is usually specified as a percentage score on each dimension with 50 percent being the mid-point. So someone who preferred solitude would score low on the extraversion dimension and someone who scored high on the conscientiousness dimension would be responsible and trustworthy.

PERSONALITY DISORDERS

The challenge for dynamic, developmental and dimensional models of personality is to explain the nature of personality disorders. The belief that there are people who have a fundamental flaw in their character or personality is widely accepted and a staple in myth and folklore dated at least to Aristotle's tragic hero. In literature, that flaw is both ironic and sad leading to a person's undoing or self-defeat on the brink of success. Think Hamlet's indecision and Othello's jealousy. In life, this deficit or excess in some fundamental trait of the person's character causes pain and problems for the person and inflicts itself on those around him.

As defined by the DSM-5, psychiatrists diagnose 10 types of personality disorders with an additional miscellaneous category. To qualify for an official DSM personality disorder, the person must manifest an enduring pattern of behavior that is contrary to general social expectations, that is persistent and rigidly inflexible, and that causes the person distress and impairment in multiple areas of their life. This pattern of thinking, perceiving and behaving must be stable over time and be traceable back to adolescence or early adulthood.

The official psychiatric approach to diagnosing personality disorders involves a simple—and largely unproven—combination of the dimensional and categorical approaches. To diagnose someone with a personality disorder the clinician must ensure that the patient meets a minimum number of overall criteria, which are often composed of a Chinese menu-like list of symptoms or behaviors. The DSM approach to diagnosis is imposed on mental health clinicians of all disciplines, who must bill insurance companies or governmental agencies for their services.

The scientific community has widely criticized the DSM approach. They say it depends too much on historical assessment of clinical symptoms and behaviors and lacks scientific data to support most of the personality disorder diagnostic categories (Morey et al., 2007). Others, however, have found empirical alignments between developmental attachment categories or specific patterns of dimensional personality factors and certain of the DSM personality disorder diagnoses.

The goodness of fit between psychological models of 'the personality' and psychiatric personality disorders is an ongoing debate that will remain with us for the foreseeable future given the enormous differences in the ways that the various camps look at the issues and interpret the data.

A MUCH BIGGER PROBLEM

The larger problem with all of these modern ways of thinking about personality and personality disorders: none of them explain people like the anti-gay politician who is gay himself, the minister who preaches hellfire and damnation and yet embezzles church funds, the timid librarian who moonlights as a stripper, or the nationally beloved father figure who leads a secret life drugging and raping aspiring young actresses. All of the current ways of thinking about personality require that it be viewed as a set of fixed, persistent, and globally defining traits that pervade all of the person's interactions with the world, for better or for worse.

But people like the politician, minister, teacher, and comedian simultaneously have a foot in two worlds: a public one in which they display socially approved character attributes and behaviors, and a private realm where they engage in secret, illegal, and socially deviant behaviors. So which is their real personality?

A STATE MODEL OF PERSONALITY

Another way exists to explain the duplicity—or, perhaps more correctly, the duality—of personality. The state model is a complementary way of viewing the complexity of an individual's personality. It defines personality as the collective dynamics of a person's set of identity, emotional, and behavioral states. The model also allows for a wider range of disparate behaviors, and it can account for abrupt personality changes. Plus it incorporates most of the phenomena covered by the current developmental and dimensional approaches.

Dissociative identity disorder—also known as multiple personality disorder—provides an extreme example that allows us to see more deeply into the state nature of personality. The personality of people with dissociative disorders, such as Polly and Ansel Bourne in Chapter 5, is composed of a collection of separate and distinct identity states that may have little or no awareness of each other and thus often behave in conflicting, contradictory, and self-defeating ways. Or as William

James observed in his famous lecture on the divided self, *"There are persons whose existence is little more than a series of zigzags"* (James, 1901–1902 p. 142).

The rest of us have our own sets of identity states created for and always evolving within the changing contexts in which we live and function. In general, we have a greater—but certainly not perfect—self-awareness and memory of how we behave in our different roles, and for that reason we feel a sense of self-continuity that spans the varied contexts of our lives. Our different identities live and appear within specific states of consciousness. And those states may be further grouped into repeating sequences or cycles that come to constitute complex behavioral sequences recurring enough to serve as prominent features of our personalities influencing how we act and react.

The state model defines personality as the integration of a person's identity, emotional, cognitive and other relevant states of being weighted by the history of their recurrent interactions with the person's inner and outer worlds integrated over time. Obviously this is not a solvable equation, but it does hint at the potential size and shape of state-space that an individual's personality inhabits—and suggests the possible range and complexity of a person's behavior at a given point in their life.

As we learned in Chapter Two, a healthy newborn infant has half-dozen or so behavioral states that exist within a relatively small state-space. These basic states cycle in the familiar infant rhythm: sleeping, waking, fussiness, feeding, alert quietness, drowsiness, and sleeping as diagramed in Figure 2-1 (see Chapter 2).

At the other end of the lifespan, a mature adult with a wide range of life experiences will command a far larger collection of distinct states of being. Some of these dominate their daily life; others may only arise in specific situations or contexts. These rarely expressed but sometimes extreme states of consciousness provide the unexpected responses—and at times shocking—differences in behavior seen in people who lead double lives. Given the many degrees of behavioral freedom available to adults, efforts to map their states of being are usually confined to narrow contexts, such as Horowitz's coding of a patient's mental states during a therapy hour (see Chapter 5).

State Developmental Model of Personality

All of us are—always—in one or another state of being. Waking, sleeping, daydreaming in a default mode resting state, or even comatose:

this is an inescapable fact of the human mind. The number and nature of an individual's states of being—and therefore the complexity of the person's "personality"—is a function of both nature and nurture. Someone in a coma may have only a few states of being to an observer, and what appears to be little or no personality. A normal adult may have many and varied states of being, which reflect a complex personality. An individual's genetic makeup may confer some unique potential, or may contain some inherent vulnerability, but the degree to which these different states of being recur is largely a function of the individual's history and environment, especially early life experiences.

In this way, the state model resembles the traditional psychodynamic and modern developmental models of personality. Early life experiences matter because they profoundly shape an individual's core social and emotional states. The critical attunement between mother and infant is essential for a child to develop self-control over social and emotional states. Children show a gradual mastery of self-control by an increasing ability to modulate their emotional state. And as they mature, they learn to match and maintain a state that fits the situation. They get better at self-soothing and recovering from distractions and disruptions. And they begin to consolidate all of their identity states into a more self-directed and coherent personality. For greater success in life previously state-dependent knowledge, skills, talents and capacities must become more available and generalized across many states of being and situations.

State Dimensional Model of Personality

Basic personality factors (e.g., extroversion, agreeableness, conscientiousness, neuroticism and openness to experience) that statistically emerge as "traits" from dimensional models of personality reflect the intrinsic properties of a person's habitual mental states. They capture the main perceptive, cognitive, and emotional operations of the individual's usual states of being. Dimensional personality factors reflect how predictable and stable a person's state systems will be in the face of environmental stress. They also implicitly address the individual's ability to consciously monitor and modulate their different states of being.

Indeed, some of the Big Five personality factors are literally defined in terms of their dominant mental states. Neuroticism, for example, is defined as a persistent tendency to display negative emotional states. High scorers are characterized as frequently swinging between states of anxiety, anger, guilt and depression. Stress can trigger these states—and even minor stresses can seem hopeless or overwhelming to people who score high on this dimension.

Other Big Five factors such as agreeableness are defined in terms of how the individual's demeanor and interpersonal style affects others. High scorers on agreeableness are sunny and optimistic about people and the world. They are empathetic, friendly, generous, cooperative, and likable. These qualities reflect the person's largely upbeat mood states, the optimistic ways in which they respond to stresses in daily life, as well as their ability to positively influence the mood states of those around them.

State-Space Mapping of Personality

If we could map an adult's set of mental, emotional, physical, behavioral, identity, and other relevant states into a pre-defined, multidimensional, state-space—such as we did using actual data for an infant in Chapter 2 (Figure 2-1)—it might look something like Figure 6-1.

The isomorphic relationships among levels of state (see Chapter 3) allow the three axes shown (out of the many dimensions that exist) to be defined for an individual at a brain state level, or at a bodily physiological level, or at a personality factor level or in terms of the moods and behaviors (see Figure 3-7). At each of these levels of analysis, the spatial configuration of the states and the pathways connecting them would look somewhat different, but there would be an isomorphic coherence in the overall pattern that cuts across levels (See Chapter 3).

In Figure 6-1 different states of being are represented by shapes, colors, and shadings intended to denote unique state-dependent qualities of perceiving, thinking, and responding. Related states share colors and shading and are clustered in different regions of state-space defined here by the X, Y, and Z-axes of: energy level, emotional valence and self-esteem, respectively. The states are not located at precise points in multidimensional state-space, but rather occupy fuzzy volumes that dynamically expand and contract as a given state waxes and wanes over time.

The states are clustered into larger groups linked by spiraling arrows symbolizing recurring cycles within the clusters that constitute larger mood or identity states. The lines connecting the different clusters of states represent probabilistic switching pathways with the arrows showing the predominate direction of switching among the clusters of mood, identity and behavioral states.

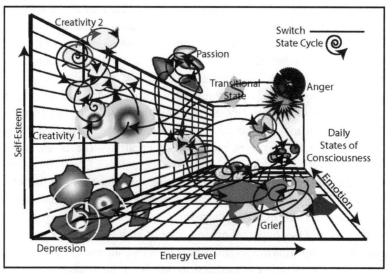

Figure 6-1 Hypothetical Map of an
Individual's Personality as States of Mind

At any given moment the individual's locus of being is centered within one of those potential states that is nested within a larger cycle of related states. Each and every state of being acts as an organizing function for consciousness—whatever consciousness is. Waking or sleeping, happy or sad, transcendent or traumatic, every state serves to shape a person's awareness, thinking, feeling, and behaving.

In this hypothetical schema the person—let's call him Jim—spends much of his time in four clusters of states of being that constitute his normal daily states of consciousness. These four clusters occupy the middle ground in our state-space map. Jim cycles within each cluster and then exits that cluster for another one. Perhaps these four clusters represent Jim's daily routines: morning, noon, evening, and night or home, work, parenting and as a spouse.

At times, triggered by events at work or home, Jim veers off into anger (he does have emotional control issues) represented by the jagged states in the far background. He returns to his normal states of mind through another pathway that passes through a transitional cool down state as his anger subsides before re-entering the larger cycle of four clusters that constitute his normal states of consciousness.

On occasion, Jim may pass on through normal consciousness into a cluster of states labeled "grief" for a deep personal loss that is psychologically related to his outbursts of anger. He may either return to the cycle of normal states or, at times, switch into a cluster of states that constitutes depression. The pathway out of depression, however, is not back through grief, but instead a switch back into one of the clusters that constitute the larger cycle of normal states.

On other occasions Jim may jump from normal states of consciousness into states of passion (whatever turns him on). From this perch of consciousness he may ascend into an even higher plane and complex cluster of states that constitutes moments of creativity (he is an artist). Creativity, in turn, occurs at two levels. The lower level, Creativity 1, consists of a ragged cycle of states that constitute much of his routine artistic efforts. Rarely he reaches a higher realm, Creativity 2, in which he produces art inspired by a deeper vision.

This schema is a hypothetical snapshot of an individual's personality (necessarily simplified to a few mood and identity state cycles) at a moment in time. Jim's personality is manifest to others by the amount of time he spends in each cluster of states and the largely predictable ways in which he moves about within his larger state-space.

An individual may spend most of his time inhabiting a restricted set of states of being that encompass their day-to-day activities and roles—normal, everyday consciousness. Periodically people feel a strong urge to break out of the humdrum of their usual states in search of intellectual, emotional, or sensory stimulation, novelty, or excitement. They usually do this by engaging in an activity meant to shake things up—watching a horror movie or a comedy, practicing yoga, riding a motorcycle, cranking up their music, reading a good book, taking a tranquil walk, a hard workout, masturbating, getting drunk, or smoking pot.

Such pursuits serve to force a transition out of a person's usual states of consciousness aimed towards a very different region of state-space. These infrequent states are often very separate from everyday states of mind. They lie closer to the boundaries of the person's state-space map. Still, they often play critical roles in defining personality. Deny someone REM sleep and it will hurt his mental health. Deprive him of a nonessential but well-loved state of being—a daily yoga routine, an evening cocktail, or jumping out of an airplane on weekends—and it still will affect a person's mood, behavior and outlook on life, even if it isn't as harmful.

Some people are driven to continually impulsively push against the edges of their state-space. It's like an addiction—they seek more and more extreme states of being, perhaps in an effort to distance themselves from pain associated with other mental states. Others systematically expand their state-space envelope in order to pursue a personal goal—mental, physical, or spiritual—that more sharply defines who they are. These special states of being have powerful and enduring effects on an individual's core sense of self.

This hypothetical map (Figure 6-1) is a snapshot taken during a period of someone's life. As the person grows and ages, new states of being appear. New connections and sequences are formed and older ones decay as they are bypassed by new life routines. States of being dating back to earlier life periods end as life circumstances change, or as age and infirmity take their toll. The twenty-something single who rock-climbed or skydived for thrills on weekends becomes the harried thirty-something parent of colicky twins. Those adrenalin-charged states of youthful daring and triumph become distant memories to the sleep-deprived, anxious parent.

The sense of self or identity associated with these earlier life experiences may still influence a person's personality and sense of self. Certain painful early life states, especially those linked to childhood maltreatment, may become inaccessible at certain stages of development, sealing off memories and behaviors that reappear only much later in life.

Regimens are the clusters of states most likely to endure over a lifetime: personal routines such as eating, sleeping, sex, hygiene, and dressing. These are domains that span one's life, its changing circumstances and allow for the most personal control. States that depend mainly on context, something unique to a certain job or intimate relationship, often disappear in life's rearview mirror when the situation changes.

What the State Model Offers

The state model of personality readily accounts for features of human behavior beyond those covered by the psychodynamic, developmental or dimensional models. The state model also allows for occasional behavior that seems like a total contradiction. And it allows individuals to make precipitous, profound, and enduring changes in who they are and how they think about themselves—for example, the life-changing conversion of some born-again Christians (see Chapter 10). It also offers a mechanism by which life experiences can change brain networks and activity patterns to firmly entrench new mental, emotional or behavioral states of being.

The state model of personality allows a politician to be vehemently anti-gay in public while a practicing homosexual in private. The politician may even conduct multiple sex lives with all manner of partners, each one associated with unique states of being. These sexual orientations remain largely insulated from each other within the politician's state-space, and thus coexist without overt dissonance. One's experience of the politician's "personality," that is, the way he relates and acts, would be very different if you saw him with different sex partners. He might be dominant and demanding with one and submissive and compliant with another.

Because new states of being can be created and old states of being may be essentially deleted by altered life circumstances, people remain capable of making sudden, dramatic changes—for better or worse—in their personality and behavior. In many cases, powerful external factors, such as losing a longtime job or ending an intimate relationship, or conversely, a new relationship or the birth of a child, may initiate profound changes in personality.

This capacity for radical personality change, to generate new states of being in response to external or internal events, bestows an enormous flexibility to human behavior. It allows people to rapidly adapt to drastically altered life circumstances. It also creates a huge liability: that we are vulnerable to the possibility that trauma and adversity will spawn dysfunctional states of being that become a fixture of our personality. It gives us a reason to hope that troubled people can change for the better— and reason to fear that trauma and tragedy may permanently scar us or those we love.

HOW STATES CAN BECOME "TRAITS"

Classical and Operant Conditioning
The principle that over time any state could eventually become a "trait" is part of state-based theories of human behavior from William James forward. It posits that a mental or emotional state (or sequences of those states) triggered over and over again comes to look to others like the expression of a personality trait.

In every personality model, whether it is psychodynamic, developmental, or dimensional, personality traits are seen as enduring patterns of character and behavior a person uses to respond to common events in life. Repeated activation of a given state or cyclic cluster of states would fit this definition because it would lead others to make reasonable predictions about how a person would most consistently respond to similar circumstances.

Classical and operant conditioning are two ways in which behavior—be it man or mouse—can be permanently changed in response to specific cues or contexts. Classical conditioning involves repeatedly pairing two stimuli, like the ringing of a bell and a puff of air that causes an eye blink, until the ringing of the bell alone will cause the subject to blink his eye. The ringing bell is called the conditioned stimulus and the puff of air is called the unconditioned stimulus. The eye blink in response to the bell alone is called a conditioned response.

As first described by the Russian psychologist Ivan Pavlov, classical conditioning can take many forms. One important form is *fear conditioning*, which plays a critical role in quickly (often instantly) teaching an animal or human to avoid danger. In the lab, subjects from snails to undergraduates are fear-conditioned by pairing an induced state of pain, fear or anxiety (perhaps elicited with a threatening noise or electric shock) with a conditioned stimulus of some type, such as seeing a rattlesnake or hearing a buzzer. Specific brain structures, including the amygdala, hippocampus and associated areas, are known to mediate forms of fear conditioning.

Operant conditioning was first described by Edward Thorndike, who was studying cats learning to escape from puzzle traps. But it was B.F. Skinner and his famous Skinner Box that permitted the scientific study of this subtle, but extraordinarily powerful, tool for changing behavior. Operant conditioning involves reinforcing or punishing a selected behavior after it occurs spontaneously.

Positive reinforcement rewards the target behavior in some fashion (food, money, sex, airline bonus miles etc.); negative reinforcement reduces some unpleasant experience—quiets an obnoxious noise or dims a blinding light—and thus reinforces the target behavior by decreasing discomfort. And a specific behavior can also be punished positively or negatively in order to decrease its frequency. Both approaches help the shaping of behavior in complex but powerful ways.

Both classical and operant conditioning produce long-lasting or permanent changes in behavior. Classical conditioning can even be demonstrated in simple neural circuits, such as a detached pair of insect legs kept alive in a Petri dish. Operant conditioning activates the very powerful pleasure circuit in the brain, known scientifically as the ventral tegmental dopamine system.

In the mid-1950s two Canadian researchers, James Olds and Peter Milner, discovered the existence of pleasure centers in rat brains.

Laboratory rats with electrodes implanted in certain brain regions would press a lever hundreds to thousands of times an hour to stimulate these pleasure centers with tiny pulses of electricity. Some would press the lever rather than eat and ultimately starve to death. Similar pleasure centers in the human brain were subsequently identified in neurosurgical patients. When electrically stimulated, patients often describe intense sexual feelings.

We now recognize that many of the brain pleasure centers Olds and Milner identified are parts of a larger brain system loaded with opiate receptors and capable of producing strong feelings of pleasure. This is the brain system most closely linked to sexual arousal, orgasm, cravings, and addiction. Experiences and substances that activate the ventral tegmental dopamine system are powerfully rewarding for both mice and man. Stimulate this system too much and out-of-control behavior and addiction follows.

Classical and operant conditioning are both believed to strengthen brain pathways so that the conditioned cue more readily activates the target behavior in the future. Exactly how the underlying pathways are strengthened is the focus of much research and beyond the scope of this chapter.

In addition to conditioning, scientists have also identified use-dependent neuronal changes. These changes appear in two contexts: brain development and brain plasticity. Studies of brain development show the existence of periods in the growth of animal and human brains when environmental events can alter things for better or worse. Known as sensitive or critical periods, they are times of heightened sensitivity to environmental influences. One example: the powerful negative effects of a mother's depression on her infant compared with other points in childhood.

Nobel Prize winners David Huble and Torsten Wiesel first identified a critical point in the development of parts of the brain needed to see correctly. If one eye is prevented from seeing (Huble and Wiesel sewed shut the unopened eyes of newborn kittens), for example, vision fails to develop normally. Despite later cutting the sutures so that the eye can finally now open and "see," after a certain passage of time the kittens' blindness becomes irreversible. The sensitive period when the kittens' visual system develops is now over.

Cruel as the research sounds, it revolutionized our understanding of the development of the visual system and led to successful treatments to correct vision problems early in life before damage becomes irreversible. When you see a small child with a patch over one eye (their good eye), chances are that they have those poor kittens to thank for their normal vision later.

Less extreme examples include the effects of enriched early environments on learning, memory, problem solving, and motor skills. Baby mice growing up in roomy pens filled with mousy toys like tunnels, ramps and ladders, running wheels, and Ping-Pong balls far outperform their littermates raised in barren cages on learning and recalling mazes and other tests. Recognizing that similar effects occur in very young children has led to preschool programs designed to enhance early childhood brain development—with wonderful success in the very best examples. Now researchers are beginning to pursue promising effects of enriched environments on mental functioning in Alzheimer's and other degenerative brain diseases.

Neuroplasticity

In humans, brain plasticity—also called neuroplasticity, cortical plasticity or cortical re-mapping—is one of the most hopeful discoveries of modern neuroscience. It's best seen in how a person recovers from a serious brain injury. Even in adults, the brain is capable of remarkable feats of plasticity. In stroke patients who gradually recover use of a paralyzed limb or the ability to speak again, areas of the brain spared from the injury can take over some functions lost when other areas are destroyed. Research conducted at many levels, from single synapses to complicated behaviors, finds that the brain can rewire, rebuild, and reprogram itself either because of new experiences or as a response to insult or injury.

Researchers are just beginning tests in patients with brain damage or spinal cord injury, but the discovery that even adult brains are capable of meaningful change has forever changed the thinking about what is possible. Even more remarkable is the possibility that mere thoughts can change brain structure and functioning. Experiments with Buddhist monks and other meditators show that certain mental states such as deep meditation can produce long-term changes in brain structure and brain activity that correlate with increased mental and physical capacities. (see Chapter 10).

There is much to learn about the neurobiological mechanisms underlying these various forms of change. Even the evolutionarily old "primitive" regions of our brains have demonstrated that they can change. Both classical and operant conditioning can create new neuronal networks and rework brain structure. Recurrent mental states, nurturing or traumatic, appear to play an important role in both brain development and plasticity.

THE MIND

The human mind is a thing of mystery. It is far, far greater than the sum of its parts—at least the parts that we know something about. Philosophers ask: Is the human mind capable of understanding itself? Or is the human mind like the infinity of the universe—impossible for us to fully comprehend?

THE UNCONSCIOUS MIND

Any model of the human mind worthy of consideration must account for the unconscious mind. Most people acknowledge that there are times when they say or do things out of character that they do not realize at the time. Only later, perhaps after someone has pointed out the inconsistency, do we begin to recognize that we were unaware of the motivation or meaning behind our actions. At other times, we may be on automatic pilot and not remember much of anything about performing some routine but nonetheless complex activity, such as driving home from work.

The recognition that human behavior is influenced by processes outside of our usual awareness dates back thousands of years. The Hindu Vedic texts, written between 1500 and 600 BCE, make reference to unconscious levels of the mind. More recently in Western civilization, the writings of philosophers such as Spinoza, Leibniz, and Nietzsche anticipated the psychological models of the unconscious or subconscious mind proposed by Janet, Freud, and others in the late nineteenth century.

The Freudian concept of the unconscious mind as revealed in dreams, slips of the tongue, and mental blocks is essential to psychoanalysis. Psychoanalysis focuses on making conscious—and therefore potentially within an individual's volitional control—the unconscious ideas and emotions believed to underlie a person's symptoms and problematic behaviors. Until biological psychiatry, which relies on medications to modulate brain state, began displacing psychoanalytic treatments in the late 1960s, it was conventional wisdom that unconscious conflicts caused neuroses.

For a couple of decades after the biological psychiatry revolution, a scientist was ridiculed if she dared mention the "unconscious" in a professional meeting. It was considered impossible to prove or disprove the existence of an unconscious mind, and for that reason it could not be studied scientifically. Fortunately, this narrow mindset is changing. Once again scientists are investigating mental processes that lie outside our normal awareness but still influence our feelings, thinking, and actions.

Today, cognitive scientists investigate unconscious mental phenomena under labels such as "disjunctions between implicit and explicit memory systems," "subliminal perception," "procedural memory," "priming," "associative processing," and "aberrations in information processing." High-speed functional brain imaging demonstrates that an enormous amount of mental activity occurs before we become consciously aware of seeing, thinking, or doing something. Brain imaging shows that sometimes the neural activity underlying a complex action begins well before the person believes that he's decided to act. Experiments in which subjects are shown subliminal images of positive rewards demonstrate that people will work extra hard for goals that they are not aware of (Custers & Aarts, 2010). We are all good at rationalizing that we really 'meant' to do whatever it was that we just did—although we can't always explain why.

A STATE MODEL OF THE UNCONSCIOUS

As his thinking matured, William James increasingly invoked the idea that there existed a subconscious mind that strongly influenced an individual's behavior through processes largely outside of the person's awareness. In *The Varieties of Religious Experience,* James discusses out-of-the-blue switches in emotional state:

> *Moreover, all these influences may work subconsciously or half unconsciously. And when you get a Subject in whom the subconscious life- of which I must speak more fully soon- is largely developed, and in whom motives habitually ripen in silence, you get a case of which you can never give a full account, and in which, both to the Subject and the onlookers, there may appear an element of marvel. Emotional occasions, especially violent ones, are extremely potent in precipitating mental rearrangements. The sudden and explosive ways in which love, jealousy, guilt, fear, remorse, or anger can seize upon one are known to everybody* (James, 1901–1902 p. 163).

David Rapaport

The Hungarian-born psychologist David Rapaport was one of the first modern researchers to grapple with reconciling Freudian notions of the unconscious with altered states of consciousness. Appointed as chief psychologist at the Menninger Institute in 1940 and later at Austin Riggs until his untimely death at the age of 49, Rapaport was a masterful psychoanalytic theoretician as well as an early advocate for bringing quantitative, empirical psychological testing to psychiatric diagnosis.

A complex man, Rapaport is described alternatively as fiercely proud and genuinely humble, an upholder of the establishment and a fearless iconoclast, as generous with credit but relentless with a grudge, an in-your-face advocate for his ideas and a crafty behind-the-scenes manipulator. In his eulogy, Merton Gil observes that Rapaport would express his opinions with "... *the fervor of a political orator and the thunder of a Hebrew prophet*" (Gil, 1996 p. 5).

Rapaport's central interest was scientifically measuring the quality of an individual's thinking—which he believed varied across different states of consciousness. His measure of a person's quality of thinking spanned a continuum that was anchored at each end by the Freudian concepts of primary and secondary process thinking.

Primary process thinking is considered to be the thinking of the Id, and is conducted in the form of symbols and metaphor, along with evocative visual imagery. It tolerates contradiction of facts and beliefs. It seeks to gratify desires and impulses and does not acknowledge the constraints of reality nor follow a coherent time line. It is the logic of dreams, hallucinations, and to some extent, idle fantasy.

Secondary process thinking is linear, logical, and time- and reality-bound. It seeks to rationally accommodate the id's impulses and desires within the constraints of reality. In Freudian terms, it is the thinking of the mature ego mediating between the conflicting pressure of the impulsive id and punitive superego.

Rapaport sensed that there were multiple blends of these two forms of thinking that could be discriminated along a set of dimensions such as visual versus verbal modes, degree of self-awareness and self-reflection, and the extent to which internal versus external perceptions dominated the individual's sense of reality. To extract these dimensions, Rapaport focuses on what he termed "varieties of consciousness" using dissociative states, dreams, and Korsakoff syndrome as exemplars for the power of mental states to influence the quality of an individual's thinking (Rapaport, 1996).

His first example is a case of dissociative fugue, in which police bring a man to the hospital who is wandering along the Hudson River, behaving oddly. The man does not know who he is and can provide no information about his identity. Under the influence of the sedating drug sodium amytal, he remembers leaving the house after a violent argument with his wife but cannot recall anything else until the police found him. Two weeks later, during another amytal interview, he is able to recount the intervening events and strong emotions that included suicidal thoughts and murderous impulses towards his wife.

This case, Rapaport observes, illustrates the larger pattern seen in such patients in whom there is first the loss of memory for personal identity followed later by an awareness of this loss. The two-part (biphasic) response illustrates a state-dependent change in reflective self-awareness. Rapaport believes that a critical dimension of thinking in general is the individual's degree of self-awareness and self-reflection—which varies as a function of the person's state of consciousness.

To further illustrate how the degree of self-awareness fluctuates across different states of consciousness, Rapaport draws upon himself as a subject:

> *What I did was to train myself to rouse at night as much as possible after each dream, reverie, and hypnagogic hallucination, to record them. The state in which I recorded was one of drowsiness; I recorded in the dark, remaining in the supine position in which I aroused, and transcribed the record the next morning, in so far as I was able to: at times these records are unreadable. Writing under these conditions becomes to a considerable extent automatic: at times one knows and records that just a moment before one has been writing something and knows not what. The hand writes without any subjectively experienced decision or intent—as one observes it sometimes in subjects doing automatic writing in hypnosis or otherwise* (Rapaport, 1996 pp. 392–393).

Examining these records made in different states of consciousness about different states of consciousness, Rapaport observes that as he edges closer and closer to a state of dreaming sleep his reflective self-awareness diminishes. The nearer he is to a dream state, the less he is able to exert his will upon his thinking and mental imagery and the more he becomes a passive observer rather than the thinker of his thoughts. The closer he is to dreaming, the more visual imagery becomes his major mode of thinking. He notes a splitting in his sense of self. In which, in his own words, he becomes a multiple personality:

> *For curiosity's sake, I would like to mention that in states very close to dream states, at times the record takes on the form of a conversation between two parts of a multiple personality. There are six examples of this in the records I obtained. What generalizations can one make about such observations? When there is no, or a decreased amount of, external stimulation available or admitted to consciousness, the internal motivations come more and more to expression in consciousness. Paralleling the degree to which external stimulations are admitted to consciousness, we find form varieties of consciousness differing from each other in decreasing availability of reflective awareness, verbalization, syntax, logic, explicitness and effort* (Rapaport, 1996 p. 397).

In Chapter 5 we learned about people with Korsakoff's syndrome, who cannot form new day-to-day autobiographical memories but can learn and remember complex tasks such as solving the Tower of Hanoi puzzle, even though they deny having ever seen the puzzle before. They also may confabulate—make up an implausible story—to explain their behavior. What interests Rapaport is that Korsakoff patients believe their own confabulations. They do not recognize that they have fabricated or imagined the events that they relate, but rather believe what they say is a true fact or a real memory. Rapaport regards this difficulty in separating imagined events from actual life experience as one of the dimensions along which the quality of a person's thinking varies by mental state.

Rapaport concludes:

> *The gradual development corresponds to varieties or forms of consciousness in which various balances are struck between perception of internal and external reality, in which internal experience is to various (ever-decreasing) degrees experienced as external reality, and in which internal and external perception (thought and perception of reality) are differentiated with increasing clarity. Correspondingly, the thought forms consciously*

experienced change gradually from prelogical to logical, from syncretic to abstract, from idiosyncratic to socialized . . . This gradual development is reflected in those forms of conscious experience which I have described in reporting on the preliminary studies of my recording of dreams, reveries, daydreams, etc. (Rapaport, 1996 p. 402).

In dreams, of course, we all become multiple personalities; we create and control all of the people and creatures in our dreams, though we experience them as separate and autonomous. Aware of this paradox, St. Augustine wrestled with the question of moral responsibility for our thoughts and actions while dreaming. Noting that since his conversion to Christianity, his former pagan personality no longer existed when awake but continued to be active in his dreams. In his *Confessions*, St. Augustine agonized:

Am I not myself, O Lord, my God. And yet, there is so much difference between betwixt myself and myself within the moment wherein I pass from waking to sleeping or return from sleeping to waking
(Ellenberger, 1970 p. 126).

The leading psychodynamic empiricist of his era, Rapaport was forced to rely on introspective observation to provide data on changes in reflective self-awareness and shifts in modes of thinking across different states of consciousness. All who knew him well describe David Rapaport as brilliant. Although technically not a psychoanalyst (he was not a clinician), he was a fervent believer in Freudian theory and yet one of its most passionate critics. By focusing on changes in self-awareness and reflective functions, modes of thought, and degree of reality testing, he sought to reveal dimensions that could be used to differentiate the quality of a person's thinking across different states of consciousness. In his later work on the organizing role of the ego in the continuity and integration of behavior, he anticipated future research on metacognition, described later in this chapter.

Charles Tart

In his important book *States of Consciousness,* psychologist Charles Tart adopts a distinctly Freudian view of the unconscious mind (Tart, 1983).

Although he substitutes the term *subconscious* for *unconscious,* Tart specifically includes classical Freudian notions. In addition, he adds creative processes, various forms of intuition, holistic reasoning, and right-hemisphere thinking. Tart believes that these important, but non-rational, mental operations occur outside of our awareness in ordinary states of consciousness. In certain altered states of consciousness an individual may become aware and take control of subconscious processes and use them to gain insight into self or the universe. However, in other altered states, painful emotions, memories, or other warded-off unconscious material can flood an individual's awareness in an over-whelming fashion. Examples of the latter would be a bad trip on psyche-delic drugs or a flashback to past trauma.

Tart is interested in a scientific approach to altered states of con-sciousness to reveal these subconscious processes and gain control over them, in order to achieve higher states of consciousness in which truth is directly knowable. In this respect, Tart grapples with the same questions that were raised for William James after his experiments with nitrous oxide.

James revisited the question of accessing truth through altered states of consciousness at several points in his career. In his final essay, "A Pluralistic Mystic," published a month before his death in August 1910, he confesses to the life-long influence that Benjamin Paul Blood had on him. It was Blood's self-published philosophical tract, *Anesthetic Revelation*, that induced the young William James to experiment with nitrous oxide. At end of his life, James quotes Blood in that he "*believes in truth and reason, but only as mystically realized, as lived in experience*" (James, 1987 p. 1308). Tart also believes that there are higher planes of consciousness—or, in his terms, "*ways out*" of ordinary consensus reality. We will take up these questions again in Chapters Ten and Eleven.

Mardi Horowitz

Mardi Horowitz is a leading figure in the psychoanalytic community and thoroughly steeped in Freudian notions of the unconsciousness. In his book *States of Mind,* however, he points out another, non-Freudian, hidden influence on behavior. Mental states that are not currently active can nonetheless have powerful influences on a person's current mental state (Horowitz, 1979).

Horowitz observes, "*. . . because states are experiential they can be remembered or fantasized as well as expressed. Past states as well as* *possible future states are contemplated, and the desire for or fear of such states can play an influential role in mental life and in choice of actions* (Horowitz, 1979 p. 40)."

In other words, even if a particular, recurrent state of consciousness—such as a distinct identity state—is not active at the moment, it can still exert an influence on a person's behavior. The mechanisms of this influence may be through semiconscious processes such as fantasy, intrusive memories, trains of associations, or through psychological defensive reactions such as avoidance of emotionally charged stimuli or situations.

Horowitz illustrates that avoidance process in his central case example of Janice described in Chapter 5, who had the catastrophic grief reaction following the death of her younger brother. Whenever she felt herself slipping into an especially painful mental state characterized by feelings of intense self-disgust, shame and despair, Janice would preemptively switch into the *"Tra-la-la"* state in which she appeared animated and cheerful but actually felt that she was only putting on an act for the benefit of others. Thus the *"Tra-la-la"* state served as a psychological defense against experiencing the painful state of self-disgust.

Observations such as these suggest that states can compete and override each other and that psychological conflicts are revealed when one mental state reverses another. Clinically, rapid switches in mental state are understood as key indicators of psychological conflict, such as the revolving door (see Chapter 4) and shimmering states (see Chapter 5).

PSYCHOLOGICAL CONFLICT

How is it that we find ourselves struggling mightily with ourselves about what we do, what we think, and what we want? Why do we sometimes hate ourselves? Why do we do things that go against our core values and beliefs?

When we examine the sources of psychological conflict we find that we harbor inside ourselves a realm of contradictory emotions, beliefs, ideas, loyalties, values, identities, impulses and behaviors. We may be able to keep mutually exclusive beliefs, values, or behaviors separate most of the time. But sometimes they collide with unforeseen circumstances that demand we come down on one side or the other of our internal divisions.

The "Adolescent Identity Crisis"

Adolescence is usually the time when individuals first experience significant psychological conflicts about who they are, what they believe, and how they should behave. With their increasing independence and growing social networks, adolescents frequently find themselves facing demands to believe and behave in different ways depending on whom they are with and where they are. Their school friends may be experimenting with sex and drugs, while their church youth group embraces abstinence. School, team sports, cliques, clubs, jobs, even posses and gangs—all require unique behaviors and new social roles. What's more, intense friendships and romantic relationships wax and wane. And no matter what teenagers say, parents and family usually remain powerful influences on their values, behavior, and identity.

The adult world considers these conflicts an identity crisis, which sometimes persists into adulthood. Erik Erikson, a developmental psychologist and psychoanalyst, first suggested the concept. *"It is a state of being and becoming,"* he wrote . . .

> *. . . that can have a highly conscious (and, indeed, self-conscious) quality and yet remain, in its motivational aspects, quite unconscious and beset with the dynamics of conflict. This, in turn, can lead to contradictory mental states, such as a sense of aggravated vulnerability, and yet also an expectation of grand individual promise* (Erikson, 1975 p 53).

Resolving the identity crisis is believed to be important in the formation of a more stable sense of self, needed to cope with the demands of adulthood.

For an impressionable teenager, each distinct group and the contexts associated with their unique social interactions create patterns of behavior that elicit different mental states—each with its own sense of identity. Because most teenagers compartmentalize these identities, they are usually not in open psychological conflict. As long as the contexts in which the different identities express themselves do not collide, they can coexist more or less comfortably. That makes it possible to behave one way in English class compared with gym class or after school hanging out with friends. Psychological conflicts arise when one context intrudes on another. Friends from one clique may strongly disapprove of friends from another. Parents may learn about friends they don't like, or learning about others they don't know existed.

Susan Harter

Developmental psychologist Susan Harter and her colleagues at the University of Denver have studied psychological conflict in teenagers as they grapple with multiple roles and identities—a process foreshadowed by William James in what he called the "*conflict of the different ME's*" (Harter, Bresnick, Bouchey, & Whitesell, 1997). Evoking different contexts (e.g., school, friends, romantic interests, best friend, mother and father) to define social roles, Harter asks teenagers to list their personal attributes in each setting. For example, a teen may describe herself as "responsible, serious, withdrawn, cooperative, and respectful" in the classroom but "rowdy, talkative, cheerful, assertive, outgoing, and sarcastic" with peers (Harter et al., 1997).

As they grow, teenagers gradually become aware of these situational differences in their identity and behavior. In early adolescence, they do not experience these contradictions as frequent or troublesome. By mid-adolescence, however, the differences between how they feel about themselves and the way they behave bothers them. State theory predicts it: contexts that differ along many dimensions produce the greatest contrasts in behavior and sense of self—and the greatest likelihood of psychological conflict. Many (though not all) studies find that the number of role-related psychological conflicts decreases in late adolescence, particularly for boys. This decline suggests that teens are able to reconcile their many identities and emerge with a more unified sense of self.

Girls report having more contradictory attributes—and as a result more conflicts in sense of self and behavior—than boys at every developmental stage. One common conflict revolves around the profound differences when they are alone with their mothers as compared to their fathers. Girls with strong feminine gender orientations seem to be especially vulnerable (Harter et al., 1997). Theorists have explained these parental effects by the differences in social roles of girls in the traditional family as compared to the more independence in social roles accorded boys. Of course, adolescents can easily be caught between warring parents who demand that the child assume dramatically different versions of self when in their presence.

For teens, the most troubling question raised by their growing awareness of self-contradictions is: *Which one of these selves is the real me?*

Harter observes:

> *Our own work has revealed that this proliferations of selves does engender problematic questions for adolescents about which is "the real me," particularly when attributes in different roles appear contradictory (e.g., cheerful with friends but depressed with parents). During our multiple-selves procedure a number of adolescents spontaneously agonized over which of the attributes represent their "true self"* (Harter et al., 1997 pp. 843–844).

By mid-adolescence, Harter and others have found, teens are very concerned about which of their many selves is their "true self." They distinguish their true self as being the *"real me inside"* that says what they believe. They are aware when they are displaying a false self—for example, saying what they think that others want to hear (Harter et al., 1997):

> *Conflict is significantly more likely to occur among attribute pairs in which one characteristic of the self was judged to be true self-behavior, whereas the other was deemed false self-behavior... Less common were conflicts between two attributes both judged to reflect true self-behavior... Conflicts between two false self-attributes were negligible... Thus, it is those opposing attribute pairs representing one false and one true self-behavior that are particularly problematic in proving conflict with the adolescent's self-theory* (Harter et al., 1997 p. 844).

UNIFICATION OF THE SELF

If we are so divided, how is it that we usually manage to bind our different identities into something that is experienced by everyone—including ourselves—as a unique personality? Is there something that melds together our many identity and emotional states into a more unified self?

Many theories of human development stress the benefits of integrating childhood and adolescent identities into a more coherent adult sense of wholeness. In the state model, this consolidating requires assuming a psychological mechanism that bridges the many different identities and emotional states attached to all of our social roles.

To work, this mental mechanism would have to make autobiographical memory and state-dependent knowledge easier to access, so that recall of every identity and their SDLM information is more available in other states of being. This bridging mechanism would also provide a person with some degree of psychological distance from which to observe and recall their behavior—a perch that would allow them to see themselves as others might. Being able to do all of these things would make it a lot easier to learn important lessons from past experience and improve self-control over powerful or dangerous impulses. It would also unify the sense of self in more areas of a person's life.

Authorities in different disciplines claim such a bridging mechanism exists. Psychotherapists call this function the observing ego. Cognitive psychologists speak of metacognition. And developmental psychologists refer to these processes as executive functions. They may theorize from different perspectives and refer to different data, but all of them are talking about psychological mechanisms that bridge gaps in self-awareness, observe, weigh, and integrate life experiences, and reflect on and learn from past behavior. From each perspective, these processes provide the self-awareness and psychological tools needed to adapt to life's changing circumstances.

The Observing Ego

The observing ego is the part of us that pays attention to what we say and do. In therapy, it allows a person to look at her own behavior and examine it with the therapist's help. Out in the world, it can help the person to make better choices. The therapist must nurture the patient's observing ego and help that part of the patient tolerate the inevitable anxiety that arises when one's own conflicted behavior is subjected to close scrutiny. After all, few people enjoy having their behavior, innermost thoughts and fantasies critically examined.

The goal of developing the patient's observing ego has progressed far beyond the psychoanalyst's couch. Cognitive behavioral therapists, who help their patients identify and correct dysfunctional ways of thinking, rely on the patient being able to monitor and accurately report their thoughts, feelings and behaviors. To help, they often require that their clients keep daily "thought records" to review during sessions. Writing down thoughts at the time makes them more reflective of the immediate conflict and easier to examine in therapy later.

Group therapists incorporate observations of members into their interpretations to help people become more aware of how others perceive them. Some forms of therapy use videotaping so the patient becomes more self-aware by seeing himself as others do. Meditative therapies teach mindfulness techniques to increase awareness of one's behavior. The fact that different approaches to psychological treatment all have techniques for increasing self-awareness or mindfulness shows that psychotherapists of many stripes know the importance that a healthy self-monitoring function plays in therapeutic success.

Metacognition

Descartes' enduring statement—*Cognito ergo sum* or *"I think, therefore I am"*—shows that people have long considered an awareness of mental life essential to being human. Modern psychologists investigate this knowing that we know under the labels of metacognition and metamemory. They study mental processes that at least partially relate to the clinician's observing ego, but which also generalize to many other mental operations related to perceiving, remembering, thinking, and doing.

The term *metacognition* was coined to characterize developmental changes in self-awareness (Metcalfe & Shimamura, 1994). It is being implicated more and more in studies of learning, memory, thinking, problem solving and decision-making.

In some respects, William James and other nineteenth-century pioneers who emphasized introspection when studying human thought and stream of consciousness foreshadowed current research on metacognition. But modern psychologists eschew the subjective nature of introspection—instead, they require controlled experiments that look at recall and use of acquired knowledge across different contexts.

Like the clinicians' observing ego, metacognition presumes that there is a higher system of observing and monitoring in the human mind that can draw upon acquired knowledge to modify a person's current emotional state, thinking, or behavior. Many experiments focus on one or more of three basic metacognitive functions: ease of learning, judgments of learning, and feeling of knowing.

Ease of learning involves subjects making predictions about how easy or difficult it will be to learn something before they try to learn it. In judgments of learning, subjects predict how well they learned something and how well they will do when tested on it. And feeling of knowing revolves around how likely some previously learned but forgotten material may be recalled in the future. These three markers of metacognitive functioning are not strongly correlated, suggesting that there may be separate metacognitive systems analogous to separate memory systems (see Chapter 5).

Executive Functions

Developmental psychologists view the ability to self-monitor, self-regulate emotion, control impulses, and focus attention as examples of executive function. First articulated by Lezak (1983) and subsequently expanded by many others, the concept converges around the idea that this ability is essential to adapting to a demanding and complex world:

> *In a constantly changing environment, executive abilities allow us to shift our mindset quickly and adapt to diverse situations while at the same time inhibiting inappropriate behaviors. They enable us to create a plan, initiate its execution, and persevere on the task at hand until its completion. Executive functions mediate the ability to organize our thoughts in a goal-directed way and are therefore essential for success in school and work situations, as well as everyday living* (Jurad & Rosselli, 2007 p. 214).

Developmental psychologists disagree on how executive functions work—whether they reflect different expressions of a single underlying process, like general intelligence or working memory, or if they come from the interaction of several independent functions such as planning, setting goals, working memory, and self-awareness. Evidence from neuroimaging studies of brain activity largely supports the latter position: that executive functions consist of a set of semi-independent processes that must be coordinated to achieve success.

Executive functions appear and mature over time as a child develops. Infants largely live in the immediate present, but by preschool age, children are able to think about the past and plan for the future. The ability to resist distraction and focus on a task first appears around age six and begins to approach adult levels by age 10. The ability to plan for the future shows its greatest development between the ages of 5 to 8, but improvement continues well into adulthood.

Although different executive capacities first appear at different points in development, most show their greatest gains during childhood in spurts that correlate with the maturation of the frontal lobes (Jurad & Rosselli, 2007). Executive functions decline in old age, particularly with dementia, sometimes resulting in a childlike performance on standard tests.

A growing child's executive functions are shaped and nurtured by interactions with role models—parents and caretakers, teachers, peers and significant others. Competent and caring adults who demonstrate good emotional regulation, problem-solving skills, cognitive flexibility, and goal-directed behavior are considered critical to forming healthy executive functioning. Trauma and family dysfunction, social adversity and chaos, and early stress and deprivation, are known to impair development of effective executive functioning in children. Certain types of psychopathology, such as borderline personality disorder, have been conceptualized as failures in the development of executive function.

Clinicians, developmental and cognitive psychologists all agree that these self-monitoring, self-directing mental processes are essential for success in life. For the psychotherapist, success means helping the patient develop an observing ego that allows the person to willfully avoid or reverse negative states of mind and to inhibit or redirect destructive behaviors.

For the cognitive and developmental researchers defining success is a bit more complicated. Like other scientists, they tend to have strong opinions and differing interpretations of the data. But across most authorities, there is a consensus that an ability: (1) to know and make use of what you "know" across contexts; (2) to monitor and control your emotions and behavior in different circumstances; (3) to reflect on and draw important lessons and generate life rules from past experience; and (4) the ability to anticipate and plan for the future are all independently associated with higher performance on tests of problem solving, knowledge, and intelligence.

METACOGNITIVE/EXECUTIVE FUNCTIONS DYSFUNCTION

If these concepts are really that important, failures of the processes should result in serious mental, social, or behavioral problems. Researchers have found that failures of metacognition are associated with difficulty developing abstract concepts, solving problems, developing rules, reasoning by analogy, classifying information and generally thinking "outside of the box."

The prototypical "metacognitive disorder" is Korsakoff's syndrome, a disorder of memory. You recall that Korsakoff's patients can learn to solve complex puzzles like the Tower of Hanoi about as well as normal people (see Chapter 5). But each time they are presented with the puzzle they deny ever having seen it before or confabulate seeing it in some improbable context. Their implicit and explicit memory systems have separated—Korsakoff's patients don't know that they know how to solve the Tower of Hanoi puzzle. They have a failure in the metacognitive function of knowing what you know.

In that common experience known as a tip-of-the-tongue moment (labeled a "ToT" by researchers), we momentarily experience another type of metacognitive failure. Everybody has had one: a moment in which we can almost remember that person's name, or what this thing-a-ma-jig is called, or the perfect word that describes a situation, but it just isn't quite there. In our case, we know that we know it—but we just can't quite recall it. It's a frustrating feeling. What many people discover is that if they can just stop trying so hard to remember, the information eventually pops into their mind.

When a ToT moment happens, we are having a momentary disjunction between memory systems. If you examine your ToT moments and the spontaneous recall of information that follows, you will note that the recovery of the missing memory often occurs after you have switched states or changed contexts. The apocryphal anecdote is the guy who wakes up his wife in the middle of the night to tell her the fact that eluded him at dinner.

METACOGNITIVE/EXECUTIVE FUNCTION PSYCHOPATHOLOGY

For psychotherapists, the classic 'observing ego disorder' is borderline personality disorder (BPD). The DSM-5 defines BPD as "*a pervasive pattern of instability of interpersonal relationships, self-image, and affects, and marked impulsivity that begins by early adulthood and is present in a variety of contexts*" (American Psychiatric Association, 2013).

For example, to be diagnosed with BPD, the individual's behavior and life history must be filled with examples in which they exhibit at least five out of nine sets of symptoms or patterns of behavior: fears of abandonment, unstable interpersonal relationships, an unstable sense of self, impulsivity, recurrent suicidal behaviors or self-mutilation, mood swings, chronic feelings of emptiness, inappropriate and intense anger, and paranoid or dissociative symptoms. To meet the criterion for impulsivity, for example, the patient must exhibit two or more types of self-damaging impulsivity for behaviors such as sex, substance abuse, reckless driving, or binge eating. The clinician must also determine that a persistent pattern of these behaviors extends back to adolescence or early adulthood.

Borderlines are notorious for having unstable interpersonal relationships in which they flip back and forth between idealizing someone then utterly devaluing or hatefully blaming the same person for some small affront. Their own sense of identity undergoes rapid shifts that play out as ever-shifting beliefs, values, and goals. They are impulsive and self-destructive. Their moods are mercurial. They can explode with righteous anger one moment and wilt in self-loathing the next.

A research study using electronic diaries found that women with BPD exhibited sudden, large swings from positive to negative mood states compared to women without the disorder (Ebern-Priemer et al., 2007). Borderlines may also have brief episodes in which they appear to be in psychotic or dissociative states. They often complain about feeling unreal or depersonalized—as somehow if they didn't exist.

Judy Herman and Bessel Van der Kolk

In 1981, Judith Herman broke through psychiatry's massive wall of denial with her landmark book, *Father-Daughter Incest.* A professor of psychiatry at Harvard University and co-founder of the Victims of Violence Program, Cambridge Hospital, Dr. Herman has made seminal contributions to understanding the effects of childhood sexual abuse, rape, and gender-based violence including first articulating a staged model of trauma treatment and the now widely used concept of Complex PTSD (Post-Traumatic Stress Disorder) to describe adult outcomes of chronic, repetitive childhood trauma, especially incest (Herman, 1997).

Bessel van der Kolk is arguably the single most influential figure in the field of traumatic stress disorders. Energetic and charismatic, Bessel was born and raised in the Netherlands but attended college and received his medical and psychiatry training in the U.S. He quickly developed a worldwide network of friends and collaborators that informs his thinking and theories. Calculatingly provocative at times in his efforts to move the trauma treatment field forward, Bessel has integrated attachment theory, neurobiology, memory and cognition into a more comprehensive understanding of the effects of psychological trauma (van der Kolk, 2015).

In the mid-1980's Herman and van der Kolk teamed up to bring their expertise to bear on Borderline Personality Disorder (BPD):

> On the basis of our work with incest victims and Vietnam veterans, we proposed (Herman & van der Kolk, 1987) that trauma, especially prolonged trauma at the hands of people on whom one depends for nurturance and security, will significantly shape one's ways of organizing one's internal schemes and ways of coping with external reality. We theorized that the characteristic splitting of the self and others into "all-good" and "all-bad" portions represents a developmental arrest—a continued fragmentation of the self and a fixation on earlier modes of organizing experience. We proposed that self-mutilation, which is often experienced by therapists as a display of masochism or as a manipulative gesture (van der Kolk et al., 1991), may in fact be a way of regulating the psychological and biological equilibrium when ordinary ways of self-regulation have been disturbed by early trauma (Herman & van der Kolk, 1987). In this framework, psychotic episodes in borderline patients can be understood much like the flashbacks seen in Vietnam veterans: as intrusive recollections of traumatic memories that were not integrated into the individual's personal narrative, and instead were stored on a somatosensory level (van der Kolk, 1996 p. 201).

Decades later it is now well documented that the majority of people meeting diagnostic criteria for BPD report a history of childhood sexual, physical and/or emotional abuse.

One of the most successful treatments for BPD is Dialectical Behavior Therapy (DBT), developed by psychologist Marsha Linehan. For years the story of how Linehan came to create DBT implied that it emerged from a happy coincidence between her therapeutic work with self-destructive and suicidal women and her private study of Zen meditation. Reportedly she simply took what she learned from Zen practice and applied it in her therapy—and voila, you had DBT. But of course, such acts of creation are rarely random, and people do not always understand at the time why they do the things that they do. In 2011, at the age of 68 saying that she did not want to die "*a coward*,"

Marsha Linehan revealed the true story behind the creation of DBT (see Chapter 10).

DBT strives to find a balance in the psychological conflicts between opposing ideas, emotions, or impulses. But the essence of DBT lies in the act of a radical acceptance of the self and of life, as it is opposed to how one thinks it is supposed to be. The self-destructive and suicidal impulses, the emotional storms, the irrational rages towards others, the self-hate, the feelings of emptiness and depersonalization, the fears, the depression, and the anger—all are reframed as understandable responses that must be changed through mindful awareness. This mindfulness is a control over thoughts and actions and a better ability to stay in the moment. Patients learn to recognize what they are really feeling and then sometimes deliberately do the exact opposite of their impulses.

Central to DBT theory is the idea that symptoms and strange behaviors spring from an inability to regulate emotional states. The root cause of that inability lies in growing up in what is called an invalidating environment—anything from severe maltreatment to milder forms of parent-child emotional tension. By increasing emotional regulation to reduce anxiety and arousal, DBT helps to steady the Borderline patient's sense of self and improves tolerance of perceived affronts.

The effectiveness of DBT is proven by randomized clinical trials, particularly for suicidal and self-destructive behaviors. In practice, it is often combined with antidepressant or antianxiety medication. It has also been successful in treating anorexia, bulimia, substance abuse and other mental disorders known for rapid shifts in sense of self and behavior.

SYNTHESIS

The goal of Chapter 6 is to illustrate three major points. The first is that this nebulous entity that we call "personality" can simultaneously host discrepant versions of self as most dramatically manifest by people who lead deviant secret lives. Secondly, although all of the conventional models account for important aspects of personality, none explains people with secret lives. Lastly, the state model, which views personality as the aggregation and integration of an individual's states of being, is complementary with current psychodynamic, developmental and dimensional models of personality.

Who knows how many people lead a secret life? Secret lives are exposed often enough, especially involving sexual behavior, however, that they are clearly a fact of human existence. Not all secret lives are immoral or illegal—there are also secret do-gooders out there. Once we get over the shock of disclosure, society tends to view such behavior as duplicitous or hypocritical. The state model suggests that it is more complicated than that.

The state model conceptualizes personality as the public expression of an individual's collection of states of being, many organized into cyclical subsystems, interconnected by brief transitional events (switches) that exhibit properties of probability and directionality. Different contexts will repeatedly activate different subsystems of states, thereby expressing different facets of the individual's personality that over time come to act like fixed character traits. Thus it is possible for a person to harbor diametrically opposed aspects of their personality compartmentalized within subgroups of states that are largely isolated from each other by SDLM. At times, these subgroups of states come into conflict with each other, vying for control of the individual's thoughts and actions.

If this formulation is correct, some sort of mental meta-mechanism is necessary to bind together our diverse collections of states of being into the more or less unified sense of self that most of us experience. Different academic disciplines conceptualize this mechanism from diverse perspectives, but all agree that it includes the ability to generalize learned information across contexts and to new situations, to self-monitor one's behavior, to reflect on and learn from past experience, and to anticipate and plan for the future. Failure to fully develop these meta-capacities—often associated with early childhood maltreatment and family dysfunction—leads to fragmentation in a person's sense of self, self-destructive and high-risk behavior, and difficulty forming trusting relationships with significant others.

Trauma and Addiction

The Convenience Store Clerk

When I was an intern (1975–1976), a woman was brought to the hospital emergency room. Found wandering in a bad section of Indianapolis, she told a horrific story. She was a clerk in an all-night convenience store. Some guys had come in and started blatantly shoplifting. When she told them to stop, they attacked her. She was gang raped and left pinned under store shelves that they toppled on her. Managing to free herself, she was looking for help when found and brought to the hospital.

There was an immediate sympathetic response from the ER staff. A hospital bed was prepared and the psychiatry resident called. Her dramatic story was retold across shifts and among staff during the rest of the night (this was long before medical privacy laws took effect). The only problem: the next day, we learned there was no evidence that the attack had happened. The police said that no convenience stores had been robbed. The store where she said her assault took place didn't exist.

A wave of hurt and anger swept through the hospital staff. She was a fake! A fraud! She had taken advantage of our gullibility—she had duped us! We found no physical injuries or evidence of rape. She was not psychotic or suicidal, so we complied when she angrily demanded to be discharged.

It might have ended there, except that one of my fellow interns looked a little farther. He learned that there once had been a convenience store located where our patient said. There had also been a robbery in which a woman employee was reported injured. But that robbery had happened years earlier—on the same date.

The woman had experienced an unconscious flashback that can occur on the anniversary of a traumatic event. While rare—or at least rarely recognized—similar cases of an unconscious reenactment of a traumatic event are scattered through the clinical literature. Blank, for example, describes a Vietnam veteran who robs a store while in the grip of an unconscious flashback that symbolically acted out his recurrent traumatic nightmare (Blank, 1985).

In his landmark book, *Psychological Trauma,* Bessel van der Kolk tells the story of Ms. D., a survivor of the Coconut Grove nightclub fire in November 28, 1942. With 492 dead and hundreds more injured, it was the worst fire of its kind up to that point. Pictures of bodies piled high at the malfunctioning exits and jammed in the revolving door led to new fire safety codes. Doctors treating the hundreds of victims of burns and smoke inhalation pioneered new treatments, including the first use of penicillin to treat skin graft infections. Their success led the War Department to order vast quantities of the new antibiotic for the armed forces, ultimately saving tens of thousands of wounded soldiers. Studies of the survivors and victims' families by Erich Lindemann and Alexandra Adler proved classic accounts of what would later become known as Posttraumatic Stress Disorder.

Ms. D's story went like this: It was the first day of her new job at the Coconut Grove for the 19-year-old Ms. D. She was excited by the glamour, the famous performers, and the celebrity guests. All of a sudden she heard a commotion. She looked up at the ceiling:

The wires—the fire was spreading in the wires. Then the whole room filled up with gases—choking gases. It looked as if the ceiling—the roof—were opening up—I saw people sitting there, not moving, with grotesque faces—and ash black, all black. I don't know how I got out (van der Kolk, 1987 p. 174).

Ms. D testified about the fire at hearings held the following March, but soon afterwards she said she "*forgot*" about the event. About 40 years later, she began having serious psychiatric problems that were ultimately traced back to the fire. At times she behaved bizarrely—pulling fire alarms, shouting for people to flee buildings because of the gases. Once she tried to organize fellow patients in an evacuation of the hospital, saying, "*I'm going to be the last one out, to make sure everyone gets out. All of the doors are coming off today. No more doors.*" On another occasion, the police brought her to the hospital after she started yelling in a supermarket that the "*gas from the ceiling will kill all of the shoppers*" (van der Kolk, 1987 p. 176).

It can, however, be difficult to convince a judge or jury that a hidden traumatic memory drove the unlawful or bizarre act in question. People who experience an unconscious flashback are usually perplexed by their own behavior and rarely connect it to their past trauma. When that connection is made they become emotional, vividly recalling the event and related memories.

POSTTRAUMATIC STRESS DISORDER

In many respects, the modern era of clinical and experimental research on the long-term psychological and medical effects of trauma begins in the Vietnam War era. Back then a few mental health professionals tried to understand and treat the emerging problems of combat veterans. But scholars have since rediscovered medical and literary descriptions of posttraumatic reactions from earlier wars. Most authorities acknowledge a historic cycle of waxing and waning awareness of trauma and its effects. For example, Jonathan Shay's fascinating book, *Achilles in Vietnam,* is an illuminating reinterpretation of Homer's *Iliad* from the perspective of Posttraumatic Stress Disorder (Shay, 1994).

From the Civil War on, each new conflict has briefly focused attention on the impact of traumatic experiences. And almost as quickly, each intervening period of relative peace has led both professionals and the public to forget or dismiss those effects. The social dynamics driving this cycle of discovery and rejection reflect a collective wish to not think about trauma—even though violence, disaster, and gruesome death are central to so much of our commercial entertainment.

The DSM-III

The now-official DSM diagnosis of Posttraumatic Stress Disorder (PTSD) first appeared in 1980 as part of a dramatic revision in the way in which mental conditions were diagnosed. Generally known as the DSM-III, the Diagnostic and Statistical Manual of Mental Disorders (Third Edition) was published to cries of acclaim and alarm from the mental health professions (American Psychiatric Association, 1980). The DSM-III was a radical departure from what had been the usual way in which psychiatric disorders were diagnosed. Prior to the DSM-III, psychiatric diagnosis was a *highly* subjective process strongly influenced by the clinician's theoretical orientation.

In the beginning it did not matter much what diagnosis was bestowed because treatments were directed at a patient's symptoms, not his diagnosis. But by the second half of the twentieth century, psychiatric treatments were becoming more effective and more diagnosis specific—especially for schizophrenia and depression. Now diagnosis did matter and pressure was building for a more scientifically based classification system.

In response to this need, and building on pioneering research on psychiatric diagnosis by Feighner and colleagues, the DSM-III sought to impose a set of requirements that must be satisfied before a patient could receive a given psychiatric diagnosis. Each of the disorders listed in the DSM-III had a set of diagnostic criteria, usually expressed in the form of specific constellations of symptoms, that must be present—or conversely, in some cases, must be absent—before the patient received a given diagnosis.

In reality, not every clinician explicitly checked off all of the criteria before bestowing a diagnosis, but the DSM-III's overall effect on the standardization of psychiatric diagnoses was profound. The US and much of the rest of the world continues to live with the benefits—and with the unintended consequences—that are the legacy of the DSM-III revolution.

Starting in 1975, the DSM-III was drafted by a series of workgroups of leading clinicians and scientists. It was then vociferously critiqued by others in the field, and finally tested at selected locations prior to its official release in 1980. My introduction occurred in the Yale-New Haven Hospital Emergency room where, as the psychiatry resident on duty, I was required to complete voluminous checklists and symptom assessments on everyone I saw as part of a pre-release field trial.

I hated it! I resented the time it took and the fact that it trumped MY clinical judgment. Yet, when the field trial was over, and we were allowed to lapse back into making psychiatric diagnoses in our previous impressionistic fashion, I realized that the way in which I saw my patients was now different. I was now also seeing larger syndromic patterns not just individuals with problems. Having now treated or supervised the treatment of thousands of people—adults, adolescents, and children—I appreciate the inherent tension between seeing the person and seeing the syndrome. Effective treatment requires a therapist to see both simultaneously and understand how each influences the other.

What you "see" when you make a psychiatric diagnosis is a function of how you organize the enormous amount of information potentially available from the person's history and interactions with you. For me, a core lesson came from a Vietnam veteran I was treating. During my first year (1976) of clinical rotations through the psychiatric units at the West Haven Veterans Hospital, I encountered many Vietnam veterans. They were being given all sorts of psychiatric diagnoses. Borderline personality disorder and antisocial personality disorder were popular with many VA psychiatrists. And then there was a whole ward of Vietnam veterans diagnosed as schizophrenic by the psychoanalysts. I soon learned that my supervisors strongly disagreed about what was going on with these men.

Larry

One of these supervisors, Arthur Blank, was a Vietnam veteran himself. He was supervising my treatment of a seriously suicidal young man—I'll call him Larry here—who had served three consecutive tours as a Marine stationed along the demilitarized zone separating North and South Vietnam. Like many veterans, Larry didn't seem ill when he first came back. A couple of years later, however, he began to drink heavily and was unable to hold a job. Over time he increasingly withdrew from friends and family. Eventually he stabbed himself in the chest with his bayonet from Vietnam—when his father found him, he was close to death. When it was certain that he would live, he was transferred to our psychiatry ward and assigned to me.

I was having trouble understanding what was going on in Larry's mind. Most days when I saw him for therapy sessions, he was lucid, logical, and articulate about his anger towards the military, the government, and American society in general. They all had betrayed him, he said, but most importantly, they had betrayed his buddies who died for what was now a lost and despised cause. He talked about the books he was reading about the war, expressing anger at both the anti-war protesters (of whom I had been one) and at the government for lying about the war. But at other times on the ward, especially at night, he seemed to be back in Vietnam. Then he could be dangerous, responding to attempts to help or control him as if we were the enemy.

During one supervision session, Dr. Blank handed me a creased, marked-up, draft of a paper that he was writing on diagnosing Vietnam veterans. It wasn't very long, maybe ten or twelve typewritten pages, but it painted a remarkably clear clinical picture of what we should be looking for. It forced me to think differently about the veterans I treated. I realized that many of their symptoms and behaviors began during their war experiences. It also led me to conclude that our well-intended but ignorant attempts to treat combat veterans as if they had some other disorder were akin to malpractice. A disturbing thought.

> *The essence of Dr. Blank's paper was that there were three cardinal diagnostic features in these cases: (1) the history of trauma; (2) re-experiencing the trauma, and (3) avoiding of things that were reminders of the trauma. What made the paper come alive were the vivid examples of daily life filled with symptoms of re-experiencing and avoidance in these veteran's everyday lives. These were the same men whom I was seeing but not seeing very well—mistakenly treating them as if they suffered from some other disorder.*

I don't believe that this paper was published, but in a later chapter of a book on the trauma of war that he co-edited, Dr. Blank writes:

> *To make any diagnosis, the physician must be ready, willing, and able to do so. Diagnostic ability depends mainly upon having the necessary information and recognizing patterns. Readiness requires a sufficient level of awareness to recognize patterns or clusters of information without groping. But the physician's **willingness** [emphasis in original] may be more of an issue in diagnosing PTSD than for other conditions.* (Blank, 1985 p. 101)

In my own work with dissociative identity (multiple personality) disorder patients, I would come to appreciate just how much a clinician's ability to make a diagnosis depends on a willingness to see what is in front of them. Occasionally a former DID doubter contacts me now enthusiastically describing having discovered DID in a patient—often sounding as if no one else had ever seen this before them. My first response is that they are now cursed—to see it again and again, but none of their colleagues will ever believe them.

My patient, Larry, had been traumatized in multiple ways. He had been wounded several times. His closest friend died in agony in his arms. He killed with his bayonet and then mutilated the enemy bodies. He experienced these events as intrusive memories, in nightmares, and at times he relived them in a waking dream.

During one episode he suddenly thrashed violently in bed, fighting off attempts to help him. He didn't seem to see us and was reacting to things that we couldn't see. Jumping out of bed he ran down the hall, collapsing against the wall by the ward door, sobbing violently. Crying and screaming, he was incoherent, but it was clear it was about Vietnam.

Later, I told Dr. Blank about the episode. He looked at me sadly and asked, *"Was he trying to get off the truck?"* Only then did I realize that Larry was reliving the time when the truck carrying his squad hit a mine. Larry awoke tangled in wreckage and buried under dead and dying fellow Marines. His eardrums were blown out. He had a broken arm and assorted other wounds, but he was the only one who could walk. Bleeding and deaf, he ran miles through enemy territory to get help and lead a rescue team back. When they arrived, everyone was dead.

During the time I struggled to understand patients like Larry, Art Blank, Robert J. Lifton, Matt Friedman and other therapists working with war veterans were pressing the recently formed DSM-III workgroups to include a trauma diagnosis. I know little about those discussions, but having served on later DSM workgroups, I suspect that lengthy negotiations must have happened to accept PTSD as a new diagnosis. All DSM diagnoses reflect a political negotiation among the suggestions offered by experts who represent competing academic positions or commercial interests. The result in this case was the introduction of PTSD, which continues as a diagnosis in much the same form in the current DSM.

The original DSM-III PTSD diagnostic criteria encompassed four domains. The first criterion (A) required a history of a stressful experience that would evoke considerable distress in most people, i.e., Dr. Blank's history of trauma. The next three criteria required one or more symptoms from each of three categories: (1) re-experiencing symptoms (Criterion B); (2) avoidant symptoms (Criterion C); and (3) hyperarousal symptoms (Criterion D).

The current version, the DSM-5, adds a dissociative subtype to the diagnosis of Posttraumatic Stress Disorder reflecting a growing recognition of a subgroup of PTSD patients who have significant dissociative symptoms as part of their PTSD (American Psychiatric Association, 2013). (New editions of the DSM are identified with Arabic numerals in order to allow for limited revisions, e.g., DSM-5.2.)

An account of how the DSM-III legitimatized the diagnosis of PTSD and opened the eyes of mental health professionals, and eventually others, to the effects of trauma on mental health is a story unto itself. Vietnam veterans benefitted first, although beyond having a more appropriate and respectful way to diagnose them, at first there was little treatment of proven value to offer. Rape victims benefitted next. Then came a growing appreciation of the long-term effects of child abuse—first as it affected adults, and much later how profoundly it changes the minds and bodies of children. Knowledge and treatment would come over the next decades.

At least proven treatments now exist to help the current generation of war veterans returning from Iraq and Afghanistan. These treatments are not perfect, and they don't work for everyone. When they do work, psychological scars remain. Nor are there enough trained therapists to meet what is an enormous, but largely invisible, national need. The current media focus—the horrific suicide rate in active duty and combat veterans—is really only the tip of an iceberg. Those of us who worked with Vietnam veterans know that without proper treatment a high percentage of the veterans of the Iraq and Afghanistan wars will suffer disabling, lifelong PTSD.

Resistance to the Diagnosis of PTSD

The number of people diagnosed as having PTSD or partial PTSD—those not meeting the full DSM criteria—grew substantially as clinicians and researchers improved their ability to spot different types of trauma and its effects on the human psyche. Not surprisingly, the large jump in number of cases, as well as contentious legal battles and increased disability claims, generated a backlash against the diagnosis (see, e.g., McNally, 2003). The most commonly voiced criticism is that the traumatized person is faking PTSD for money. Resistance to seeing PTSD for what it is, rather than viewing it as faking, antisocial or borderline personality disorder, schizophrenia, or bipolar disorder, often revolves around questions of just how much a person with PTSD is in control or responsible for his behavior.

Critics argue that war veterans and other trauma victims fake PTSD symptoms to get disability payments, to excuse illegal behavior, to justify drinking or drug abuse, or just to get sympathy—to play the victim. Proponents argue that people with PTSD are often seriously disabled, engage in behavior that is outside of their rational control, use and abuse alcohol and drugs in an attempt to reduce their symptoms, and generally are looking not for pity but for validation that trauma has profoundly changed them.

Flashbacks

Perhaps the single most contentious collision of these two viewpoints is the PTSD flashback. They make the news when they are raised as a legal defense for baffling or sensational crimes. In other cases, they may be cited as evidence of a persistent psychological injury that justifies compensation.

Flashbacks can be sudden and dramatic, which can make them appear as if the person is acting or faking. The person becomes markedly different from their usual self, behaving oddly or in a frightened or frightening fashion. The fact that flashbacks may be triggered by simple objects, common behaviors, or everyday events that most people regard as innocuous naturally increases skepticism. The term flashback can be confusing because it is also applied to certain drug experiences and has become part of everyday slang referring to recurrent life situations. And, of course, the flashback is a timeworn plot device in fiction and film.

Posttraumatic flashbacks are episodes in which the person acts or feels as if a past traumatic event is recurring. Blank describes four types of posttraumatic flashbacks. The first two types appear as dreams and nightmares, some that even continue after awakening. Unconscious flashbacks take the form of a vivid reliving of the experience, complete with hallucinations of sight and sound.

Even more common are conscious flashbacks that take a form in which the person feels as if his mind is splitting into two parts. One part is reliving the past traumatic event—seeing, hearing, and even smelling it. Another part of the mind remains grounded in the present and can often describe the experience with detachment. Conscious flashbacks occur along a continuum ranging from brief flashes of a traumatic memory that interrupt a person's train of thought to an overwhelming sense of being simultaneously caught in two separate, but equally vivid, realities—a foot in two worlds.

Although a person may know that he is having a flashback and may be able to relegate it to the back of his mind, it still takes a toll on attention, concentration, and mood. When common situations trigger flashbacks, people learn to avoid them and even develop phobias of these activities, places, or objects. An all-too-common and tragic example is the difficulty that rape victims have with consensual sex. Rape victims frequently describe having flashbacks to their sexual assault while making love with their partner. They are torn between their desires to enjoy intimacy and please their lover and a dread of the traumatic flashbacks that sex can trigger. Many a relationship has floundered as a result.

PTSD AS A STATE DISORDER

Flashbacks

Flashbacks are altered states of consciousness. Like panic attacks, they disrupt the person's normal stream of consciousness. Flashbacks often have an abrupt onset that resembles the rapid switches seen in mania, panic attacks and multiple personality. They tend to abate more slowly, fading by degrees. I have observed patients fluctuating between alternatingly knowing that they are having a flashback and returning to a full immersion in the traumatic memory.

During an unconscious flashback contact with the present disappears—the person acts as if he is back in another time and place. The individual may hallucinate things that are not there. They may mistake the people and places around them for things from another time. The unconscious flashback may play out as a reenactment of a traumatic memory or in a more symbolic fashion such as the convenience store clerk reliving her gang rape and Larry running down the hall in his waking dream of the truck hitting a mine.

Other State-Related Symptoms in PTSD

A number of other PTSD symptoms can be understood in terms of the states they create. The hyperarousal symptoms include problems falling or staying asleep. Sleep, as discussed in Chapter 3, is composed of a repeating cycle of discrete psychophysiological states conventionally referred to as sleep stages. PTSD researchers have found abnormalities in the sleep cycle including earlier onset of the REM state after falling asleep, correlations between certain brain wave frequencies during REM sleep and the severity of a person's nightmares, and ultra rapid transitions between REM sleep and nighttime awakening (Mellman, Pigeon, Nowell, & Nolan, 2007). Thus trauma sufficient to produce PTSD not only generates altered states of consciousness such as flashbacks, but it also distorts the temporal organization and normal flow in subsystems of states such as the normal sleep cycle. Therapists often sarcastically refer to 'trauma' as the *"gift that keeps on giving"* all of the person's life.

The DSM PTSD hyperarousal symptom cluster includes explosive anger and exaggerated startle responses to loud noises or other stimuli. People with these PTSD symptoms startle and become angry easily. Minor events or setbacks that would not faze most people are enough to trigger explosive rage reactions. With explosive anger, the person is often unaware that they have just erupted with rage until much later—or when someone tells them. Consider these kinds of reactions as rapid switches into extreme mood states.

Exaggerated startle responses reflect how trauma can condition someone who suffers from PTSD. Minor stimuli evoke an adrenaline-charged state of fight or flight. Being repeatedly startled can leave a person exhausted or paranoid if the shocks occur over a short period. Infants and toddlers have a similar reaction at fireworks displays on the Fourth of July. When they see the flash of a bursting rocket or aerial bomb, their immature nervous systems cannot suppress a startle reaction in anticipation of a loud boom the way an older child or adult's can. That is why you hear infants and toddlers crying after the third or fourth loud boom and become increasingly inconsolable as the celebration goes on around them.

A Loud Bang

I was chatting with staff in the nursing station of the West Haven VA Hospital psychiatric admissions unit, when we were startled by a loud bang coming from the patients' kitchenette. The cause proved to be a patient boiling batteries on the stove in an effort to rouse their few remaining electrons for his transistor radio. He was unhurt and after the commotion died down, we returned to the nursing station only to be interrupted by a World War II veteran having a semi-conscious flashback of his tank being knocked out while he was taking a piss behind it. Several Viet Nam veterans agitatedly paced the hall—cursing us when we tried to talk them down. One patient eloped. Another was found in a fetal position under his bed talking like a small child. There were angry demands for "PRN" (as needed) medications for sleep or nerves. It was a demonstration of how a single startling noise could set off states of fear, anger, and paranoia that lasted for hours afterwards.

The cluster of PTSD avoidant symptoms are often thought to reflect an understandable—but maladaptive—attempt on the part of the person to shield themselves from reminders of the trauma. Examples include the avoidance of thoughts, feelings, conversations, activities, places or people that arouse recollections of the trauma. Indeed, the most common thing trauma patients tell their therapists is, *"I try not to think about it."*

Amnesia for part or all of a traumatic experience is more common than people think. Often a person can't remember the worst parts of an experience and covers this gap by saying something like, "*I must have blacked out*." Some critics maintain that traumatic experiences are never forgotten—especially, they are never forgotten and then recalled many years later.

But many carefully done scientific studies document amnesia for traumatic experiences and that people report suddenly recalling them years later, often triggered by something that they heard or saw in daily life. Few people report first recalling previously forgotten traumatic memories in psychotherapy—but many people who recall troubling traumatic memories in other settings seek out psychotherapy to deal with them. This delayed recall (mislabeled by critics as "recovered memories") has proven true for virtually all forms of trauma (Putnam, 2003). The greatest amnesic effects are usually seen for childhood trauma.

In addition to avoiding situations that directly remind them of their trauma, people with PTSD also avoid situations that rouse strong emotions—even seemingly positive emotions such as laughter. They avoid sentimental movies, cheering crowds, loud music, or loving affection. They have learned that any powerful emotional situation—positive or negative—is likely to unsettle their ability to ward off traumatic images or memories. Their range of emotions (think emotional state-space) constricts—in many instances they report feeling "numb" much of the time. To become emotional in any way, positive or negative, is to risk losing control and being overwhelmed by traumatic emotions.

Avoidance can also include persistent depersonalization and derealization—in fact, they usually happen together. Depersonalization is an intense feeling that the person is somehow not real or not really present in the moment. There is often a sense of standing outside of oneself, as if watching another person. There is usually a sense of empty detachment. Derealization is the sense that the world is not real. One Holocaust survivor described it to me as if everything—people, objects, and the environment—were all two-dimensional cutouts lacking any substance or solidity. These experiences are profoundly disturbing and patients dread persistent depersonalization as much they fear depression and PTSD flashbacks.

THERAPEUTIC ABREACTIONS

All wars are ugly, but World War I was especially ghastly. Shell shock was first believed to be the result of a physical injury to the nervous system from the massive artillery bombardments common in that war. But a large percentage of shell shock cases were eventually recognized to be the result of psychological trauma. The British army suffered tens of thousands of such psychiatric causalities. Four-fifths never returned to active duty. The men's symptoms were often classically hysterical, in that they could be directly traced to their combat experiences. Soldiers who bayoneted an enemy in the throat might have trouble swallowing. Snipers might go blind. Men who strangled an enemy would struggle to breathe.

Attempts to treat these symptoms with rest, talking, or electroshock were unsuccessful. The British favored punishments and disciplinary therapies for the enlisted ranks, with rest and rehabilitation reserved for officers. The French preferred a bizarre treatment known as *torpillage*, consisting of electric shocks applied to the affected parts of the body coupled with "persuasive" psychotherapy. Although high rates of success were claimed initially, the French were forced to discontinue *torpillage* after increasing numbers of soldiers refused it, their mutiny culminating in a sensational public trial. It was briefly resurrected by the French military in 1918, leading to another soldiers' revolt.

Toward the end of the war, it became clear that talking treatments that induced an altered state by using the anesthetic ether or hypnosis produced far better results than other treatments. Such treatments, which were based on the earlier reports by Janet, Freud and James, came to be called abreactive therapy. This discovery was largely forgotten after that war, only to be rediscovered early in World War II. Ultimately, abreactive therapy became the principal treatment for what World War II British and American psychiatrists called combat neurosis or combat fatigue.

Abreactive treatments under the influence of the barbiturate sodium amytal—dubbed narcosynthesis—were first used on a mass scale by the British following their desperate evacuation from Dunkirk. In narcosynthesis, the doctor slowly injects sodium amytal or a similar drug until the soldier enters a state of twilight sleep. Usually the patient's speech slurs, and he feels relaxed. The therapist then takes the patient back to the battlefield, asking about what is happening, sometimes suggesting details, until a clearer picture of the patient's traumatic experience emerges. The therapist then helps the patient relive the experience releasing pent-up emotions, while suggesting alternative reactions and explanations to help defuse the traumatic memories.

Battlefield studies comparing abreactive treatments with hypnosis and barbiturates found they worked essentially the same. How a patient reached an altered state mattered less than a vivid reliving of the traumatic event. Compared to the dismal results of World War I, 60 percent of World War II soldiers with combat fatigue returned to their units within two to ten days (Menninger, 1945). In most instances, treatment was performed near the front line, and soldiers never left the combat zone.

Despite their initial optimism that they had discovered the answer, former military psychiatrists soon learned that therapeutic catharsis did not work for most peacetime mental disorders. Within a short time, drug- and hypnosis-induced abreaction largely disappeared from postwar clinical practice. Instead, psychiatry resumed its love affair with Freudian psychoanalysis, which had been gaining adherents since the 1920s. Although psychoanalysis traces its roots to reliving trauma and the "hypnoid" states described by Breuer and Freud in their seminal case study of Anna O, Freudians rapidly dropped abreactive treatments after Freud rejected hypnosis (see Chapter 8).

Abreactive therapy briefly returned as a treatment for Vietnam veterans advocated by former WWII combat psychiatrists such as Lawrence Kolb. Noting that many patients retained only fragmentary recall of their flashbacks, Kolb would show his patients videotapes of the sessions to help them process the traumatic memories (Kolb, 1985). In the 1980s, therapeutic abreactions were used in the treatment of dissociative identity disorder patients, who were often victims of severe child abuse.

BRAIN IMAGING OF POST-TRAUMATIC AND DISSOCIATIVE STATES

The recognition that extreme emotional states can change brain function—and perhaps even brain structure—has led to a fruitful series of research studies looking at brain activation patterns associated with traumatic states of consciousness in conditions such as PTSD. This work has highlighted individual differences in how people react to reminders of past trauma.

There are, of course, major ethical and technical limits as to what can be done in the laboratory to recreate a traumatic experience. Typical experiments expose a person traumatized in the past—someone, say, who meets criteria for a diagnosis of PTSD –to a reminder of their experience. In some studies, researchers distill the essence of an individual's traumatic experience into a short story that is read to the subject as their brain and bodily responses are measured. In others, subjects are exposed to generic traumatic reminders, such as showing Vietnam veterans graphic combat scenes from a movie such as *Platoon*. The subject's brain and body activation patterns are compared with activation patterns to neutral stimuli, such as a story of a prosaic event or clips from a boring documentary on slime mold.

Individual Responses to an Identical Trauma

Individual differences in posttraumatic response to the same trauma are dramatically illustrated by a case study published by Ruth Lanius and colleagues (Lanius, Hopper, & Menom, 2003). A husband and wife were caught in a huge multi-vehicle accident with many deaths and serious injuries. Trapped in their car, they watched a child burn to death in front of them. They escaped uninjured after the husband was able to knock out the windshield.

In the weeks after the crash, both were crippled by acute PTSD symptoms—flashbacks, nightmares, feelings that the accident was happening again, reluctance to drive, poor sleep, and irritability. The husband was jumpy; his wife felt frozen and numb.

They agreed to participate in a fMRI study in which a script describing their experiences was read to them as they lay in a brain scanner. Both reported reliving the accident. The husband felt anxious, and his heart rate speeded up. The wife still felt frozen and numb, her heart rate unchanged. Compared with a neutral script scenario, when the husband was read the trauma script his fMRI scan showed activation in brain regions associated with a classic PTSD response. In contrast, his wife's brain activity was almost shut down, except for increased activation only in the occipital regions (see Figure 7-1, next page; from Lanius et al., 2003, used by permission). The husband responded to treatment but after six months of therapy the wife remained seriously impaired, having to sell her previously successful business.

Ruth Lanius and colleagues used the results of a series of brain imaging studies to make the case that there are two forms of PTSD—a dissociative type like the wife's and a hyperaroused form like the husband's. They identified distinct patterns of brain and bodily activation that differentiate these two types of post-traumatic response.

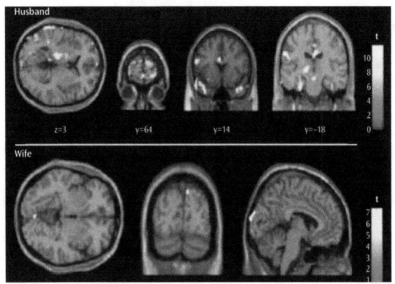

Differential Posttraumatic Brain States
in Response to the Same Trauma

For most patients with PTSD, exposure to a traumatic reminder speeds up their heart rate and produces a brain-activation pattern that shows decreased activity in the prefrontal cortex and greater activation in the limbic brain circuitry, especially the amygdala—a deep brain structure known to play an essential role in fear conditioning (see Chapter 6). They interpret this pattern as consistent with a failure of the ventromedial prefrontal or rational part of the brain to inhibit the emotional parts of the brain. People showing this pattern of brain activation often report reliving their traumatic experience in great detail.

But a minority of PTSD patients exhibit brain activity patterns marked with abnormally high levels of activation in part of the brain that modulates strong emotions. Their heart rate may not change or may even slow down. People with this pattern of brain and body responses report feeling depersonalized and unreal when confronted with reminders of their trauma. They have a sense of somehow being removed or at a safe distance from the awful experience. In extreme cases, they may have an out-of-body experience, feeling as if they are watching themselves from a distance. Clinical studies using measures of dissociation also provide evidence for a dissociative subtype of PTSD (Putnam et al., 1996). Based on this evidence, the DSM-5 committee added the new diagnosis of PTSD—dissociative subtype (Spiegel, 2010).

So, depending on the person, the same traumatic experience can produce at least two radically different PTSD reactions, an agitated state of hyperarousal or a numbed out dissociative state. Besides these polar opposite emotional reactions, it is likely that many mental and bodily functions, especially memory, also differ in these two traumatic states. Such fundamental differences in the mental states elicited by traumatic reminders likely hold important implications for the way therapists treat a given individual diagnosed with PTSD.

EVIDENCE-BASED TREATMENTS FOR PTSD

For as long as there have been healing arts, they have encountered Posttraumatic Stress Disorder in its many forms. It is unavoidable, as trauma has so many serious medical and psychological consequences. But it wasn't until the concept of PTSD was legitimized by the DSM-III in 1980, that systematic research into treatments for traumatic experiences began.

A remarkably diverse range of therapies have been tried for PTSD: various forms of psychotherapy, multiple medications (even marijuana, LSD and Ecstasy), psychosocial rehabilitation, hypnosis, music, dance and other arts, yoga, meditation, virtual reality, eye movement desensitization, adventure sports, and the martial arts. All have their advocates, and after three decades we now have several scientifically proven PTSD treatments that work—at least for a subset of people.

Of all of these, the cognitive behavior therapies or CBTs have consistently proven to be most effective for the greatest number of people, both adults and children, for more types of trauma. CBT can be tailored for different age groups and delivered in a variety of settings, from one-on-one sessions in an office to groups in schools, churches, or prisons. Despite some differences in emphasis most CBT-based treatments share common elements. The next generation of CBT treatments for trauma focus on identifying a core set of therapeutic components selected from among the most successful models that can be readily re-combined in various sets and sequences to meet a given patient's unique needs without losing an evidence-based framework (Layne et al., 2014)

A few medications, notably selective serotoninergic agents such as sertraline, paroxetine, and fluoxetine have proved to be effective in clinical trials. Differences in gender, age, and trauma have been cited as influencing whether a medication succeeds or fails in a given research study. Non-randomized studies suggest that certain other types of medication may help in refractory cases. Often, medication is combined with CBT to reduce symptoms that interfere with psychotherapy or daily life. In addition, many PTSD patients receive medications directed at commonly associated symptoms such as depression and anxiety.

A common element in current psychotherapies for PTSD is that patients must somehow express their underlying traumatic memories to detoxify the residual emotion. Treatment models differ in how graphically they seek to recreate the past traumatic experiences, but they share the idea that recall and processing of trauma must occur to defuse the memories or triggering situations that cause the person distress. Naturally, some people question the need to remember past traumatic events for a PTSD treatment to work. Research comparing PTSD treatments with and without explicit processing of traumatic memories is in progress.

At some level, all the current PTSD treatments address some of the state-related aspects of PTSD although not necessarily in a deliberate fashion. The cognitive behavioral treatments (CBT) encompass a diverse array of techniques including exposure therapies, stress inoculation training, cognitive processing techniques, relaxation training, Dialectical Behavior Therapy, and Acceptance and Commitment Therapy (Cahill, Rothbaum, Resick, & Follette, 2009). These diverse approaches seek to elicit traumatic responses, thoughts or feelings and then process them.

Exposure-based therapies seek to recreate the state of anxiety or fear with stimuli that are frightening but safe. A variety of techniques—and increasingly technologies such as virtual reality—are used to simulate the key traumatic experiences. The intensity, number and length of sessions may differ, but most include a psychoeducation component to make the PTSD symptoms more understandable and build in relaxation and meditation techniques to manage anxiety. The theory is that by vividly and recurrently recreating the emotional state associated with a traumatic event, it can be transformed through cognitive and behavioral techniques and lose its emotional potency.

Muscle relaxation or breathing techniques are taught in most CBT trauma therapies to show patients how to deliberately replace fear and hyperarousal with a more tranquil state of mind. Antidepressants and antianxiety drugs are often prescribed to modulate post-traumatic emotional states. Increasingly, psychedelic drugs such as ecstasy (MDMA) and psilocybin are used to create highly altered states of consciousness within which to examine trauma-related memories, thoughts and feelings (see Chapter 11 and Epilogue).

Alternative therapies, such as yoga, meditation, martial arts, music, and dance, seek to substitute other states of being that offer a refuge from painful posttraumatic states as well as express emotions and physical tensions that cannot be readily accessed through words alone. They provide a sense of self-mastery and, perhaps, even another identity. Some people—often those who have failed more conventional forms of PTSD treatment—respond well to one of the alternative therapies. But these unconventional treatments have not been able to muster the same level of scientific evidence for how well they work or for whom. Official skepticism (often misinformed), coupled with a conspicuous lack of research funding, has handicapped efforts to properly evaluate most of these nonstandard treatments.

The wide array of responses to different PTSD treatments highlight the need for better ways to assess individuals to predict likely benefits for any given therapy. Age, gender, type of trauma, culture, genetics, social and personal expectations and other factors influence results, but are difficult to measure. Assessing a person's altered states of consciousness elicited by traumatic reminders—e.g., hyperarousal, anxiety, paranoia, dissociation, depression—may be more helpful in identifying the best treatment for that person. This can be easily done today by taking a careful clinical history of the types of flashbacks and altered states triggered by traumatic reminders. Perhaps one day, there will be diagnostic tests measuring physiological responses to virtual reality generated traumatic reminders that help predict treatment choice.

CHILDHOOD TRAUMA

Posttraumatic Stress Disorder is an adult diagnosis, initially created primarily for Vietnam veterans. So it tells us little about the effects of a chronically recurring trauma, such as sexual or physical abuse and neglect that may happen to a child. PTSD has, however, taught us that trauma seriously affects psychological processes and biological systems that develop in early childhood. Early childhood trauma will abnormally influence the child's growth and development—and reverberate throughout the rest of the person's life.

By the time I had studied ten multiple personality cases in the laboratory and spent time talking with them about their lives, I understood that a significant connection existed between multiple personality disor-der and child abuse. All of my multiple personality research subjects shared a history of severe child abuse that started early in life and usual-ly lasted well into their teens. It typically involved multiple perpetrators, including parents or close relatives. All said that from as early as they could remember, they had been multiple, although there were always alter personalities that were unaware of it. It usually wasn't until their teen years, however, that they realized that other people were not like them. And so they learned to hide their differences.

If this were the case, I reasoned, I should be able to find children with multiple personality disorder. I would need to circulate a behavioral profile among the agencies and institutions that worked with abused chil-dren. I asked a number of the adult multiples participating in my research to help me define characteristics that dissociative children would display. Over the next couple of years we looked at family photographs, read per-plexed teachers' notes on report cards, tormented diary entries, high school yearbook salutations, and pediatricians' records. We talked at length about their childhood experiences in school and elsewhere that made them realize that they were different from other people.

Out of this came a rough profile of what a dissociative child or ado-lescent might look like to someone involved with the child, such as a social worker, foster parent, or teacher. In the mid-1980s, I circulated this profile to child welfare and child mental health agencies in the Washington, DC metro area. I expected to get maybe three or four possi-ble hits to evaluate together with a child psychiatrist or psychologist, because at the time I was trained only in adult psychiatry.

In the end, I saw well over a hundred maltreated children. Only a few seemed significantly dissociative. But most were seriously emotionally disturbed and behaviorally out of control. I kept wondering, what terrible things had happened to these children?

Dr. Edward Taylor, a child psychologist, and I continued to refine the diagnostic profile, seeking to develop both a diagnostic interview and a parent-caretaker report for pathological dissociation in children and ado-lescents. The diagnostic interview was never sufficiently validated to be released, but the parent report evolved into the Child Dissociative Checklist (CDC), now a widely used measure of dissociation in children (Putnam, Helmers, & Trickett, 1993). An adolescent self-report measure, the Adolescent Dissociative Experiences Scale (A-DES), followed a number of years later (Armstrong, Putnam, & Carlson, 1997). Both measures—as well as the current version of the adult Dissociative Experiences Scale (DES-II)—are available somewhere on the Internet for free without copyright restrictions (Carlson & Putnam, 1993).

While searching for dissociative children, my eyes were opened to the much, much larger group of abused and neglected children. To get the clinical training and credentials necessary to work with them, I started a fellowship in child and adolescent psychiatry at Children's National Medical Center part of George Washington University Medical School. Hazel Rae, the deputy Scientific Director of the NIMH Intramural Research Program, took an interest in my work and introduced me to Dr. Penelope (Penny) Trickett, a developmental psychologist studying abusive parenting in another laboratory at the NIMH. At about the same time an outside scientific review group recommended transferring me from the NIMH schizophrenia research unit at St. Elizabeths Hospital to the Laboratory of Developmental Psychology on the main NIH campus in Bethesda, Maryland.

After a year of planning, Penny and I obtained initial funding from the W.T. Grant Foundation to start a prospective longitudinal study (The Psychobiology of Sexual Abuse in Females) in December 1986 that has followed a group of sexually abused girls (ages 6–15 years at the start) and a carefully matched comparison group of non-abused girls into adulthood. (We have always wanted to do a parallel study of boys but could never get the funding.) Dr. Jennie Noll, the current primary investigator on the project, joined us in 1996. Our original children are now mothers and their children are included in this ongoing study. The research is revealing the many ways that abuse, neglect, and family violence and dysfunction harm children in generation after generation. A comprehensive summary of our three-generation study of childhood sexual abuse in females can be found in (Trickett et al., 2011).

The ACE Studies

Childhood maltreatment, a term that includes various forms of abuse and neglect, is the single most preventable cause of mental health problems. Surprisingly, it may also be the single most preventable contributor to many of the costly chronic diseases and causes of early death in our society. Effective prevention of child maltreatment and related family dysfunction such as parental alcohol and substance abuse, and domestic violence, would more than pay for itself in terms of an enormous drop in serious mental illness (e.g., perhaps half of the cases of major depression in women), especially major depression, substance abuse, and PTSD. And it would pay off in reduced tobacco use and lung disease, decreased alcohol abuse, decreased obesity with corresponding reductions in heart disease and diabetes, as well as fewer sexually transmitted diseases like HIV. These astonishing statements are scientifically supported by large-scale studies. (e.g., see Hammon, Ben-Ari, Laundry, Boyko, & Samore, 2015).

The groundbreaking Adverse Childhood Experiences (ACEs) study published in 1998 was the first research to link childhood exposure to an increasing number of different types of maltreatment with a dramatically rising risk for many of the leading causes of death (Felitti et al., 1998). The result of a long running collaboration between the U.S. Centers for Disease Control and Prevention (CDC) and Kaiser Permanente in San Diego, the ACE study prospectively investigated the relationship between early adverse childhood experiences (ACEs) and subsequent health and functioning in over 17,000 adults (Middlebrooks & Audage, 2008).

Based on answers to ten questions covering child abuse and neglect and parental and household dysfunction, an adverse childhood experience or ACE score was calculated for each subject. ACE scores could range from 0 to 8 in the first wave of subjects and were revised into a 0-to-10 index in the second wave of research participants. When an individual's ACE score was compared with a range of health outcomes, the relationship proved to be remarkably consistent.

As a person's ACE score increased, meaning that they had experienced more different types of maltreatment and family dysfunction, their risk for a myriad of health problems increased. ACE scores are significantly related to alcohol and drug abuse, chronic lung disease, depression, suicide, heart disease, liver disease, and sexually transmitted diseases. ACE scores were also correlated with risky adolescent behavior—early onset of smoking, suicide attempts, illicit drug use, early sex, and unintended pregnancies.

People with four or more ACEs often have serious mental and medical health problems. In addition, they were more likely to marry people with similar problems, increasing their risk for being involved in domestic violence, either as victim or abuser. For instance, a woman who was physically and sexually abused as a child and grew up in a home where there was domestic violence is three and half times more likely to be in a violent relationship as an adult than a woman who did not experience these childhood traumas. This, of course, exposes her children to increased health risks. And so it continues from generation to generation.

Far more than any other single study, the ACE study informed our understanding of the enormous public health costs of childhood abuse and dysfunctional home life. Later research has repeatedly confirmed the essence of the original ACE findings in study after study. An important implication of this truth: any time that we learn a child has been traumatized, we must work to prevent future trauma to that child—as trauma is cumulative. (See *CANarratives.org* for a down-loadable PowerPoint presentation on the public health effects and costs of childhood trauma and adversity.)

Certain combinations of maltreatment and adverse childhood experiences, such as being sexually abused and also living with a depressed or substance abusing parent, appear to have a combined synergistic effect that is greater than the sum of their individual effects. Sort of a $1 + 1 = 3$ situation. In our analysis of the National Comorbidity Survey—Replication Sample, we found that synergistic combinations differed for men and women. For women, sexual abuse combined with a variety of other adversities led to more complicated mental health problems. For males, the leading synergistic ACE was poverty, which amplified the effects of a range of other childhood adversities and maltreatment (Putnam, Harris, & Putnam, 2013).

SYNTHESIS

Chapter 7 begins the section, Trauma and Addiction, which examines experiences and behaviors that leave enduring marks on personality. How is it that memories of a single event, such as the convenience store clerk's gang rape or Ms. D's nightclub fire, haunt a person forever—at times taking over their awareness and displacing reality? It was only after we took another look at trauma and its persisting effects on personality that we could think to ask this question.

But first we, as a field and as individual clinicians, had to see the effects of trauma in a new way. The revolutionary diagnosis of PTSD in the 1980 DSM-III removed our blindfolds, but inevitably imposed its own diagnostic filter with its clinical and social consequences. Indeed, the continuous attack on the legitimacy of PTSD is proof of the clashing ways in which the same data can be interpreted.

Flashbacks, vivid remembering and re-experiencing of traumatic events, provide the quintessential example of the role of altered states of consciousness in PTSD. While they can look fakey as hell, the person having the flashback may be clueless or mentally torn in two by the vivid simultaneity of then and now. In addition to flashbacks, there are other powerful states of consciousness—hyperarousal, depression, anxiety, explosive anger, paranoia, and dissociation—common in PTSD. Disturbances in life energy renewing state cycles, such as sleep and play, reflect disruption of the mechanisms that modulate the normal rhythmic flow of states. Difficulties controlling powerful negative emotional states lead PTSD sufferers to adopt self-destructive strategies such as phobic avoidance of triggers or abuse of alcohol and drugs in efforts to avoid or blot out traumatic memories and suppress painful emotions.

For PTSD patients who do not respond to conventional treatments, altered states of consciousness are sometimes useful to bypass heavily layered psychological defenses erected to contain unspeakable horror, pain, and shame. From hypnosis to yoga to virtual reality to Ecstasy, the nature of the altered state doesn't seem to matter as much as the setting and intent of client and therapist.

PTSD was a diagnosis originally created for Vietnam veterans. When it was more broadly applied it becomes apparent that PTSD fails to fully describe other responses to trauma. Lanius and colleagues showed that two people exposed to an identical trauma could have virtually opposite psychological and neurobiological responses. As a diagnosis, PTSD also fails to characterize the profound effects of trauma on children, especially those who are exposed to synergistic combinations of trauma and adversity.

CHAPTER 8   DISSOCIATION

Like Mother Like Son

I was asked to evaluate a 6-year-old boy expelled from school for severe behavioral problems. His school reported bullying and fighting, sexualized behaviors, hyperactivity, and significant learning problems. A teacher described staring spells during which he did not respond to his name, commands or questions. The principal said that he would only be readmitted if I put him on a "hyperactivity drug."

Before seeing me, his mother completed the assessment measures I sent her, endorsing high levels of behavioral problems as well as self-injury and depression. During our first meeting we reviewed them together. Choosing questions such as "child goes into a trance-like state," "shows rapid changes in personality," "denies or does not remember traumatic experiences known to have occurred" that she had marked at the maximum level, I asked her to describe specific instances when he had displayed these behaviors. She couldn't give me even one example for any of the questions. Yet she vehemently insisted that her son was out of control.

Her son, whom I had not yet seen alone, was playing quietly in the corner with toy cars—seemingly oblivious to our discussion. She shot him a strange look. Immediately he began violently crashing the cars and then pushed over a dollhouse. Yelling "You God damn fucking whore" in an unnaturally hoarse voice, he threw one of the cars in her general direction.

In response, she cowed, scrunching down in her chair, head bowed, hands up as if to protect her face from blows. He kicked over the play table, and then menacingly stomped in front of her cursing, "fucking bitch, fucking bitch, fucking bitch." She sat frozen, eyes squeezed closed, her body drawn up tightly in a defensive crouch as if expecting to be viciously beaten.

I intervened, taking him to another room. He complied without resistance and began checking out the toys on the shelves. When I returned, his mother, appearing confused, asked where her son was.

Touching her face and rubbing her temples, she said she must have had one of her "migraines." She seemed to have no memory of what had just happened.

Mother and child both proved to have Dissociative Identity Disorder (DID). They had complementary pairs of alter personalities that triggered each other in a pathological dance of states. Similar reciprocal switching of parent and child DID alter personalities was first described by Richard Kluft (personal communication 4/27/13).

What happened between them is an exaggerated version of what happens between every parent and child. Children are sensitive to their caretakers' states of being. This sensitivity is exquisitely heightened in abused children who become hyperalert to any shifts in parental demeanor that may signal impending abuse. I have seen other cases of mutual DID in parents and their children marked by switches of alter personality state in one (parent or child) triggering a corresponding alter personality switch in the other. Such multi-generational cases are extremely difficult to treat and the clinician has the added responsibilities of ensuring the child's safety and reporting any suspected maltreatment.

IMPACT OF REPEATED TRAUMATIC STATES OF BEING ON CHILD DEVELOPMENT

Mortal fear, murderous rage, blind panic, indescribable pain, crushing grief, paralyzing depression, mortifying shame—these are not only extreme mental and physical states of being, they are also common responses to some children's terrible life experiences. In time they will remain as intrusive traumatic memories. Children growing up in ACE-ridden homes will repeatedly experience many of these painful and overwhelming states of being. The frequency and the types of extreme states will interact with a range of other factors, everything from the child's age at the time to the presence or absence of positive relationships in the child's life. There is no simple formula that captures all of the factors that shape a person's life.

Children exposed to repeated ACEs (Adverse Childhood Experiences) recurrently experience these extreme states of being. They are frightened, panicked, helpless, depressed, horrified, abused, neglected, troubled, and isolated—over and over and over again. Because ACEs tend to occur together (i.e., if you have one ACE you are at much higher risk for two or more ACEs), these children will accumulate a history of having repetitively experienced many types of extreme states of being. This cumulative history becomes a growing vulnerability because each time you experience an extreme state, it becomes easier to re-experience it or something like it in the future. A pathway is being formed in state-space. Thus, it becomes ever easier to switch into an extreme state of being when confronted with situations reminiscent of the initial trauma.

The residues of past traumatic experiences continue to haunt the child through intrusive memories, nightmares, and—in their most extreme form—flashbacks. Remnants of the extreme states hover in the background, at times intruding on the child's stream of consciousness and disrupting attention, concentration and thinking. The mental effort that a traumatized child must expend while trying to ignore and suppress these traumatic intrusions disrupts concentration, saps energy, and frays mood. Unfortunately, these cognitive disruptions and emotional lability are often mistaken for attention deficit hyperactivity disorder (ADHD), so many of these kids get stimulant medications rather than therapy to address trauma. Not a great idea for an already hyperaroused child.

Repeated experiences of extreme states disturb the flow and function of normal sequences of states such as the sleep cycle. The nightmares, sleep terrors, decreased time in restful sleep states, and frequent nocturnal awakenings common in traumatized children interrupt the critical repair and growth that happen during sleep. The combination of nightmares and the fragmentation of the normal sleep cycle disrupts rest, decreases energy, fogs awareness, and impairs certain types of learning that depend on sleep for memory consolidation. Many other bodily rhythms and processes are similarly disrupted. As maltreated children (especially sexually abused children) are often the most disturbed at night, those who live with them (e.g., foster parents) are troubled, inconvenienced, and sometimes frightened by the child's nocturnal behavior.

ATTACHMENT AND ATTUNEMENT

In order to better understand how extreme and painful mental and emotional states affect a growing child, we must consider how they influence the developmental stages a child must master to achieve independence. As discussed in Chapters 2 and 6 the most important task for an infant is to form a healthy attachment—usually with her mother. Developmental psychologist, Ed Tronick calls these dyadic states of consciousness.

Tiffany Field, one of the pioneers in research on mothers-infants inter-actions, describes this process as "attunement." When it occurs, the mother and infant experience a sense of connectedness that is powerfully re-inforcing and deeply soothing for each.

Disrupting this mutual experience is extraordinarily painful. The still-face paradigm in which a mother becomes passive and unresponsive for 2 minutes (described in Chapter 2) usually quickly distresses and disorganizes her infant or toddler. Even college students merely role-playing an infant or a mother in the still-face paradigm as part of a psy-chology experiment describe having unsettling and painful feelings.

When interviewed later, the students who role-played the still-faced mothers reported feeling guilty, anxious, depressed, and shameful. Students who role-played the infants described feeling anxious, vulnera-ble, angry, frustrated, sad, afraid and even panicky. Imagine what hap-pens in real life when infants and young children are confronted with angry, depressed, abusive, fearful, psychotic, drunk, or stoned mothers and fathers. What kind of attachments do they form?

And what if the parent ignores the child's needs, or is rough and abu-sive? Noxious experiences can push the child into extreme states of anx-iety, fear and panic. The cues of hunger or a full diaper, if they are met with abuse, become associated with states of pain and fear rather than relief and security created by love and care.

Abused or neglected children often withdraw into themselves. They turn within to their own meager resources and limited coping skills to quell their fears and pain—or they try to. They come to regard their care-takers with mixed emotions—both as sources of support and sources of pain. In a high percentage of cases they develop a disorganized or type D attachment style; showing extreme biological and psychological re-sponses to stress. They run a much higher risk of developing psychiatric disorders as adolescents and adults.

Repeated experiences with anxiety, anger, sadness or panic under-mine a child's efforts at regulating his emotions and controlling inappro-priate or dangerous impulses. They have a hard time empathizing with others or forming strong bonds with the important people in their lives.

Indeed, abused children may exhibit bizarre or dysfunctional responses when confronted with situations reminding them of their expe-riences with frightened or frightening caretakers. Other children pick up on their difficulties and shun them. These are the kids who are picked on, bullied, or become bullies. Teachers likewise reject them either as troublemakers or as spacey, attention-disordered, learning-impaired kids (Trickett, McBride-Chang, & Putnam, 1994). Such rejections often doom these kids to a childhood of loneliness and lost opportunity that ill prepares them for adulthood.

The caretaker's state of mind and the child's state of being constantly interact. The child often tries to reflect the caretakers' mood in some fashion that shrinks the state-space between them. In abusive relationships, the child's need to maintain an attachment dominates other needs, and the child assumes whatever state seems the least likely to provoke the caretaker—often a passive withdrawal into an inner world.

TYPE D ATTACHMENT AND DISSOCIATION

Over the last twenty years the role that Type D attachment, dissociation, and dysfunctional parenting play in cycles of family dysfunction across generations emerged from a series of research studies. The quality of the attachment formed between an infant and her caretaker plays a critical role in the individual's success in life. Based on Mary Ainsworth's research protocol, The Strange Situation, infants and toddlers are classified into three basic attachment categories (Secure [B], Avoidant [A] and Anxious/Resistant [C]) that have proven to be good long-term predictors of social and emotional adjustment. All three of these categories are considered to be "organized" attachments, in that the infant/toddler responds to the Strange Situation's sequence of separations and reunions with mother and stranger in a manner that is largely consistent with one of the three types of attachment in terms of orientation, attention, and behavior.

Researchers, however, found some children could not be classified using the Ainsworth system. A critical breakthrough in attachment theory came with the recognition by Main and Solomon in 1986 that there was a fourth, highly pathological, attachment style now known as disorganized/disoriented or type D attachment (Main & Solomon, 1986). They described infants and toddlers who entered trance-like states, exhibited disorganized or contradictory response patterns of alternating approach and avoidance, or uttered bizarre vocalizations upon the mother's return.

Although the behaviors manifest by type D children range from dazed immobility to bizarre movements, postures, and noises, they manifest a common pattern of multiple contradictory and self-conflicting responses to interactions with their primary caretaker. It often appears as if a type D child is rapidly switching between two or more distinct modes (states) of relating to his mother, but is unable to lock into a single, consistent relational pattern. Alternatively, in the case of frozen and trance states, it is as if she becomes paralyzed by an internal conflict among different ways of relating to the parent.

Other researchers, notably Dante Cicchetti and colleagues at the Mt. Hope Center in Rochester, NY, found that maltreated preschoolers had extremely high rates of type D attachment (e.g., Cicchetti & Barnett, 1991). The contribution maltreatment makes toward developing a type D attachment greatly outweighs the summed effects of the next five risk factors (Cyr, Euser, Bakermans-Kranenburg, & Van IJzendororn, 2010). During the last two decades, researchers discovered that infants and toddlers with type D attachment frequently grew up to become children and adolescents with serious emotional and behavioral problems. Type D children also respond to stress differently, usually more extremely, than securely attached children.

The discovery of biological problems in children with attachment problems is not unexpected given that John Bowlby (1907–1990), a British psychiatrist, who first described attachment, regarded it as an instinctive biological process. Some studies even find that when compared with securely attached children, type D children show virtually opposite biological and behavioral responses to separation and reunion with their caregivers (e.g., Oosterman, De Schipper, Fisher, Dozier, & Schuengel, 2010). When stressed, these children show the largest increase in stress hormones such as cortisol and the greatest changes in heart rates. Overreaction and skewing of biological stress responses is thought to contribute to the impulse control and behavioral problems prevalent among type D children.

The search to identify the cause of type D attachments points to disturbed maternal behaviors. In 1990, Main and Hesse proposed that *"frightened and/or frightening"* parental behavior associated with the parent's own unresolved experiences of trauma, caused the child's type D attachment behaviors (Main & Hesse, 1990). Later studies by Main, Lyons-Ruth and others found consistent evidence that certain ways parents interacted with their children were highly associated with their infants showing type D behaviors.

In particular, Lyons-Ruth found that a mother's *"Hostile-Helpless"* state of mind (as coded by the Adult Attachment Interview (see Chapter 6)) and a characteristic pattern of disrupted mother-infant communication were associated with borderline, dissociative and conduct problems when the child became an adult. These mothers sent contradictory cues and distressing double messages to their infants. They invited their child to join them and then moved away from the child. They did not respond or would respond inappropriately to distress in their babies. At times they seemed to be confused or frightened by their own infants. They aggressively teased, mocked, and physically intimated their babies. At other times, they needed their baby to reassure them, reversing the role of parent and child. They might suddenly begin acting seductively, talking to their baby in a hushed and intimate manner. When they held their baby it would be with stiff arms out away from their bodies (Lyons-Ruth, Brofman, & Parson, 1999). Liotti observes:

> *It is noteworthy that parents' unresolved states of mind can induce fright without solution and dissociative reactions in the infant **even when the parent's behavior does not obviously constitute maltreatment** [emphasis in the original]. For instance, while seemingly trying to sooth the infant's cry, an unresolved parent approaches her child from behind, sliding both hands around the infant's neck; other parents freeze, with a "dead" stare, unblinking, in the face of the infant's cry for help; some parents manifest a paradoxically differential attitude towards the infant; still others seem to seek safety and comfort from the infant, in a patent inversion of the attachment relationship* (Liotti, 2004, pp. 477–478).

Main and Hesse's hypothesis that these abnormal behaviors result from unresolved early trauma and loss has been partially confirmed by a number of studies (Liotti, 2004). Most of all, it is the severity of maltreatment, especially sexual abuse, and exposure to family violence that best predicts a mother's Hostile-Helpless state of mind—and that in turn, is strongly associated with type D attachment in her children (Lyons-Ruth, Yellin, & Atwood, 2003).

Building on a theoretical article by Peter Barach (1991) conceptualizing multiple personality disorder as a form of attachment disorder, Giovanni Liotti (1992) proposed that type D disorganized attachment in infancy led to a dissociative disorder in later life (Barach, 1991; Liotti, 1992). This hypothesis, that type D disorganized/disoriented attachment is an early precursor of later dissociative disorders, has subsequently received support from two prospective studies following type D children from infancy into late adolescence.

The Minnesota Mother-Child Project followed children born to mothers recruited during their third trimester from public health clinics. These mothers were considered at high risk for the poor development and treatment of their children as a result of poverty, lack of education, young age, and single parenthood. The child's attachment category was assessed during the second year of life. Dissociation in the children was measured using a subscale from the Child Behavioral Checklist (CBCL), a well-researched measure of child behavioral problems. The outcome measure was the Dissociative Experiences Scale (DES-II) administered at age 19 years (Carlson, 1998; Ogawa, Sroufe, Weinfield, Carlson, & Egeland, 1997).

Type D disorganized/disoriented attachment was consistently associated with dissociation as rated by their teachers during three periods of the child's development (30–64 months, grades 1–6, age 16–17) and as self-reported on the DES at age 19 years (Ogawa et al., 1997). The combination of a type D attachment and later trauma during adolescence was the best predictor of pathological dissociation at age 19. Three of the adolescents were formally diagnosed with a dissociative disorder.

Similarly following high risk families in the Harvard Family Pathways Study, Karlen Lyons-Ruth (2008) and colleagues found that maternal behavior, especially problems with maternal communication and emotional flatness, was associated with disorganized attachment at age 14 months and ultimately predicted high dissociation scores at age 20 years (Lyons-Ruth, 2008). Indeed, they note that,

> *"Objectively assessed quality of early care in the first 18 months of life accounted for approximately half of the variability in young adult dissociative symptoms assessed 20 years later, a surprisingly large portion of the variance over such a long time-span"* (Dutra, Bureau, Holmes, Lyubchik, & Lyons-Ruth, 2009 p. 387).

What is remarkable about both long-term studies is that attachment measured during the first two years of a child's life powerfully predicted emotional, behavioral and psychiatric problems almost two decades later. Teachers were already noticing differences in these children by second grade, including more sadness, anxiety, and social withdrawal (Lyons-

Ruth, 2008). If we, as a society, should so choose, we have ways to identify high-risk mothers and children at an early stage.

What kinds of parents do type D children become in turn? We have some preliminary evidence: they become parents who are at great risk of recreating the same dysfunctional child rearing patterns as their parents—putting their own children at risk for repeating the cycle in yet another generation.

The Minnesota Mother-Child Study found that the best predictor of which high-risk mothers did **not** have a maltreated child (neglected or abused by them or another household member) was whether the mother had talked with someone about her own childhood trauma. It did not matter to whom the mother told her story. It was the act of talking about—and thereby openly acknowledging—what had happened to her that reinforced a mother's effort to prevent the same thing from happening to her children.

They hypothesized that it was the mother's level of dissociation, not her history of child abuse per se, that perpetuated the cycle of maltreatment across generations (Egeland & Susman-Stillman, 1996). Findings from our own multi-generational longitudinal study of sexually abused girls support this observation. We found that the mother's current dissociation score on the DES-II, as well as her self-reported history of being punitively parented as a child, predicted whether she would parent her children in a positive or harsh fashion (Kim, Trickett, & Putnam, 2010). Mothers with high levels of dissociation were significantly more likely to be harsh, punitive parents; whereas mothers with low levels of dissociation were more likely to be positive parents.

Passing down dysfunction from parent to child is not inevitable. Indeed, most abused children do not grow up to become abusing parents. But the children of parents who were abused as children are at markedly increased risk (Putnam-Hornstein, Cederbaum, King, Eastman, & Trickett, 2015; Widom, Czaja, & DuMont, 2015). A critical factor is the mother's own dissociative symptoms. Mothers with increased dissociation are at higher risk for continuing the generational cycle of family violence and dysfunction as they raise their own children.

While dissociation is not the only cause of intergenerational maltreatment and family dysfunction, it is a powerful risk factor that can be targeted with Parent-Child Interaction Therapy (PCIT) or Child-Parent Psychotherapy (CPP). These therapies work to improve the bond between mother and child relationship as well as help mothers address their own histories of trauma and family dysfunction.

It has taken about two decades of research (or one generation of type D children becoming adults) to sketch out this intergenerational picture. It will take at least another decade or two to determine how well our current interventions work to prevent or correct this generational cycle of family dysfunction. Unfortunately, it is difficult to convince public or private funders to invest in projects that take decades to see if they pay off.

TRAUMATIC IDENTITY STATES

Children subjected to repeated ACEs will grow up to become adults with painful, shameful and disowned identity states that shape a disorganized, fragmented, and conflicted sense of self. When confronted with traumatic reminders, their emotions are likely to swing rapidly, their reasoning may derail, their behavior can spin out of control. They will have trouble learning from experience and forming healthy relationships. They will have trouble assessing a social situation and determining how to best fit in and make things work with others. They dislike—perhaps even hate— and distrust themselves. They will also kill themselves (deliberately and accidentally) at much, much higher rates than people with no ACEs.

If you think about it, much of children's fantasy play involves altering their sense of identity. When children pretend to be firemen, cowboys, or astronauts or dress-up, it is about becoming someone or something else. When children play with dolls, stuffed animals, or action figures, they infuse their toys with personalities, and then they set those personalities into motion in their make-believe world. When they draw people or animals, make up stories, or just sit and daydream, the people and creatures in their creations have names, identities, and character attributes. And children experience themselves as if in some sort of relationship with their pretend identities and make believe characters. Young children are primed to create and explore different aspects of identity. It is part of a primal need to find out who we are and who we might become.

As a result of who and what they are exposed to, children learn to create the identities that fit the realities of their lives. In the case of abused and traumatized children, they have powerful needs to create identities that protect them and minimize their pain. But they must also create identities that avail themselves of whatever nurturing their abusive caretakers may be capable of providing. Children are desperate for attachment, healthy or otherwise.

Because of this, abused children often have an unstable sense of their identity. They are unsure of who they really are. They don't know or understand themselves. And they don't trust themselves to act in their own best interests. Victims of child abuse typically have poor self-esteem and describe feelings of self-loathing and self-hatred. They often have mercurial moods and angrily explode for trivial reasons. They don't seem able to use what they know. They are poor at recognizing basic social patterns of cause and effect in daily life and thus continually repeat past mistakes. And they are also prone to use alcohol or drugs to manage their negative moods and painful memories as well as cope with stressful situations.

For abused children there is far less incentive to bridge their state-dependent learning and memory (SDLM) discontinuities with their incongruities in sense of self. For most children, it is a good thing to increase self-awareness and improve control over their behavior; for abused children, integrating different aspects of self means confronting emotionally disturbing material. It makes good psychological sense to evade anxiety and pain by avoiding the mental leaps needed to unify fragments of identity into a more unified personality. This is why victims of child abuse are often diagnosed with psychiatric disorders such as borderline personality disorder and dissociative identity disorders characterized by fragmentation in their sense of self.

MULTIPLE PERSONALITY AND THE DISSOCIATIVE DISORDERS

Multiple personality, now called dissociative identity disorder (DID), is an extreme result of early childhood trauma—and a prime example of how repeated trauma early in life can produce a fragmented adult personality.

DID is characterized by the presence of two or more identity (aka alter) personality states that recurrently take control of the person's behavior. When in one identity, a person may have partial or complete amnesia for his behavior in another identity state. The person's different identities usually have persistent and distinctive attributes including age, gender, predominant emotion, values, attitudes and goals that often conflict with each other. Different identities arise in specific contexts, so that people who know and interact with a person in only one setting are often unaware of his other identities.

People who live their lives switching among a set of dissociated identities have always been with us. It is possible—especially given the often short and brutal lives of people over the history of our species—that humankind was more often multiple than not. This unified sense of self, this unique and special *ME* that most of us cherish, may reflect a relatively late development in the ongoing evolution of human psyches. One might speculate that the emergence of a singular sense of self was at least partially a product of the Renaissance and reflects a modern Western conceptualization of personality. Not every culture fosters the heightened sense of individuality that ours does.

As a formal psychiatric disorder, multiple personality has been with us for well over 200 years. Cases of dual and multiple personality were among the first psychiatric conditions to be described in the medical literature. Explaining the nature of the altered states of consciousness and different identities seen in multiple personality became a central challenge for the rapidly emerging fields of psychology and psychiatry towards the end of the nineteenth century. Indeed, until about 1930 the number of case reports of multiple personality outnumbered those of schizophrenia in the psychiatric literature (Rosenbaum, 1980).

DISSOCIATION AND THE ADVENT
OF MODERN PSYCHIATRY

Nineteenth-Century Hysteria

The idea that a traumatic experience could somehow produce a splitting of a person's consciousness that, in turn, caused the patient's psychiatric symptoms became increasingly accepted by late nineteenth-century psychiatry. This splitting of consciousness was thought to be the cause of a mental disorder known then as hysteria. Today the word *hysteria* is used as an epithet. At the end of the nineteenth century it was a respected psychiatric diagnosis.

A young Sigmund Freud went to Paris in 1885–1886, where he encountered the formidable influence of Jean-Martin Charcot (1825–1893), whom he called "*the great French observer*" (Freud, 1955 p. 18), as well as other luminaries in French psychiatry, possibly including Charcot's famous protégé, Pierre Janet. We cannot be certain that Freud and Janet ever met. Freud may have attended a reading of Janet's paper on his patient, Leonie, which catapulted Janet to instant fame.

Charcot was the Director of the Salpêtrière, the French insane asylum in which Philippe Pinel (1745–1826) freed the insane women from their chains and took the first steps on the long road towards more humane care of the mentally ill. Then at the height of his career, Charcot—known as the "Napoleon of Neuroses,"—dominated the emerging discipline of modern psychiatry.

On Fridays Charcot gave dramatic public demonstrations held in a 400-seat auditorium in which female patients swooned on his command, became catatonic, or exhibited other "hysterical" symptoms. Foreign dignitaries, celebrities and distinguished scholars considered attending one of Charcot's performances at the Salpêtrière, then the leading medical institution in the Western world, an essential experience when visiting Paris. Following his sudden death in 1893, Charcot would be accused of inducing these hysterical symptoms through the power of suggestion.

Asti Hustvedt provides a more sympathetic picture of Charcot as a clinician and scientist who firmly believed in the neurological nature of hysteria (although he could not find a physical cause) (Hustvedt, 2011). While some physicians under his authority performed unethical "experiments" or were sexually involved with their patients, Charcot treated patients with respect and, on occasion, kindness.

The contemporary painting, *A Lecture in the Dispensary at La Salpêtrière* (1887) by M. Andre Brouillet, shows a bulldog-like Professor Charcot standing beside a swooning patient (Ms. Blanche Wittmann) in front of an enraptured audience that is a who's-who of late nineteenth-century French psychiatry—although Pierre Janet, still a student, is absent. A painting at the back of the room, showing a patient similarly swooning, symbolizes the power of suggestion. Note Ms. Wittmann's twisted arms and backward bent wrists, a classic sign of hysteria in that era. The eroticization of hysteria is implicit in the falling blouse and the doctor's hand (Joseph Babinski—known for his discovery of the plantar reflex) near her breast. The windows look into the courtyard where Pinel unshackled the insane women. An immense artistic and commercial success at the time, a copy hung above Freud's desk in Vienna and later over his oriental rug-covered, analytic couch in London.

Figure 8-1 *A Lecture in the Dispensary at La Salpêtrière*
André Brouillet (1887)

Pierre Janet

Scholars regard the work of Charcot's student Pierre Janet with hysterical patients as the foundation for modern dissociation theory. Born in Paris in 1859, Janet grew up in turbulent times under Napoleon III and lived through the two world wars, dying in 1947. At age 15 he experienced a period of crisis and depression that changed his life, transforming him from a mediocre student to a respected scholar, innovative scientist, and sensitive clinician.

In 1882 Janet heard Charcot's famous presentation, which sought to reclaim hypnosis as a legitimate scientific subject from the wreckage of Mesmerism. Fascinated, he soon was studying hysterical patients in a local hospital ward, which he jokingly called the *Salle Saint-Charcot* (French hospital wards were frequently named for saints).

Researching hysterical symptoms, Janet discovered that the early Magnetizers had already described everything that Charcot reported to have discovered (Ellenberger, 1970). He concluded that Charcot's dramatic public demonstrations influenced the patient to conform to the audience's expectations. As a result, Janet imposed a strict set of rules upon his research. He would see all of his patients alone to avoid having the reactions of others influence the patient. He would carefully record everything that the patient said and did (which he referred to as his "fountain pen" method). Drawing on these careful investigations Janet began to cautiously articulate a dissociative theory of hysteria and develop a model for its treatment, which he called Psychological Analysis.

Janet believed that traumatic events and frightening experiences created "subconscious fixed ideas" (he coined the word *subconscious*) which were expressed through hysterical symptoms. Janet theorized that the patient's hysterical symptoms and dramatic crises were, in fact, disguised or symbolic reenactments of subconscious fixed ideas derived from the traumatic events that gave rise to them. The fixed subconscious ideas created divisions within the person's consciousness that became semi-autonomous entities capable of independent behavior. Janet called these entities successive existences.

He treated his patients by uncovering the nature of the traumatic fixed idea underlying the patient's symptoms and replacing it with a more tolerable idea or a transformed memory. He believed that merely making the fixed idea conscious was not enough, as it was likely to lead to an obsessive neurosis in which the patient ruminated on what had been revealed. Instead, Janet would try to transform memories of the traumatic event into a more benign recollection.

Seeking to discover subconscious fixed ideas, Janet experimented with a range of psychotherapy techniques. He used hypnosis extensively, but also investigated automatic writing in which the patient allowed her hand to write in a mindless fashion. He pioneered automatic talking, similar to what later became known as free association. Janet emphasized the important role that the doctor-patient relationship played in finding and changing the traumatic experiences that evoked the fixed ideas. The early Magnetizers first described the function of the doctor-patient rapport in curing symptoms. It would later be appropriated and revised by Freud as transference, in which the patient acts out early relationship problems within the therapist-patient relationship.

In therapy sessions, Janet would sometimes join his patients as they relived their frightening experiences and rework their traumatic memories with his suggestions. In the case of *Justine*, for example, he used hypnotic suggestions to progressively transform her terrifying memory of a diseased and naked corpse into the image of a comically clothed Chinese general, who gets up and acts silly. After eliminating a traumatic fixed idea, Janet prescribed educational exercises such as reading and mathematics to strengthen the patient's intellect, as he thought that the power of these fixed ideas reflected an intrinsic weakness in a patient's mental capacities.

At the start of the twentieth century, Janet's fame was at its peak. Many assumed that he would found a new school of psychology. He started an institute devoted to advancing the science of psychology that boasted an international board of famed advisors, including William James. Yet within a few years, Janet's institute failed and his theories were abandoned.

Sigmund Freud

The events that led to the decline of Janet and the corresponding rise of Sigmund Freud were set in motion by the publication of *Studies on Hysteria* in May 1895 (Breuer & Freud, 1957). The publication of *Studies* is widely regarded as the beginning of psychoanalysis (Ellenberger, 1970).

Coauthored with Josef Breuer, *Studies* articulates the prevailing late nineteenth-century psychological theories on the traumatic nature of hysterical symptoms. Janet can claim to have said much of this first, but Breuer and Freud say it more clearly (at least in the English translation). Although they scatter brief mentions of Janet throughout the book, they cite him in support of their theories rather than as the originator.

At first Janet responded positively to *Studies,* but then became increasingly hostile as he perceived Breuer and Freud taking sole credit for having discovered the cause of hysterical symptoms and inventing psychotherapy. He fought back, writing scathing reviews of Freud's work and contemptuous critiques of psychoanalysis in general. In one article, Janet sarcastically observed that he was "*happy to see that the results of my already old findings have been recently confirmed by two German authors, Breuer and Freud*" (Taylor, 1982 p. 63).

In response, Freud became increasingly condescending towards Janet and remained silent as his disciples accused Janet of plagiarizing Freud's ideas. Yet when Freud was criticized at a French scientific meeting held on the eve of World War I, Janet rose to defend him despite the anti-German sentiment permeating France.

Many years later, Janet wrote to Freud that he was coming to Vienna and would like to meet him. Freud replied that when he received Janet's letter, he had considered writing back that he would be away, but had instead decided to tell Janet directly that he did not care to meet him. There is no further record of contact between the two men. For the next half century, Freudian psychoanalysis would dominate psychiatric theory and practice. Janet outlived Freud, but his treatment of *psychological analysis* became a mere footnote—though we owe much to Janet's observations and theories about the effects of trauma on the psyche.

William James also reacted to *Studies on Hysteria* in a series of public lectures titled *Exceptional Mental States*. Commenting on Breuer and Freud's claim of discovering a "talking cure," he declared that he has already published a paper describing the method.

> *"The cure is to draw the psychic traumata out in hypnotism, let them produce all their emotional effects, however violent, and **work themselves off** [Emphasis in the original]. They make then a new connection with the principal consciousness, whose breach is thus restored and the sufferer gets well"* (Taylor, 1982 p. 65).

Hypnoid States

In the words of Breuer and Freud, *Studies* is a book about "*abnormal states of consciousness*" (Breuer & Freud, 1957 p.12). The essence of Breuer and Freud's theory of hysteria is that traumatic events that usually happen in childhood give rise to what they label hypnoid states, which "*intrude into waking life in the form of hysterical symptoms*" (Breuer & Freud, 1957 p. 13):

> *The longer we have been occupied with these phenomena* [hysterical symptoms] *the more we have become convinced that the splitting of consciousness which is so striking in the well-known classical cases under the form of 'double conscience' is present to a rudimentary degree in every hysteria, and that a tendency to such a dissociation, and with it the emergence of abnormal states of consciousness (which we shall bring together under the term 'hypnoid') is the basic phenomenon of this neurosis.* (Breuer & Freud, 1957 p. 12)

One of the most often quoted observations from their book is "*Hysterics suffer mainly from reminiscences* (Breuer & Freud, 1957 p. 7). In the introduction, Breuer and Freud express great surprise and delight in their discovery that each hysterical symptom "*immediately and permanently disappeared*" (Breuer & Freud, 1957 p. 6) when the traumatic memory of the event that provoked it was finally recalled and examined in the greatest possible detail, translating the emotions into words. They refer to this therapeutic process both as catharsis and as abreaction. They say that traumatic experiences produce unique kinds of memories that take the form of *hypnoid* or abnormal states of consciousness that hover largely outside of normal awareness—as a result they preserve an unprocessed vividness and emotional intensity.

Fräulein Anna O

Breuer and Freud provide a series of treatment case histories to support their observations, the most famous of all is the patient known as Fräulein Anna O. Anna was Breuer's patient, whom he had treated more than a decade (beginning in 1880) before he and Freud published *Studies.* She was twenty-one when she first came to medical attention suffering from blurred vision and intermittent paralysis of her right arm and both legs. Soon other symptoms appeared. She had trouble speaking and was revolted by the sight of food. As her behavior became increasing erratic, she complained of having two selves—one real and one evil. In desperation, Breuer examined her. He confirmed two states. In the first state Anna was normal, though anxious and depressed. In the second, she hallucinated and could become vicious, abusive and destructive.

Using hypnosis, Breuer probed for details. It became clear that two distinct mental states existed side by side but were unaware of each other. Anna would rapidly change from one state to another, particularly when she was confronted with the sight of an orange, which reminded her of her father's fatal illness during the year prior to her own deterioration. She had been his devoted nurse, remaining at his bedside for days at a time sustaining herself by eating oranges.

In her normal state Anna spoke in French, Italian, and her native German. In her abnormal state, she spoke in English or a garbled mixture of multiple languages. At times, another part of Anna reported being aware of her erratically changing behavior and described itself as a *"clear-sighted and calm observer sitting in the corner of her brain and looking on at all the mad business"* (p. 46).

Breuer treated her with hypnosis and psychotherapy for about 18 months. It was Anna who first used the term *"talking therapy"* to describe her treatment. She also referred to it as *"chimney sweeping."* In 1882 Breuer suddenly terminated his treatment of Anna, reportedly at the insistence of his wife, who felt that he was becoming much too involved with his attractive young patient. Anna was hospitalized several times after that, but by 1889 she was well enough to resume an active and eventful life. What makes Anna so interesting is that we now know who she was and what she accomplished in the years following her treatment.

Anna O was Bertha Pappenheim, a pioneering social worker and an aggressive advocate for women's rights. She was renowned for her fearless raids into brothels in Eastern Europe and Russia to free women held as sex slaves. Under the pseudonym Paul Berthold, she wrote stories, plays and essays that attacked the sexual exploitation of women. She founded a women's rights organization and ultimately confronted the Nazis, dying of cancer in 1936 shortly after an interrogation by the Gestapo regarding anti-Hitler remarks.

All the while, she carried on a full and rich second life as a member of the cultural and artistic bourgeois of Vienna. She collected lace, china, and glassware. She wrote short stories, children's tales, travelogues, and translated ancient Jewish texts. Friends marveled at her "double life" as a radical feminist and as an aristocratic member of an elite social circle. It is said—but difficult to verify—that when she died, she left two wills—each written in a different hand.

Studies, with its central case of *Anna O,* transformed psychiatry. But within a year of the publication of their landmark book, Breuer and Freud became estranged over differing interpretations of Anna's case, and parted ways. A second edition appeared in 1908 with dueling prefaces written by each man. Breuer says that he "*could add nothing fresh to what was written in 1895*" (Breuer & Freud, 1957 p. xxxi).

Freud agrees to republishing the 1895 text unaltered only because:

"*. . . my views during the course of thirteen years of work have been too far-reaching for it to be possible to attach them to my earlier exposition without entirely destroying its essential character*" (Breuer & Freud, 1957 p. xxxi).

In other words, he had changed his mind so completely that it was not possible to connect his current theories with his earlier ideas in *Studies.* Thus Freud recommends the book only to those interested in learning how "catharsis" evolved into psychoanalysis and thus "*. . . follow the path which I myself have trodden*" (Breuer & Freud, 1957 p. xxxi).

Freud's Seduction Theory of Hysteria

It is well known that Freud initially theorized that hysterical symptoms in female patients were caused (in the language of the time) by being "seduced" by their fathers. In April of 1896, shortly after publication of *Studies,* Freud presents a paper, "The Etiology of Hysteria," at a meeting of the local society of Psychiatry and Neurology. He boldly proposes that childhood sexual abuse is the cause of hysterical symptoms. Invoking the metaphor of an archaeologist exploring a half-buried ancient city, he urges the audience to dig for the truth.

Believing that he has solved this ancient riddle and, in his words, shown his colleagues *"the source of the Nile,"* he is stunned by their cold response. The distinguished chairman of the meeting, Baron Krafft-Ebing, promptly pronounces Freud's theory a *"scientific fairytale"* (Ellenberger, 1970 p. 448). In a letter to his closest friend, Wilhelm Fliess, Freud ruminates on his *"icy reception from the donkeys"* concluding, *"They can all go to hell"* (Masson, 1984).

Yet, little more than a year later, Freud seems to come to a similar conclusion—writing to Fliess (9/21/1897) that he has lost faith in his seduction theory. *"Let me tell you straight away the great secret which has been slowly dawning on me in recent months. I no longer believe in my **neurotica**. [Bold is italics in original] (S. Freud, 1897/1954 p. 215). Freud details a number of "factors" that led him to reject the seduction hypothesis. The first being his recurrent failure to bring his psychoanalytic treatments to a therapeutic closure.

> *Then there was the astonishing thing that in every case . . . blame was laid on perverse acts by the father, and realization of the unexpected frequency of hysteria, in every case of which the same thing applied, though it was hardly credible that perverted acts against children were so general* (Freud, 1897/1954 pp. 215–216).

Rather than feeling chagrined at his "mistaken" seduction theory of hysteria, Freud concludes that his error is just one more step along the road to a better understanding:

> *Now I do not know where I am, as I have failed to reach theoretical understanding of repression and its play of forces.*
> *Were I depressed, jaded, unclear in my mind, such doubts*

might be taken for signs of weakness. But as I am in just the opposite state, I must acknowledge them to be the result of honest and effective intellectual labour, and I am proud that after penetrating so far I am still capable of such criticism. Can these doubts be only an episode on the way to further knowledge? (Freud, 1897/1954 pp. 216–217).

Freud wondered how so many women could have been sexually abused by their fathers without anyone noticing? Could he really trust his patients' memories of their childhood? Freud soon came to regard such reports as fantasies. Rather than being seduced by their fathers—these girls were actually fantasizing about seducing their fathers. The incestuous impulses resided in the young girls, not in their fathers. Of course, we now know that at least one in every five (20%) U.S. women report a history of childhood sexual abuse—usually by a family member.

Although distrusting his patients' memories of their childhoods, Freud becomes increasingly focused on his own childhood as the source of data for his theories about psychosexual development (see Chapter 6). It was during this period that Freud conducted his famous "self analysis," a feat that—according to admirers—has never been duplicated. He wrote to Fliess, ". . . *the main patient who keeps me busy is myself*" (Ellenberger, 1970 p. 446).

In this self-analysis Freud sought to examine every aspect of his mental life—his dreams, his fantasies, his memories, his desires, his neurotic symptoms and his inhibitions. The culmination of this period of intense introspection was the publication of his seminal book, *The Interpretation of Dreams* (1900) (Freud, 1913). This is the underpinning of Freudian theory, as we know it today. And, it is largely based on Freud's theories about his own psychosexual development.

In 1905, Freud publicly rejected his seduction theory of hysteria. Subsequent generations of psychoanalysts blindly accept Freud's formulation that childhood memories of incest are actually the disguised sexual fantasies of young girls about their fathers. Tragically, I have read this erroneous formulation in the psychiatric case notes of young women who attempted suicide after being told that their allegations of incest were really only their sexual fantasies.

Fortunately the story does not end there. In 1984, Jeffery Masson startled the psychoanalytic world by filling in the missing sections of Freud's letters deleted by his daughter, Anna Freud. As Director of the

Freud Archives, Masson had unrestricted access to all of Freud's private letters including his correspondence with Fliess during that critical period. In letters to Fliess and later ones to Freud's late-life confidant, Sándor Ferenczi, Masson found evidence that Freud's thinking about the reality of incest was more far complicated than the public record reflected.

Despite what he said publicly, it appears that Freud continued to privately hold out the possibility that these women were telling the truth. Their fathers had in fact, sexually abused them. When Masson confronted Anna Freud about the pattern of deletions in her father's letters, she defended the editing as necessary to prevent doubt in readers about his ultimate rejection of the seduction theory of hysteria (Masson, 1984).

Blindly following Freud's lead—as many orthodox Freudians seem to want to do—the field of psychoanalysis rejected hypnoid states, catharsis, abreaction and divided consciousness along with the sexual seduction theory of hysteria. In their place, they embraced theories such as infantile psychosexual symbolism, ego defense mechanisms, forbidden wishes expressed in dreams and fantasies, and the repression of memories and affects as the casual mechanisms for their patients' symptoms. They ceased to see—with a few notable exceptions—the divided consciousness and multiple identities of some under their care.

Multiple personality disorder (now Dissociative Identity Disorder), however, continued to exist as a psychiatric diagnosis after Freud's rejection. But it no longer was at the center of psychological inquiry and clinical interest. Rather, cases of multiple personality continued to be reported—but usually in the vein of a medical oddity discovered by accident. Many of these case reports have a *"you will never believe what I found"* incredulous quality that reinforced a growing sense that such patients were exceedingly rare freaks of nature—if not outright frauds. A few clinicians, most notably a group at the University of Kentucky in Lexington headed by the distinguished departmental chair, Arnold Ludwig, and including Cornelia Wilbur, later of *Sybil* fame, continued to publish careful case reports of multiple personality patients. These included some of the first scientific data that demonstrated physiological differences across personality states.

Similar to the recognition that the DSM-III brought to PTSD, the pivotal event that reinvigorated the recognition of multiple personality disorder was the publication of the DSM-III in 1980 (American Psychiatric Association, 1980). Although the diagnosis of multiple personality was included in all of the prior versions of the DSM, the articulation of a clear clinical profile in the DSM-III helped clinicians to see the dissociative disorder patients whom they were mistakenly treating as if they were suffering from conditions like schizophrenia and bipolar illness. As a result, the 1980s saw a dramatic rise in multiple personality cases diagnosed. Researchers began to publish quantitative studies of the disorder based on evaluations of dozens to a hundred or more patients.

The research all pointed to early childhood trauma as a cause of multiple personality (dissociative identity) disorder. Most adult patients reported histories of horrendous childhood physical and sexual abuse, neglect, and often what amounted to systematic torture by their caretakers, mainly parents. These memories were typically restricted to specific identity states—often the very same ones that caused major life problems through self-destructive and risk-taking behaviors.

Constellations of alter identity states—a host, protectors, personalities of the opposite sex, and child personalities—regularly surfaced in treatment. Therapists found they often fulfilled similar roles in patients' lives. Laboratory studies found consistent physiological differences across the alter personality states of a given patient (See Chapter 4). But this research also found evidence for other physiological and psychological continuities that crossed identity states and thus contradict the alter personalities' claims of total separateness.

Approaches to treating these newly recognized cases of multiple personality (the condition was renamed Dissociative Identity Disorder (DID) in the 1994 DSM-IV (American Psychiatric Association, 1994)) coalesced around a trauma-focused psychotherapy that drew inspiration from Janet, Freud, as well as the World War II abreactive treatments for combat neurosis. The articulation of this treatment approach to MPD largely paralleled but rarely intersected with the simultaneously emerging treatments for the newly minted diagnosis of PTSD.

Despite developing in parallel, treatments for these two trauma-related conditions (PTSD and MPD/DID) remain conceptually distinct. With few exceptions, authorities in each area rejected the other side as failing to "see" the essential clinical phenomena considered to be the source of the patient's problems. However, as demonstrated by the brain imaging studies discussed in Chapter 7, there is growing evidence supporting the existence of a dissociative subtype of PTSD (Lanius et al., 2010; Spiegel, 2010).

PTSD therapists and researchers typically focus on the hyperarousal and avoidant symptoms. Dissociation and amnesias for traumatic events are noted, but not specifically targeted for treatment. In contrast, therapists in the MPD/DID camp focused on re-experiencing symptoms, amnesias for traumatic memories, and, of course, the existence of alter identity states.

Both groups founded professional societies, The International Society for Traumatic Stress Studies (ISTSS) [1985] and the International Society for the Study of Multiple Personality and Dissociation (ISSMP&D) [1984]—later renamed the International Society for the Study of Trauma and Dissociation (ISSTD) [1994]. Membership was largely separate and remains so today. This professional divide is a revealing example of the much larger problem of the compartmentalization of trauma-related disorders and types of trauma, often further subdivided by profession.

RESISTANCE TO THE DIAGNOSIS OF MULTIPLE PERSONALITY/DISSOCIATIVE IDENTITY DISORDER

Satanic Ritual Abuse

In the late 1980s to mid-1990s, the dissociative disorders field experienced a major schism around the question of whether satanic cults existed that were responsible for the horrendous "ritualistic" abuse reported by a relatively few DID patients. "Satanic" patients dramatically described being forced to participate in demonic cult rituals including eating their own newborn infants and suffering massive sexual abuse perpetrated by entire congregations of Satan worshipers, who masqueraded as upstanding citizens by day. Therapists working with these "satanic" cases frequently seemed to lose their objectivity, becoming strong advocates for their patient's version of events. Notwithstanding the lack of credible independent evidence for the widespread existence of baby-eating satanic cults, the popular media often featured such patients—usually together with their therapist who vouched for the claims. Dramatic books about such cases, frequently jointly coauthored by patient and therapist, sold well.

A number of us warned publicly and privately against the proliferation of these unsupported allegations of baby rape and human sacrifice and questioned the ethics of sensational first-person accounts cowritten with their therapists (e.g., Putnam, 1991). We were not successful. Ultimately, a series of hefty malpractice settlements and professional censure put a damper on the satanic ritual abuse movement, but such claims continue to be made by a few patients and their therapists. Although examples of individuals or small groups (e.g., Charles Manson) practicing "satanic" rituals exist, no allegations of large-scale satanic cult abuse have ever been independently substantiated.

False Memory Syndrome

Predictably, a backlash developed that, for complicated reasons, became focused around what is referred to as false memory syndrome. This pseudoscientific "syndrome"—for which there is no clinical or experimental evidence—has been aggressively advanced by the False Memory Syndrome Foundation (FMSF), founded by Peter and Pamela Freyd in 1992 after their eldest daughter accused her father of childhood sexual abuse. Other family members support her allegations (Whitfield, 1995).

A major critic of the diagnosis of Dissociative Identity Disorder and a member of the FMSF Advisory Board is Paul McHugh of Johns Hopkins University. Dr. McHugh and I have debated the validity of the diagnosis of MPD/DID in person and in print.

In one instance, Dr. McHugh opens his side of the debate with the rhetorical question, *"Where's hysteria now that we need it?"* (McHugh & Putnam, 1995 p. 957). His major thesis is that individuals with DID/MPD are "hysterical" in that they are assuming a "sick role" that is being wittingly or unwittingly suggested by their therapists when they interact with the person's alter personality states. McHugh writes:

Such an identification can provide these "sick" individuals with certain social privileges, i.e., rest, freedom from employment, and support from others during the reign of the condition (McHugh & Putnam, 1995 p. 957).

Interestingly, Dr. McHugh cites Charcot's public demonstrations as central to the origin of multiple personality. However, he views this history through the eyes of Charcot's other famous protégée, Joseph Babinski, who assumed leadership of the Salpêtrière following Charcot's sudden death:

Psychiatrists have known about these matters of social and psychological dynamics for more than 100 years. They were brought vividly to attention by the distinguished pupil of Jean-Martin Charcot, Joseph Babinski (he of the plantar response). Like Sigmund Freud and Pierre Janet, Babinski had observed Charcot manage patients with, what Charcot called, "hystero-epilepsy." But Babinski was convinced that hysteroepilepsy was not a new disorder. He believed that the women at Charcot's clinic were being persuaded—and not so subtly—to take on the features of epilepsy by the interest Charcot and his assistants expressed. Babinski also believed that these women were vulnerable to this persuasion because of distressing states of mind provoked in their life circumstances and their roles as intriguing patients and the subject of attention from many distinguished physicians who offered them a haven of care (McHugh & Putnam, 1995 p. 958).

McHugh believes the appropriate therapeutic response is to ignore the alter personalities and other dissociative behaviors and to isolate the patient from people (therapists, friends, family) who reinforce the "sick role" with their attention and fascination. He opines: *"We refuse to talk to "alters" but rather encourage our patients to review their present difficulties, thus applying the concept of "abnormal illness behavior" to their condition"* (McHugh & Putnam, 1995 p. 595).

I countered that the diagnosis of DID should be judged by the same criteria that we set for all other psychiatric disorders. This requires that psychiatric diagnoses satisfy three separate forms of validity: content validity, criterion-related validity, and construct validity (McHugh & Putnam, 1995 p. 961). Content validity requires that there is a specific and highly detailed clinical description of the disorder such that other clinicians can readily recognize the condition. Criterion validity requires that there are specific tests—chemical, imaging, or reliable psychological measures—that are consistent with the clinical picture. Construct validity (sometimes called discriminant validity) requires that the disorder can be reliably distinguished from other disorders.

DID/MPD readily satisfies all three forms of validity. DID/MPD is a well-defined clinical syndrome, specified and detailed both in the DSM criteria and as a distinct, clinical profile that has been replicated many times across international samples by independent investigators. In addition to the brain imaging differences between PTSD and dissociation described in Chapter 7, the core psychopathological process, dissociation, can be detected and measured by a number of well-validated dissociation scales and structured diagnostic interviews satisfying the criterion validity requirement.

In terms of the essential psychometric properties of reliability and validity, dissociation scales and diagnostic interviews are equal to well-accepted measures of depression and anxiety. Using cut-off scores and subscale profiles on dissociation measures; DID/MPD cases can be readily distinguished from other psychiatric conditions thereby satisfying construct (discriminant) validity.

Dr. McHugh and I do agree, however, that whatever the mechanism (fascination or dissociation), affected individuals are truly suffering and in need of effective treatment. In many ways, the argument about the nature of MPD/DID is going to be settled by which treatment approach proves most effective in alleviating symptoms and restoring function in the lives of these individuals.

DID AS AN IDENTITY STATE DISORDER

The Alter Personalities

When you ask the alter personality states about themselves—what they see themselves as, how they came to be, what their role or purpose is? They often talk about either specific life events or recurring situations that brought about their creation. Many of these identity states date back to childhood. Some will have first emerged in the context of a specific trauma; others will have been created to encapsulate reoccurring abuse, such as incest. At least a few will have emerged to take advantage of some nurturing or positive situation and remained to infuse continued hope.

Some of the child alters are frozen in time, remaining forever the age at which they were created. Others grow up to a greater or lesser extent, providing developmental threads that mature over time. Sometimes a number of different versions of nominally the same alter personality emerge, as if psychological development consisted of a series of snapshots rather than a smoother continuum of maturation. Clinically, having many child identity states implies that a person may retreat into severe regression when stressed.

We all have aspects of ourselves that have matured at different rates—and we all have some childish parts of our personality that have not matured in step with the rest of us. What makes people with multiple personality disorder unique is that these different sides of themselves are frequently cut off from each other by SDLM discontinuities in memory and awareness. One identity may know little or nothing about the history and activities of another. Within a given patient there is usually an internal hierarchical organization which determines which identity states can "see" and "monitor" the behaviors of which other identities. Therapists have come to refer to this collection of identity states as the "personality system."

In the nineteenth century, clinicians tried to classify multiple personality cases according to the pattern of self-awareness among the facets of their personality system. They soon gave up, as it became clear that all manner of permutations exist among the identities of MPD/DID patients, and that these internal relationships continuously change with time and treatment.

Frequently a therapist will encounter an identity state that describes itself as able to "see" all of the other identity states—like Anna O's clear-sighted and calm observer sitting in the corner of her brain. This identity state has come to be called, "the internal self-helper" or "Ish," after the fashion of Ralph Allison, one of the therapists bringing attention to the disorder in the late 1970s and early 1980s.

Does every DID patient have an Ish? Is every Ish, all-knowing and wise? I don't know, but split-off parts of dissociative patients often show insight into the patient's behavior and will ally themselves with the therapist around the goals of treatment. These metacognitive fragments are one of the salvations of what are otherwise long and difficult treatments characterized by a roughly upward saw-toothed pattern of improvement and relapse—in much the same way that treatment for an addiction typically proceeds.

Many DID patients have long histories of treatment for other psychiatric diagnoses, notably schizophrenia and bipolar disorder. These treatments seldom worked because they did not address the patient's core problems. Effective treatment of DID requires working with the patient's split-off identities. There is no getting around this if you want to help the person gain more positive control over their personality system writ large. Many of the identity states encapsulate painful memories, which will disturb and disrupt the person's functioning when they are more widely shared across the larger personality system. This must be repeatedly worked through at multiple levels until the person can do this for herself.

How far the patient and therapist progress varies by case and circumstances. A few multiple patients become essentially like the rest of us—more or less self-integrated individuals depending on our current stress level. Others, probably a majority, progress toward greater self-integration but retain clusters of separate identity states. In these cases, decision-making and goal setting occurs through a sort of internal executive committee influenced by the hierarchical dynamics of the individual's personality system. This is often less than a perfect solution, but it usually represents a considerable improvement over life before therapy.

RESEARCH ON THE TREATMENT OF DISSOCIATIVE DISORDERS

Research to determine how effective different DID treatments are faces enormous resistance from many sides. There is a PTSD-only reviewer lobby that blocks funding for dissociative disorder treatment studies at the NIH grant review level. The National Institute of Mental Health also unofficially discourages dissociative disorder treatment research at the program level such that preliminary inquiries about NIMH's interest in potential dissociative disorders treatment studies are quickly nipped in the bud. The status of DID as a legitimate psychiatric disorder is under continual attack by members of the False Memory Syndrome Foundation. As a consequence of all these impediments and controversy, there has been little federal interest and no research funding for the kind of multi-million dollar, gold standard, randomized clinical trials necessary to evaluate the effectiveness of dissociative disorder treatments.

Until recently, the best evidence for the efficacy of dissociative disorder treatment were case series contributed by therapists from their clinical practices. I was among several experts who authored books in the late 1980's and 1990's attempting to distill personal clinical experience into an organized approach to treatment (Putnam, 1989, 1997). In many respects our individual efforts were remarkably congruent. Out of this shared experience, a basic, staged, treatment model emerged—for which many deserve (and claim) credit. While promising, this is a weak form of evidence on which to base an expensive, time-consuming treatment for a seriously impairing and financially costly condition.

The TOP DD Study

Fortunately a foundation, local grants and individuals provided funding for an important prospective, longitudinal study that examined the efficacy of this general staged treatment approach with an international sample of clinicians treating dissociative disorder patients. The Treatment of Patients with Dissociative Disorders (TOP DD) project is run by Professor Bethany Brand and her students at Towson University in Maryland. A Scientific Advisory committee (including myself) helped design and support the study. We've even held a 'bake sale' to support the project. Run on a shoestring budget, the TOP DD study is a naturalistic observational study that followed the treatment courses of dissociative disorder patients (primarily DID patients) over 30 months. The DD patients and their therapists independently completed scales and questionnaires about symptoms and treatment techniques at four time-points, entry into the study, and 6, 18 and 30 months later. See the TOP DD website for a more complete discussion and scientific publications (http://www.towson.edu/topddstudy).

As is true of trauma treatment studies in general, there was substantial attrition over time (226 patients started the study and only 119 remained at 30 months), although the group retained did not differ from the dropouts on critical demographic variables or comorbid psychopathology. Most often patients dropped out of treatment for financial reasons, relocation, or therapist retirement. Participating therapists were largely recruited from the International Society for the Study of Trauma and Dissociation (ISSTD) and included a subgroup that had graduated from the ISSTD's Dissociative Disorder Psychotherapist Training Program. Other mental health therapists treating DD patients were recruited through mental health list serves. Therapists enrolled consenting patients, who independently completed packets of self-report measures that were returned separately to the study staff. Therapists completed their own measures on their patient and themselves. These data were analyzed both cross-sectionally (Brand, Classen, Lanius, et al., 2009) with patients grouped by treatment stage and longitudinally as symptom and behavioral trajectories over 30 months (Brand et al., 2013).

The results of the TOP DD study and a meta-analysis of other DD treatment studies support the general efficacy of the current mainstream approach to treatment of these complex patients. Cross-sectional analyses grouping patients by treatment stage found that both patients and therapists reported that patients in the last stage of treatment had significant improvements in measures of social adaptation and daily function, fewer hospitalizations, and lower levels of PTSD and dissociative symptoms compared with patients in early stages of treatment (Brand, Classen, Lanius, et al., 2009).

The longitudinal analyses revealed significant levels of improvements in dissociation, PTSD, general distress, substance abuse, physical pain, and depression over 30 months for those patients who remained in treatment (Brand et al., 2013). Patients reported increased socialization, returning to school or volunteer work, and generally feeling better. Their therapists reported decreases in self-injurious behaviors, fewer hospitalizations, and increased global functioning on standard measures.

Thus, the TOP DD study found that when classified by treatment stage according to predetermined criteria, dissociative disorder patients in later stages of treatment are significantly better off than those just beginning treatment. When patients in all stages of treatment were followed over the course of two and half years, there were significant improvements with time for most of them. The TOP DD study cannot by itself establish the efficacy of current treatment for dissociative disorders (it lacks a standardized intervention and randomized control group among other things), but it does indicate that the current mainstream approach to treatment deserves research funding (at least several million dollars over a period of three to five years) to conduct the same kind of rigorous randomized clinical trial required to establish the efficacy of all medical and psychiatric treatments.

Several medical economics studies find that dissociative disorders are among the most costly of all psychiatric disorders in terms of their rates of treatment utilization (Brand, Classen, McNary, & Zaveri, 2009; Brand et al., 2013). An innovative, Internet-based treatment study (The TOP DD Network Study) is underway directed by Dr. Brand with the same advisory board as The TOP DD Study (http://www.towson.edu/topddstudy).

Establishing the effectiveness of current treatments and conducting the necessary research to systematically improve treatment will ultimately result in decreasing costs and improving treatment efficacy in the future. Treatment of DD patients is only one of the many human and social costs of child maltreatment. Prevention of child abuse is ultimately the most cost-effective investment.

SYNTHESIS

The effects of childhood trauma and adversity reverberate across generations. One mechanism through which they pass from parent to child is through the sharing of mutual states of being. Before there are even words, mutually shared states of being are the language of attunement and attachment. Even when there are words, they are never sufficient to convey or to mask the meta-messages communicated by a caretaker's state of mind.

When we think of emotional, physical or sexual abuse, for example, we tend to forget about the perpetrator, most often a parent, who is inflicting the maltreatment. To put it crudely, for every maltreated child there is at least one adult who is screaming at, hitting and/or sexually molesting that child. In addition to the acts of maltreatment per se, the child is repeatedly exposed to a primary caretaker in an altered state of consciousness (e.g., rage, intoxication, sexual arousal).

The closest thing that we have to investigating the long term effects of such childhood adverse experiences are longitudinal studies of mothers with ACEs parenting their own children, who, in turn, grow up to become parents (often at an early age). Although few in number, the prospective longitudinal nature of this research allows us to make causal inferences about the role of type D attachment in infancy increasing the risk for dissociative and hostile maternal states of mind that, in turn, increase rates of Type D attachment in their offspring. And so it goes, across generations. But this cycle is not inevitable. Some individuals overcome their ACEs, while prevention and treatment can decrease the numbers of others who are affected.

Recurrent childhood maltreatment creates traumatic identity states that compartmentalize the emotions, sense of self, and memories of those abusive experiences. Trauma undermines the development of healthy metacognitive/executive/observing ego mechanisms that integrate different states of being into a more global sense of self, further contributing to psychiatric disorders characterized by personality fragmentation such as multiple personality/dissociative identity and borderline personality disorder.

Historical cases of traumatic identity fragmentation such as *Fräulein Anna O* played important—although largely unacknowledged—roles in the genesis of modern psychology and psychiatry, especially the origins of psychotherapy. Yet, for many reasons, acknowledging the often incestuous and abusive etiology of these disorders was unacceptable to authorities of the time.

Despite multiple lines of clinical and experimental evidence supporting DID, vehement rejection of the diagnosis and its traumatic etiology continues even today. Arguments against the dissociative disorders (some version of this diagnosis has been included in every version of the DSM from DSM-I to DSM-5) often harken back to critiques made by nineteenth-century skeptics rather than addressing the literally thousands of peer-reviewed research studies across cultures and types of trauma virtually all of which find undeniably strong associations between trauma and dissociation.

Ultimately the only proof that really matters, however, is which side of the debate is able to help dissociative disorder patients lead more harmonious and productive lives. Despite never receiving a federal grant for a clinical trial, the DID therapeutic community has pioneered grassroots, Internet-based, international, research studies that demonstrate that current mainstream treatment approaches produce significant clinical improvement in objective measures such as number of hospitalizations and suicide attempts as well as patient and therapist reports of greater well-being.

CHAPTER 9   DRUGS AND ADDICTIONS

Aldous Huxley

In 1953 Aldous Huxley took 400 milligrams of mescaline mixed in a glass of water and sat back to await the results. Seriously vision-impaired as a result of an illness in his teens, he expected to see intense mental imagery. Instead he was surprised by the transformation of his vision for plain objects. A simple arrangement of three flowers became a beatific vision filled with the Dharma-Body of the Buddha.

> *"I continued to look at the flowers, and in their living light I seemed to detect the qualitative equivalent of breathing—but of breathing without returns to a starting point, with no recurrent ebbs but only a repeated flow from beauty to heightened beauty, from deeper to ever deeper meaning. Words like "grace" and "transfiguration" came to my mind . . .* (Huxley, 1954 p. 18).

Huxley's *The Doors of Perception* remains a seminal account of a psychedelic "trip" (Huxley, 1954). A member of the famous British family of scientists and writers, Huxley was introduced to mescaline by the psychiatrist Humphrey Osmond, who was among the first to try mescaline and LSD as a treatment for alcoholism and psychiatric disorders. Best known for coining the term, "psychedelic," by which he meant, "mind-manifesting"; Osmond is believed to have been with Huxley during his mescaline trip.

Checking his recollections against a tape recording made during the experience, Huxley described how the change in the way that he saw the physical world reorganized his understanding of what was important in his life. During the mescaline trip, he finds deep and universal meaning in the colors, shapes, and placement of common objects; the differing intensities of their internal glow dictating their relative intrinsic values. He becomes entranced by the legs of a chair, which then becomes a recurrent visual theme during the remainder of his Mescaline trip.

> *"A rose is a rose is a rose. But these chair legs were chair legs were St. Michael and all angels"* (Huxley, 1954 p. 28).

Huxley explains these "visions" of the deeper meaning implicit in everyday things and activities as the opening up of a new "door of perception"—likening our brains to a "reducing value" that narrows the flow of information and filters out all manner of sensation, perception, and information about the world except that which we absolutely need to survive. Huxley believed that certain people—artists, musicians and people with conditions like schizophrenia—had leaks or breakdowns in their filtering process. Thus they were exposed to much more of the "real" nature of the world than "normal" people. Artists seek to capture or represent this heightened perception of reality. But, Huxley reasoned, for some the breakdown in their filtering process with its resulting heightened intensity and enormous volume of sensory information could be overwhelming.

For Huxley, his mescaline trip was a moment of clarity:

I am not so foolish as to equate what happens under the influence of mescaline or of any other drug, prepared or in the future preparable, with the realization of the end and ultimate purpose of human life: Enlightenment, the Beatific Vision. All I am suggesting is that the mescaline experience is what Catholic theologians call "a gratuitous grace," not necessary to salvation but potentially helpful and to be accepted thankfully, if made available. To be shaken out of the ruts of ordinary perceptions, to be shown for a few timeless hours the outer and the inner world . . . as they are apprehended, directly and unconditionally, by Mind at Large—this is an experience of inestimable value to everyone and especially to the intellectual. (Huxley, 1954 p. 73)

Huxley continued experimenting with mescaline and LSD for the remainder of his life. In the introduction to *Perennial Philosophy*, he writes, "*Knowledge is a function of being. When there is a change in the being of the knower, there is a corresponding change in the nature and amount of knowing*" (Huxley, 2004 p. vii). Hours before dying from cancer at the age of 69, he asked for an injection of LSD.

Mind Altering (Psychoactive) Drugs

To the extent that we can interpret the images, inscriptions, and artifacts of long-extinct cultures, it appears that psychoactive drugs have played important roles in worship and religion, healing and health, and easing of pain and fatigue. From the Neolithic period we have tantalizing indirect evidence, primarily seeds of psychoactive plants such as betel nut and cannabis associated with cave and rock art pictures of shamanistic ceremonies that may have used these drugs. Evidence of opium use as far back as 7,500 years ago has been claimed, but can only be reliably dated to about 2,500 years ago. The *Iliad* mentions the cultivation of poppies and Aristotle specifically identifies them as a narcotic.

Marijuana's use as a medicine has existed for about 5,000 years. The world's oldest existing medical textbook, the Chinese *Shen-nung Pen-tshao Ching* (the *Pharmacopoeia of the Heavenly Cultivator*) prescribed marijuana for rheumatism and digestive problems. Nineteenth-century Western medicine expanded the list to include neuralgia, convulsions, hysteria, and depression. Marijuana was routinely prescribed in the United States until the Federal Marijuana Tax Act of 1937 severely restricted its use, imposing a $100 per ounce tax and onerous legal paperwork. At the same time the government distributed publications and movies such as the now-pop classic, "Reefer Madness," with dramatized accounts of degradation and moral decline associated with marijuana use. Medical use virtually ended within a few years. Recently, an increasing number of states have passed laws allowing prescription for medical and compassionate use—and a few for recreational use.

Long lists of herbal pharmaceuticals that include psychoactive plants have been translated from Egyptian, Indian, Chinese, and Greco-Roman medical texts attesting to their utility and ubiquity in ancient civilizations (Sneader, 2005). In the Americas, early Spanish explorers reported the medicinal uses of coca leaf and other plants by native peoples to relieve fatigue and cold as well as a variety of ailments. Mescal beans and remains of peyote (a mescaline-containing cactus) have been found associated with rock art drawings of dancing hunters or warriors in the Rio Grande region of southwest Texas.

Alcohol was—and still is—the single most widely consumed psychoactive drug. Whether beer or wine came first is a matter of debate, but firm evidence in the form of chemical residues on drinking and brewing vessels has been found at Neolithic sites. The oldest of these are Chinese, dating back at least 9,000 years. Beer is frequently mentioned in Sumerian texts and by the time of Homer's Troy ornate silver and gold chalices attest to the importance of alcohol in ceremonies. Not all cultures were familiar with alcohol, however, and its introduction into North America by early European settlers had devastating effects on native peoples.

Psychoactive drugs alter the dimensions of state of being, and so we commonly categorize psychoactive drugs by the kinds of state-altering effects that they induce. Some change mood—they can boost alertness and physical energy. Others alter sensory awareness, including perception of pain. Psychoactive drugs change how we think about things and what information we recall and incorporate into our immediate worldview. They can change how we think about ourselves and what we tell others about who we are and what we stand for. A powerful psychoactive drug frequently affects many of these dimensions of state-space simultaneously, producing a markedly altered state of being.

Psychoactive medications are often grouped together based on their most pronounced effect on the person's state of being—for example, sedatives and hypnotics, analgesics, stimulants, antidepressants, mood stabilizers, antianxiety, antipsychotics, and psychedelics. But the same drug can have markedly dissimilar effects in different people. These classifications are only generalizations.

By their nature, psychoactive drug-induced states of being are transient. The drug must be taken each time the individual seeks to enter an altered state that they have come to associate with a particular drug. But even the same drug and dose does not guarantee the same desired effects each time that it is taken. Other factors, such as the individual's mental state or setting at the time that they take the drug, can influence the person's overall drug-induced state of being. As a result, frequent users develop habits and rituals and use props and settings in an effort to create a favorable context in which to get "high."

Many individuals will have at least one class of drugs that produces psychoactive effects that differ markedly from the norm. Genetic factors, tolerance as a result of prior exposure, interactions with other drugs, general physical and mental health, possible exposure to toxic environmental agents, and a myriad of other factors and unique circumstances limit our ability to predict exactly how an individual will respond to a specific psychoactive drug at any given time.

Individuals differ in which side effects they experience with a given medication. They may tolerate some medications and have adverse reactions to others prescribed for the same medical problem. Many medications used for medical conditions have powerful psychological side effects, e.g., depression, mood swings, suicidal thoughts, paranoia, confusion. In the next TV drug commercial, ignore the enticing images of the now-happily adventurous, former sufferer enjoying life to the fullest.

Instead, listen closely to the long list of possible side effects reeled off in a hurried, hushed voice—many reflect negative states of mind.

Likewise drug users who have sampled many psychoactive drugs will have clear favorites and avoid others. An individual seeking a mescaline-induced religious vision may disdainfully eschew smoking pot as trivial mellowing out without spiritual inspiration. The stuporous heroin junkie avoids the crack user's frenetic high. The two-fisted whiskey drinker scoffs at the white wine sipper's subtle buzz. For every drug user there are certain drugs that do it; and others that are a turn-off or ineffective at best.

A BRIEF SURVEY OF PSYCHOACTIVE DRUG STATES OF BEING

ALCOHOL

Stone Age alcoholic beverages, especially beer and wine, are well documented in a variety of cultures. From India, Persia, Egypt and China, researchers have found alcohol residue in jars, cups, and brewing vessels. Fermented rice, honey, and fruits were often the basis for these early drinks. Early writings such as the famous Babylonian Code of Hammurabi mention alcohol and often praise moderation or prescribe abstinence. Alcohol was also a feature of daily life and religious ceremony in pre-Columbian Mesoamerica, although with exception of the Southwest, it was largely absent from the rest of North America.

Alcoholic intoxication at banquets and festivals was considered socially desirable. The ancient Greeks regarded inebriation as a sign of manhood. Wine deities like Dionysus for the Greeks and Bacchus for the Romans were common to many other cultures. These deities were often considered "liberators" because they freed an individual from his usual sense of self.

Alcohol intoxication is an altered mental and physical state of being. Progressive alcohol intoxication is marked by loss of coordination, slurred speech, confusion, loss of memory, and lethargy. In extreme cases it can result in respiratory depression and death. Alcoholic blackouts are often regarded as a cardinal sign of alcoholism. Most authorities recognize two types of alcoholic blackouts, "en bloc" and "fragmentary." In an en bloc blackout, the individual loses memory for any and all events for a distinct period. In a fragmentary blackout—the most common type—the individual may recall some events but is unable to remember others from the same time.

Laboratory research on alcohol-induced memory impairment demonstrates a number of state-dependent features. The degree and nature of memory disruption is most strongly related to the rate of change in blood alcohol level rather than the absolute level, which may vary significantly across individuals. As people become drunk, short-term memory is most affected as compared to when they are sobering up. Memory tasks involving the explicit memory system such as recalling word lists show the greatest impairment. Implicit memory tasks such as recognition are less affected. Alcohol-induced impairments of memory differ depending on whether someone is switching into or out of an intoxicated state. Different memory systems show greater or lesser sensitivity to the effects of an intoxicated state.

SEDATIVES AND HYPNOTICS

In 1794 the inventor William Murdock used coal gas to light his house and transformed man's relationship with the night. Within a few decades, major European cities were brightly lit by streetlamps fueled with coal gas. The light left a dark byproduct: huge amounts of coal tar, a waste product of manufacturing coal gas. German chemists began exploring possible uses of coal tar giving rise to the modern chemical and pharmaceutical industries heralded by the founding of the Bayer aspirin company. The early synthesis of phenol from coal tar provided Joseph Lister with the antiseptic with which he transformed the practice of surgery, saving enormous numbers of lives by reducing the high rates of post-operative infections.

Another family of synthetic drugs that sprung from these chemical manipulations were the sedatives or hypnotics. The synthetic hypnotic chloral hydrate was created in 1832 by Justus Liebig. In Berlin the pathologist Oskar Liebriech discovered that chloral hydrate calmed disturbed mental patients. Within a short time after the publication of his findings in 1869, physicians all over the world were using chloral hydrate as a sedative to quiet agitated or anxious patients.

Sold across the counter as a sleep aid, the increasing popularity of chloral hydrate soon led to a steep increase in price. Recognizing a market, the Schering company in Berlin built the world's first large scale pharmaceutical factory to meet growing demand. Within a decade, consumption in the U.S. and Britain exceeded a ton a day far surpassing any medication of that era (Sneader, 2005). Chloral hydrate was the Valium or Prozac of its time.

Barbituric acid, first synthesized by von Baeyer in 1864, was another discovery of the new science of synthetic drugs. Reportedly named after his first love, barbituric acid is the parent compound for a huge class of synthetic hypnotic drugs commonly known as the barbiturates. Sold on the street as barbs, block busters, Christmas trees, goof balls, pinks, red devils, reds and blues, and yellow jackets, barbiturates are downers that depress the central nervous system. In low doses they produce a calming effect, relaxing the individual and reducing anxiety. In moderate doses they cause a drunken euphoria with slurred speech, impaired judgment, and loss of coordination similar to the effects of alcohol for many people. In high doses they induce stupor to the point of surgical anesthesia.

An overdose can easily be fatal. Tolerance develops rapidly, requiring increasing doses to achieve the same effect. Addiction is common. Withdrawal brings tremors, sweating, increased heart rate and blood pressure, and sometimes seizures—it resembles alcohol withdrawal.

Until the mass marketing of benzodiazepines in the 1960s, the barbiturates in their many forms dominated both medical use and the illicit drug trade.

The immense popularity of these sedative/hypnotic drugs in their time and their frequent flagrant and widespread abuse tell us something about the lure of the particular altered states of consciousness that they produce. A chloral hydrate high is not like a barbiturate high, which, in turn, differs from a benzodiazepine high. In fact, these drugs don't produce a high at all, but rather they share a powerful antianxiety effect associated with a peaceful sense of slowing down of the mind. Indeed, one of the common uses on the street for barbiturates and benzodiazepines is to mellow out the otherwise crashing withdrawal associated with stopping stimulant drugs such as amphetamines and cocaine.

STIMULANTS

Cocaine

Written accounts of the use of the coca leaf by Inca nobility date to the mid-sixteenth century. In 1569, the Spanish passed a law making Coca leaf freely available to all Indians, thereby undermining the ruling Inca elite and facilitating the conquest of Peru. Cocaine was first synthesized from the coca leaf by Albert Niemann in 1860. It became widely available in nineteenth-century Europe and the U.S. in the form of medicinal drinks and lozenges, including Coca-Cola, which was reformulated in 1903 to eliminate the cocaine.

Sigmund Freud first came to international attention in 1885 through the glowing reviews of his paper, "*Ueber Coca*" (On Coca), on the effects of cocaine. He was a user and for a time an enthusiastic promoter, until the disastrous attempt to treat his friend Ernst von Fleischl-Marxow's morphine addiction increased his caution. Freud's personal use, however, continued until at least 1895.

In some respects, Freud may be regarded as among the first psychopharmacologists, experimenting on himself in an attempt to delineate cocaine's many effects (Byck, 1974). He was especially interested in its energizing effects, which distinguished it from the sedative and hypnotic drugs that constituted the major psychiatric medications of the time. It was Freud's assistant, Carl Koller, however, who identified cocaine's most important medical effect, topical anesthesia. Within a short time after Koller's presentation on its numbing effects to the Opthalmological Society in Heidelberg, cocaine anesthesia became a staple of surgical practice throughout the world. Today its medical use is largely limited to topical anesthesia for surgery of the nose and throat.

Known on the street as coke, flake, snow, blow, toot, nose candy, and lady, among other names, cocaine is the leading stimulant drug abused in the U.S. It is often referred to as the Cadillac or Champagne of drugs. The illicit drug of choice for physicians, lawyers, brokers, celebrities, and athletes, cocaine can be snorted as a powder, smoked as crack, injected, or mixed with alcohol.

Cocaine is powerfully addicting. It can be fatal as an overdose or cause sudden death by inducing a heart attack. Users feel a sense of euphoria, increased energy, and excitement. They are happy, talkative and social. They have a grandiose confidence in their abilities and an exaggerated sense of their physical strength. This can progress to a paranoid mental state, characterized by mental flightiness, irritability, explosive anger, confusion, restlessness, agitation, tics, tremors, clammy sweats, and tactile and visual hallucinations nicknamed cocaine bugs or snow lights. A full-fledged psychotic state may occur that resembles paranoid schizophrenia.

Amphetamines

In Europe and Asia a small shrub (*Ephedra vulgaris*) was the source of a widely used stimulant, Ephedrine, which was imbibed as tea made from dried leaves and branches. Ephedrine became an important early treatment for bronchial asthma. An acute shortage of the plant in 1927 led chemist Gordon Alles to synthesize a cheap alternative, amphetamine.

During World War II all sides used amphetamines to increase alertness and fight off the effects of fatigue and sleep deprivation. The Germans mixed it with chocolate and issued it as candy bars to aircraft and tank crews. Hitler received daily injections; its psychosis-inducing effects probably contributed to his infamous paranoid rages. Post-war Japan suffered an epidemic of methamphetamine abuse in the early 1950s, when old military stock found its way onto the street. In the U.S., the general public was introduced to this family of stimulants in the form of the famous Benzedrine inhaler, which was finally banned in the 1960s.

Medical uses of amphetamines include the treatment of a rare neurological disorder, narcolepsy, in which individuals lapse into periodic bouts of sleep during the daytime. It was once widely used as a diet drug, but is now highly restricted. However, forms of amphetamine and a derivative, methylphenidate—brand name Ritalin—are still widely used in children to treat attention deficit hyperactivity disorder (ADHD).

Several drugs in the amphetamine family have become major drugs of abuse in the U.S. The most commonly abused form, methamphetamine, is a central nervous system stimulant that increases alertness and energy, produces a sense of euphoria, and decreases appetite. It also increases heart rate and blood pressure and raises body temperature.

Easily synthesized in garage and basement meth factories from over-the-counter cold and allergy medications containing ephedrine (which is why buyers of certain over-the-counter allergy medications are required to show a picture ID), methamphetamine is known on the street as "ice," "crystal," "bitch," and "glass" among other names. It can be ingested, inhaled, smoked, injected, or even taken as a suppository. Users rapidly develop tolerance making it powerfully addicting. The drug can cause sudden death from a heart attack, stroke or hyperthermia. It depletes the brain of important neurotransmitters, such as dopamine and it can cause brain damage. Withdrawal is intensely unpleasant and often accompanied by deep depression. Relapse is common.

The meth head and the crack addict are two examples of the frenetic, self-destructive addictive behavior that stimulant drugs can induce in users. Both have profound effects on a brain circuit known as the "mesolimbic pathway," commonly referred to as the brain's "pleasure" or "reward system." This brain system can be activated by a variety of pleasurable activities such as sex and eating as well as by drugs. Dopamine is the major neurotransmitter in the brain's pleasure pathway and abuse of these drugs damages dopamine neurons inflicting long-term brain damage including Parkinson-like symptoms.

The initial attraction of these drugs are the states of intense pleasure, sense of power and grandiosity that users feel. Cocaine and methamphetamine are frequently used in conjunction with sex as they heighten pleasure, increase libido, and prolong performance by delaying orgasm. With long-term abuse, they often lead to indiscriminate, violent, and self-endangering sexual behavior. The individual's moral judgment, social- and self-awareness, and other protective metacognitive capacities disintegrate. Physical health deteriorates and is marked by visible stigmata such as the ragged, rotten teeth known as meth mouth and the abscess-ridden, pockmarked skin caused by scratching cocaine bugs.

OPIATES

Initially published anonymously in *London Magazine* in the fall of 1821, *Confessions of an English Opium Eater*, served to initiate the literary reputation of its author, Thomas De Quincey, becoming the authoritative account of opium addiction for the next century. In his extended confession, De Quincey blames a painful medical condition as the root of his addiction (De Quincey, 1821).

> *It was not for the purpose of creating pleasure, but of mitigating pain in the severest degree, that I first began to use opium as an article of daily diet. In the twenty-eighth year of my age a most painful affection of the stomach, which I had first experienced about ten years before, attacked me in great strength* (De Quincey, 1821).

Although he writes at great length about the role of opium as relief for his pain, both physical and mental, De Quincey also acknowledges it as a source of pleasure. But he assures his readers that "... *nobody will laugh long who deals much with opium: its pleasures even are of a grave and solemn complexion* ..." (De Quincey, 1821). He revised *Confessions* several times over the next decades, expanding it into a book in 1856 with explanatory footnotes including tallies of daily use that reveal sudden relapses as he continued to struggle with his addiction.

Not surprisingly, De Quincey was vehemently attacked for tempting others –including several notable English writers—with his dramatic and sensual descriptions. The French poet Charles Baudelaire further amplified this appeal in his *Les paradis artificiels* (or *Artificial Paradises*); his 1860 account drew heavily on *Confessions* and advocated opium as an aid to reaching humankind's ideal world.

At its core, however, *Confessions* is an account of De Quincey's self-observing his many states of being and their mutually destructive conflicts. He speaks of bodily states both painful and pleasant, of states of cloudless serenity, of torpid states and unutterable irritation, of imbecility, of exaltation, and of gloom. Indeed, the popular appeal of *Confessions of an English Opium Eater* may have come as much from its novel and graphic portrayal of an individual recurrently cycling through extreme states of being as from any glamorization of opium intoxication. In many respects, De Quincey's *Confessions* is an early example of what have come to be known as "recovery stories" in the field of substance abuse treatment.

Oliver Sacks

The noted neurologist and best-selling author, Dr. Oliver Sacks (1933–2015), wrote a revealing New Yorker magazine essay on his use of drugs (Sacks, 2012). Although primed by reading De Quincey's *Confessions,* Baudelaier's *Artificial Paradises* and Huxley's *Doors* in school, Sacks says that he did not try mind-altering drugs until he was a thirty-year-old neurology resident. Starting with marijuana, he moved on to a variety of drugs, experimenting with combinations and attempting to mentally control the hallucinatory experiences. Initially he restricted his drug exploration to weekends, but during a three-month gap between finishing his residency and starting a research fellowship, he "*descended deeper into drug-taking, no longer confining it to the weekends.*"

The research fellowship did not work out. Despondent, Sacks began to self-medicate with that old reliable, chloral hydrate:

Depressed and insomniac, I was taking ever-increasing doses of chloral hydrate to get to sleep, and was up to fifteen times the usual dose every night. And though I had managed to stockpile a huge amount of the drug—I raided chemical supplies in the lab at work—this finally ran out on a bleak Tuesday a little before

Christmas, and for the first time in several months I went to bed without my usual knockout dose (p. 46).

Feeling a bit under the weather, Sacks thankfully did not ride his motorcycle to work as usual, but took the bus. Stopping first for a cup of coffee, he was startled to find the cashier had the face of an elephant seal. Next, all the passengers on the bus had glittering insect eyes that moved in sudden jerks. To gain some degree of control at work, Sack relied on a personal coping strategy, writing:

. . . by describing in my lab notebook what was going on, I managed to maintain a semblance of control, though the hallucinations continued, mutating all the while (p. 46).

Once safely back home, he called a physician friend, who asked what he had taken. When he replied "nothing," she wisely asked what he had just stopped taking:

"That's it!" I said. "I was taking a huge amount of chloral hydrate and ran out of it last night."
"Oliver, you chump. You always overdo things," Carol said.
"You've got a classic case of the DTs, delirium tremens" (p 46).

Continuing his personal explorations, Sacks found that he especially enjoyed amphetamines. His usual amphetamine trips consisted of spending a weekend high on the drug but doing nothing in particular. But one Friday in February 1967, he was exploring the rare book section of a medical library and a book on migraine headaches, written in 1873 by one Edward Liveing, MD, caught his eye. Taking the book home he imbibed his *"bitter draft of amphetamine-heavily sugared, to make it more palatable."* Soon thereafter he was captivated by Liveing's humanity and sensitivity to his patients.

I wanted nothing but to enter Liveing's mind and imbibe the atmosphere of the time in which he worked. In a sort of catatonic concentration so intense that in ten hours I scarcely moved a muscle or wet my lips, I read steadily through the five hundred pages of "Megrim" (p. 47).

This experience changed his life. Coming down, Sacks noted that he did not experience the usual depressive crash, but retained a sense of *"illumination and insight"* (p. 47). Realizing that he could be *"the Liveing of our time"* (p.47), Sacks declares that he never took amphetamines again. His subsequent books are amazing clinical accounts of unusual neurological conditions and circumstances that have won prestigious awards, as well as serving as the basis for movies such as *Awakenings* starring Robin Williams and Robert De Niro.

PSYCHEDELICS

Scientists, philosophers, therapists, and other seekers of knowledge seem drawn to psychedelic drugs such as mescaline and LSD for a set of related reasons. They want to learn about the human mind and believe that these drugs will open up new ways of seeing and thinking. They want to understand, and perhaps to empathize, with the inner world of the seriously mentally ill and believe that these drugs simulate the experience of being "mad." They wish to have mystical religious experiences and regard these drugs as potential openings into the spiritual world. Or they believe that these drugs can offer a psychological perspective from which they may gain deeper insight into themselves.

But they all seek to profoundly alter their state of consciousness—to have a transformative experience that changes the way that they see the world and how they think about life. They intend to bring insight back from these trips that will change their life or will help them to understand and help others. Many professionals who have experimented with psychedelic drugs for these reasons become vocal advocates for their use to treat mental health problems, substance abuse, PTSD, or to invite self-discovery.

LSD and Its Ilk

The paragon of psychedelic drugs, LSD (lysergic acid diethylamide), was first synthesized by the Swiss chemist Albert Hofmann in 1938. Research with psychedelic drugs began in the late 1950's as the CIA and U.S. military searched for a 'truth serum' for interrogation and for drugs that would allow 'mind control'. Researchers conducted top-secret human experiments at a number of government facilities, including the National Institutes of Health, military bases, and federal psychiatric hospitals such as St. Elizabeths in Washington, DC. In addition to military "volunteers," LSD was eventually used on the unwitting public (Lee & Shalin, 1985). Project MK-Ultra, a series of CIA-run psychedelic drug experiments on unsuspecting subjects, is believed to be one of the more extreme examples of these clandestine programs. But who knows?

The intertwined activities of three groups gave birth to the psychedelic movement in the late 1960s (Lee & Shalin, 1985): the hippies, the therapists, and the spies cross-pollinated each other to create a brief but vibrant psychedelic drug culture that continues to influence art and society. Each group had its share of proselytizers and groupies, who freely dispensed LSD (and other psychedelics) to spread the good word. Some would cross paths or join forces in surprising ways with each seeking to use psychedelic drugs to advance their vision of the truth.

Ecstasy et al.

Alexander Shulgin (1925–2014) was a psychedelic drug developer credited with synthesizing over 200 psychoactive compounds and best known for popularizing the powerful mind-altering drug MDMA or ecstasy (Methylenedioxymethamphetamine). Trained in biochemistry and psychopharmacology, Shulgin worked as a senior researcher for the Dow chemical company until the mid-1960s. He left to set up a private laboratory after Dow grew uncomfortable with his creating and promoting psychedelic compounds. His home laboratory, built on the foundation of a derelict cabin near San Francisco, reportedly resembled a medieval alchemist's lair, complete with walls of shelves crowded with beakers, flasks, and jars of exotic potions covered in cobwebs and guarded by legions of spiders.

In 1991 Shulgin and his wife, Ann, published *PiHKAL: A Chemical Love Story* (Shulgin & Shulgin, 1991). *PiHKAL* stands for "Phenethylamines I Have Known and Loved." The first half of the large volume is a transparently autobiographical novel detailing their individual and joint personal explorations with psychedelic drugs, as well as accounts drawn from a select group of friends. The second half of the volume is devoted to a detailed compound-by-compound description of the steps required to synthesize such drugs, how much to take, how long their effects last. It also rates the psychedelic properties of more than 175 phenethylamine-derived compounds.

Within two years of *PiHKAL's* publication, the U.S. government shut down Shulgin's private laboratory for alleged paperwork deficiencies, an act he regarded as retaliation for publishing what has been construed as a cookbook for creating your own psychedelics (provided you are a first-rate chemist). He nonetheless vowed, *"to continue to devote myself to the work of discovering new keys to an understanding of the human mind, and to the widest possible dissemination of whatever knowledge and information I have been able to gather."* (Shulgin & Shulgin, 1997 p. xxvii).

Despite the legal problems he encounters, the scientific problem Shulgin faces is how to reliably and validly measure the unusual mental and physical experiences that his many psychedelic drugs produce? How to capture and quantify the essence of the alternative states of consciousness that his drugs unlock? Recognizing that individuals respond differently to the same drug, he created a simple 6-point scale running from Minus (no effect) to Plus Four ("peak" experience) for rating drug experiences.

After trying each new phenethylamine compound on himself, Shulgin brought in his wife Ann as a second tester for drugs that score a Plus-Two or higher. If their joint experiences were interesting or desirable, he then tested it with a team of about a dozen experienced people, many of them mental health professionals or scientists. The group experiments were conducted according to some simple rules. Participants had been drug free for at least three days. They met at someone's home prepared to spend the night if necessary. There was an agreement about how a member could express a serious concern or veto a group activity. Disagreements and problems that occur were handled in a process manner, by neutrally exploring the underlying psychological issues.

He investigated over 100 psychedelic compounds using this method. The teams' collective ratings and comments, together with Shulgin's more detailed accounts of his personal experiences across multiple trials and different dosages served to characterize a given drug's effects. He often adds comments about the longer-term effect of the drug on his sleep and dreams that night and his mood and energy the next day.

Obviously *PiHKAL* is a very limited and highly subjective account drawn from a non-representative sample of users. Shulgin's "get-high" scale is overly simplistic from a psychometric point of view—but it does serves a purpose of helping to sort and quantify initial psychedelic effects. Despite these significant limitations, *PiHHKAL* remains one of the more systematic and comprehensive accounts on the effects of psychedelic drugs in settings where they are commonly used.

Like Huxley, Shulgin sees psychedelic drugs as keys to hidden doors within the mind that when opened offer wisdom, greater self-awareness, and spiritual attunement. With fellow scientists he would invoke Huxley's premise that psychedelic drugs mimic the experience of insanity. After all, he pointed out, the two major classes of psychedelic drugs, phenelthylamines and tryptamines, are chemically related to two major neurotransmitters, dopamine and serotonin respectively. Most of his colleagues seemed to accept this argument.

In his introduction to *TiHKAL* (Tryptamines I Have Known and Loved), the sequel to *PiHKAL,* he downplays the scientific justifications that he offered his academic colleagues. The real reason Shulgin reveals is that he believes that he is developing a set of mind tools—tools that

> *might allow each human being to more consciously—and more clearly—communicate with the interior of his own mind and psyche. This might be called a vocabulary of awareness.* (Shulgin & Shulgin, 1997 p. xxii)

Shulgin was not the first to synthesize MDMA, but he is closely associated with promoting it among a small group of psychotherapists who used it (as well as LSD and mescaline) in the treatment of selected patients. His notes on MDMA (also known as Ecstasy), a drug Shulgin believes opens up hidden mental passages and sparks insight and personal change, provides a flavor for his qualitative descriptions. After ingesting 120 milligrams, he writes:

> *I feel absolutely clean inside, and there is nothing but pure euphoria. I have never felt so great, or believed this to be possible. The cleanliness, clarity, and marvelous feeling of solid inner strength continued throughout the rest of the day, and evening, and through the next day. I am overcome by the profundity of the experience, and how much more powerful it was than previous experiences for no apparent reason, other than a continually improving state of being. All the next day I felt like "a citizen of the universe" rather than a citizen of the planet, completely disconnecting time and flowing easily from one activity to the next* (Shulgin & Shulgin, 1991 p. 736–737).

Bad Trips

While Shulgin might wax ecstatic about his ecstasy experience on one occasion, he records that on another a lower dose produced feelings of anxiety and dread, tiredness and negativity. He observed that the state of mind that one brought to the situation could color the experience, as could the setting and mood and personalities of others present.

The beat poet Allen Ginsberg took his first LSD trip as part of a scientific experiment. In a small room crammed with intimidating medical equipment, men in white coats subjected Ginsburg to psychological and intelligence tests and drove his brain waves with a flashing strobe light. Although an experienced user of other drugs, Ginsburg freaked out:

Suddenly I got this uncanny sense that I was really no different than all of this mechanical machinery around me. I began thinking that if I let this go on, something awful would happen. I would be absorbed into the electrical network grid of the entire nation. Then I began to feel a slight crackling along the hemispheres of my skull. I felt my soul being sucked out through the [strobe] *light into the wall socket and going out* (Lee & Shalin, 1985 p. 59).

Huxley, likewise, had a dark moment during his first Mescaline trip as he looked inward. He did not see the Dharma-Body of the Buddha within as he expected. Instead, he saw something he labeled as *"cheap"* that he also realized was his *"own personal self."* His inner mental landscape seemed to be made of *"tin"* and *"plastic"*—a mere symbolic substitution for the Dharma-Body he saw radiating from the objects of his external world (Huxley, 1954 p. 44–45).

These negative experiences, however, did not dissuade Huxley, Ginsburg, or Shulgin from becoming strong advocates for the use of psychedelic drugs as a means to achieving what they called higher states of consciousness. Like William James before them, drug-induced altered states of being seemed to evoke mystical experiences and to take them to places in their own minds that were inaccessible in normal consciousness. James wondered whether these experiences were truly mystical, or merely the illusions of a drug-addled brain. Huxley, Ginsburg, and Shulgin don't seem to have entertained similar doubts. All, however, say that these experiences changed their lives.

MARIJUANA

In 1970, as the psychedelic drug movement was peaking, psychologist Charles Tart sought to study the effects of marijuana intoxication. Trained by Professor Ernest Hilgard (see Chapter 10), a leading authority on hypnosis and altered states of consciousness, Tart was interested in identifying the "common effects" of marijuana. Like Shulgin, he recognized the enormous range of individual personality differences, physical health, past drug use, and mental differences that interact with a drug in the laboratory to shape a psychedelic experience. Tart reasoned that if you could poll a large number of experienced marijuana users about their repeated recreational use, many of their idiosyncratic effects would cancel each other out and the results would reflect the more universal or pure effects that occur in natural settings (Tart, 1970).

Scientifically studying a large number of illegal drug users is, of course, a difficult task. The best that Tart could do was to creatively distribute a lengthy anonymous questionnaire in hopes that frequent users would find it and respond with an honest appraisal of their experiences. Addressed to *"Anyone who has smoked marijuana more than a dozen times,"* an accompanying letter appealed to the users' 'expertise' to set the record straight and mail the questionnaire back to Tart, who, in return, promised to make reprints of the research results easily available. The results were published in the prestigious journal *Nature* and subsequently expanded into a book, *On Being Stoned,* that remains a classic (Tart, 1971/2000).

Measuring "Stonedness"

The questionnaire consisted of over 200 statements about possible marijuana effects (e.g., *"I can see new colors or more subtle shades of color than when I'm straight."*). Each statement of possible effects was ranked on two scales, a 5-point (Likert) scale measuring how frequently the effect occurred ranging from "never" to "usually" (almost always). Beneath each question was a second scale asking how "stoned" the user was when the given effect first occurred.

The "stonedness" scale ranged from "just stoned" to "LSD," which Tart apparently equated with the maximum possible psychedelic effect. He was trying to approximate a "dose effect" curve—i.e., identify certain experiences that occurred at only low or very high degrees of being stoned. Lacking the ability to independently verify users' reports, Tart included a "validity" subscale consisting of 14 experiences that he considered highly unlikely to be effects of marijuana intoxication.

About 20 percent of the questionnaires were returned in their stamped envelopes. The respondents were primarily under thirty and lived in California or on the East Coast. They were mostly male, well educated, had regularly used marijuana for more than six months and three quarters had tried LSD at least once. Four percent had been arrested for using marijuana.

Tart's strategy for identifying "pure" marijuana effects was to determine which experiences were most frequently endorsed and typically occurred at low to moderate levels of being stoned. He labeled such effects as characteristic because many users experienced them. Indeed, users reported a number of common effects that broadly define the dimensions of that region in state-space known as being "stoned."

On Being "Stoned"

Vision alters. Hearing sharpens. Touch and feel take on sensuous qualities. Taste and smell are similarly enhanced with a new appreciation of subtleties in foods and odors. The user's sense of time and space are expanded. Distances seem greater and simple actions take longer. Time slows down.

In his chapter on the perception of time, William James similarly observes that hashish—a purified, compressed preparation of marijuana resin—stretches time.

> *In hashish-intoxication there is a curious increase in the apparent time-perspective. We utter a sentence, and ere the end is reached the beginning seems already to date from indefinitely long ago. We enter a short street, and it is as if we should never get to the end of it* (James, 1950 p. 639–640).

Tart's survey users reported that the perception of their body changed or suddenly seemed strange; often some overlooked body part seems to clamor for attention, while other familiar parts, such as the user's hands, suddenly seem strange or disappear from awareness. Pain is easier to tolerate (something that cancer patients know), in part because the user seems able to more easily divert attention elsewhere. The person feels relaxed, but also perceives him or herself as able to move easily and gracefully. Sex drive goes up and orgasm brings new pleasure.

Users reported that they were less noisy and boisterous at parties when they smoked marijuana than when they drank alcohol. They were more interested in quiet conversation, which they found stimulating and meaningful. They appreciated other people's humor more and surprised themselves by saying things that they found funny.

But they also admitted to having trouble remembering what they had just said—and sometimes forgot what they were saying before they had finished saying it. A person's memory for long-forgotten events seemed to improve. But it also was easy to become confused as to whether he had actually said or done something or had just thought about it. Some users reported becoming so absorbed in thoughts, fantasies, or some activity that they didn't hear others talking to them and had to be physically touched or shaken to get their attention—the classic definition of being "spaced out."

They also reported changes in their thinking. They felt more insightful about their own behavior. Their thinking was largely focused on the here-and-now, and it seemed to them to be intuitively correct if often not entirely logical. They experienced their thinking as more efficient than usual but later, when sober, often discovered that they had not been nearly as effective as they thought at the time. They had trouble reading and concentrating. At very high levels of being stoned their mind could go blank.

Not surprisingly, frequent marijuana users endorsed the experience of feeling good when they turned on, no matter how they were feeling before. Smoking marijuana was, for them, a reliable way to feel good— powerfully self-reinforcing. If they were already feeling good, getting stoned amplified the feeling.

But the same amplification could occur for feeling bad, too, although this was rarer and usually associated with high levels of being stoned. About 10 percent of the survey's sample reported having witnessed three or more other people freak out on marijuana. About a fifth said that they had themselves been overwhelmed by upsetting emotions when stoned, but only 3 percent said that this happened often.

Shifts in the user's sense of identity often took the form of a change in the person's relationship with the world. It was common to feel a childlike sense of awe and wonderment, as was a sense of merging with another person or even becoming an object. Losing all awareness of a personal ego and feeling at one with the world was associated with higher levels of being stoned, and most common among users who also practiced mediation. Some users especially valued this state of oneness with the world.

Most users felt a sense of control over how stoned they were and claimed an ability to come down at will. Usually, they explained, they simply willed themselves straight. Many, however, reported that once they started to get high they had a compulsion to get even higher. Some used other drugs to potentiate their marijuana highs, but many described using mental techniques such as meditation, music, or simply letting themselves go.

A sizable minority of Tart's respondents—the ones he labeled "marijuana enthusiasts"—reported having unusual mental or spiritual experiences. Indeed, most of those who reported also using LSD said that they actually had more spiritual experiences with marijuana. About a fifth endorsed fairly frequent out of body experiences. About an equal number reported feeling "in touch with a Higher Power or a Divine Being" when high on marijuana. These kinds of unusual and mystical experiences were more common in females and tended to occur at much higher doses.

Tart attributes his respondents' strong interest in higher (so to speak) states of consciousness to his impression that in 1970 marijuana users were more intelligent, better educated, and more interested in self-improvement than in later decades, when pot became just another recreational drug. Of course, no way exists to determine how representative his sample was of the marijuana users of that era.

All of Tart's respondents were familiar with alcohol and had been drinking much longer than they had smoked marijuana. They preferred alcohol when in large, impersonal social situations, but noted that in comparison it worsened sensory perceptions, lowered inhibitions, impaired cognition and judgment, could contribute to violence, and had worse after-effects. Most users said that they would choose marijuana over alcohol.

In the three decades that have passed since Tart conducted his simple survey of 150 "experienced" users, research has become more sophisticated. At first considered an "anomalous" drug of abuse because it did not seem to act on the brain in the same way as addicting drugs, we now know that the main psychedelic ingredient, D^9-Tetrahydrocannabinol (THC), activates receptors in the same central brain reward circuits that are stimulated by addicting drugs, sex, and other pleasurable activities. The cellular mechanisms, however, appear to differ in important ways from addicting drugs. Cannabinoid receptors have been mapped in detail and are found all over the brain, suggesting widespread activity.

Thousands of studies have investigated marijuana's relationship to psychiatric problems, cancer, aggression, apathy, and a host of possible negative effects. A growing number of randomized clinical trials are focusing on potential medical and psychological benefits. But our knowledge of why people use marijuana—an estimated 70 million Americans have tried it and perhaps 10 million use it daily—has not advanced much beyond what Tart learned from his simple survey.

Anonymous user surveys remain a tool of choice and convenience for researchers interested in illegal drug use. The Internet has replaced the paper questionnaire as the primary medium enabling the collection of enormous international samples, but vulnerable to hacking or hidden manipulation. Some Internet surveys include video clips, such as animated examples of different types of visual hallucinations, for users to compare with their own experiences.

Charles Tart went on to investigate other altered states of consciousness. He advocated for a science of discrete states of consciousness and published seminal research papers and books on related topics. He founded a school of Transpersonal Psychology and has more recently sought to make meditation more accessible to Westerners (Tart, 2001). He is also known for his interest in parapsychology.

PSYCHIATRIC DRUGS

Many of the drugs widely abused in Western societies were first introduced for medical and mental conditions. Examples in the nineteenth century include chloral hydrate, barbiturates, heroin, and cocaine, and benzodiazepines, methamphetamine, and synthetic opiates such as OxyContin in the twentieth. Each of these drugs was initially viewed as a panacea. Only later did their tragic addictive effects emerge. Although they differ pharmacologically, all produce powerful changes in mental state that predispose a person towards addiction.

With the exceptions of benzodiazepines and ADHD-stimulants, most modern psychiatric drugs are not considered ripe for abuse. They do, however, have powerful state-altering effects that, in some users, can create their own version of dependency.

Antipsychotics (aka neuroleptics, major tranquilizers)

In the early to mid-1980s, I was stationed at St. Elizabeths Hospital in Washington, DC, an enormous old 'insane asylum' with a rich history. Originally known as the Government Hospital for the Insane, it was built in 1852 according to the prevailing asylum model, which dated to the Jacksonian era. The asylum model dictated that mental institutions be located in the country on a hill overlooking a bucolic landscape that included a body of water whenever possible. Patients worked in the fields, shops, and industries and there was often one staff member for every few patients. Before the Civil War, most mental asylums were governed by relatively humane policies for their time and achieved cure rates unmatched since.

My hospital was renamed St. Elizabeths when it was converted into a military hospital during the Civil War. Wounded and sick convalescing soldiers did not want their families to think that they were locked in an insane asylum. Following the Civil War and the waves of immigration during the 1870s, many such institutions were overwhelmed by enormous numbers of patients and became the "snake pits" associated in the public mind with insane asylums. Although many good things continued to happen at St. Es in subsequent years, it was also home to secret mind-control research, including efforts by the Office of Strategic Services (OSS), the World War II precursor of the CIA, to develop a truth serum.

I was working at St. Es because I had changed my research focus from rapid cycling bipolar disorder to dissociative disorders and increasingly, to the effects of child abuse. In order to get minimal financial support, I made a Faustian bargain that permitted me to conduct my research only after I had recruited enough patients for the NIMH schizophrenia research studies. That duty kept me pretty busy visiting the ancient wards looking for potential subjects.

At its peak St. Es housed over 7,000 patients, but in my day there were only a few hundred of the most chronic cases left, with many former patients among the homeless living on the streets of DC. I got to know many—some of whom I repeatedly visited to convince them to sign up for some research study or other.

My impression was that they were a pretty placid bunch, given to sitting quietly in their rickety chairs lined against the peeling, pee-yellow walls of decrepit dayrooms. Indeed, the whole hospital, including the staff, had this torpid, dazed, passive, detached quality that existed a world apart from the frenetic city of Washington visible across the Anacostia River. The patients, of course, were drugged on heavy doses of major tranquilizers such as Thorazine and Haldol. I can't speak for the staff.

This wasn't always the case. Before Thorazine (the trade name for chlorpromazine, the first antipsychotic tranquilizer) was discovered in the early 1950s, mental asylums such as St. Elizabeth's were the proverbial Bedlam, filled with howling, wailing, shrieking, cursing and crying patients. One elderly psychiatrist, who had worked at St. Es in the days before Thorazine, told me that you could hear the hospital from blocks away. Once inside its walls, he said, the noise was so deafening that you couldn't talk normally and often had to shout to be heard by someone in the same room. For him, Thorazine was truly a miracle drug.

Antipsychotic medications such as Thorazine calm agitated individuals and help them to stabilize their thinking—often slowing down racing thoughts and organizing scattered ones. Hallucinations fade or at least lose some of their frightening intensity. When these drugs are working well people report being able to think more clearly and to be more present. They feel more emotionally stable and more in control of their thoughts and behavior. But they also complain about feeling less spontaneous and creative, of having difficulty concentrating, of thinking more slowly, and of not being as interested in social activities.

Many other antipsychotic medications followed Thorazine. Some work better than others for a given patient, but when differences in potency are controlled for, they have roughly equal antipsychotic effects. The most common serious side effects of the early antipsychotic medications were primarily neuromuscular symptoms such as tics, tremors, and severe muscle stiffening. The more recently introduced "atypical antipsychotics tend to have serious metabolic side effects such as significant weight gain and diabetes. The benefits of these drugs—which do improve the lives of many people and their families—also come with substantial long-term risks.

Individuals who benefit from antipsychotic medications often must take them for years. If they stop their medication, they risk slipping back into a psychotic state. I have heard this dilemma described as having to daily make a choice between re-experiencing a frightening loss of contact with reality—perhaps accompanied by exhausting paranoia or berating, condemnatory auditory hallucinations—or living with a straitjacket wrapped tight around your mind.

When used in high doses over a long period of time, antipsychotic medications contribute to the spaced-out, low energy, emotionally flattened state that I saw so often at St. Es. Many other things also contribute to this state: the devastating effects of the illness itself, years of being in an institution, a lack of social stimulation, and a profound disconnection from the outside world. I don't doubt that in some ways such numbness is more comfortable than the tormented life of a chronically psychotic mental patient before antipsychotics. But we can do a lot better—and that will take more clinical research.

Antidepressants

Morphine, St. John's Wort, and a variety of natural preparations were tried as antidepressants until the early 1950s, when drugs being tested with TB patients were discovered to have powerful antidepressant effects. Initially promoted as "psychic energizers," their liver toxicity forced withdrawal from the market in the 1960s. But, by then the three-ringed or tricyclic antidepressants with tradenames like Elavil, and Tofranil, were emerging as effective and safer alternatives. The tricyclics, in turn, were largely replaced by the equally effective, but safer and better tolerated, selective serotonin reuptake inhibitors (SSRIs), of which Prozac, is the best known.

Today, many classes and subclasses of antidepressant medications exist and are among the most widely prescribed of all medications. In addition to depression, antidepressants are prescribed for a wide variety of psychiatric conditions as well as used to supplement the effects of other psychiatric medications. It has been estimated that 1-in-10 women and 1-in-20 men in the U.S. is taking an antidepressant for some reason—not necessarily for depression.

As antidepressants, these drugs reduce the mental and physical symptoms associated with depression. They lift up mood, speed thinking, and free up energy. Sleep and appetite improve, sex once more becomes pleasurable, and social interaction is easier and more desirable. Life gets better.

The problem: often, as people begin to feel better, they decide they no longer need their medication. An abrupt stopping of many antidepressants often produces a serious relapse—or switch back—into deep depression. People whose depression responds to an antidepressant usually need to keep taking that medication for months—and sometimes years—beyond the point that they first feel better. Stopping an antidepressant should be only done in consultation with a doctor. It usually requires a careful tapering of dosage while checking to make sure depression does not return. These drugs don't cure depression. They only keep it at bay.

Anxiolytics (aka minor tranquilizers, nerve pills)

Medications used to treat states of intense anxiety, panic attacks, and phobias are collectively referred to as anxiolytics. Early sedatives like chloral hydrate and various barbiturates were among the first anxiolytics, but are no longer used for this purpose. Miltown (meprobamate), named after a small town in New Jersey, became the first drug to be marketed as a "tranquilizer" (Balon, 2008).

Created in 1946 by the Czech-born microbiologist Frank Berger, meprobamate was another one of those serendipitous drug discoveries, like lithium, Thorazine and Librium, that changed psychiatric practice. Berger sought a drug to prolong the action of penicillin, then a new—but scarce and expensive—"wonder drug" for previously lethal infections. He observed that meprobamate tranquilized animals. Trying it on himself, Berger noted that it induced a mild euphoria and a sense of inner peace. To convince executives at his drug company, he made a movie of its calming effects on monkeys. Miltown was soon widely prescribed for what was then termed "nervousness." Only later did it become apparent that it could be powerfully addicting and an overdose quickly lethal. While still available, meprobamate has lost market share to the benzodiazepines.

Benzodiazepines now dominate the anxiolytic market. Indeed, many authorities simply divide all anxiolytics into two groups: the benzodiazepines and everything else, reflecting the enormous popularity of benzodiazepines like Valium®, Xanax®, Ativan®, and Klonopin®. Beginning with Librium®, (chlordiazepoxide) and subsequently eclipsed by Valium®, (diazepam), the much safer and better-tolerated benzodiazepines supplanted meprobamate and the barbiturates both medically and increasingly on the street.

Literally thousands of variants have been synthesized, replacing barbiturates as the drugs of choice for sedation and reducing anxiety, as well as being excellent anticonvulsants and muscle relaxants. Although often used to reduce symptoms of alcohol detox, abrupt benzodiazepine withdrawal shares many of the same symptoms, including increased anxiety, altered perception, and, in rare instances, seizures.

Overusing benzodiazepines can lead to tolerance and dependence. One variant, Rohypnol ("Mexican Valium"), is ten times as potent as Valium and induces stupor within a half hour. Rohypnol is notorious as the "date rape" drug and is illegal in the US. The benzodiazepines—and most of the sedative, hypnotic and minor tranquilizers used before them—have a high potential for addiction. Their ability to suppress anxiety and panic and substitute detached tranquility makes them the drug of choice for people with gnawing fears or recurrent states of panic.

As a consequence, it is recommended that benzodiazepines only be taken for short periods of time, only be prescribed intermittently, or only taken on an as-needed basis. Total daily dosage should be carefully monitored. In reality, however, high-potency benzodiazepines are often prescribed chronically and many patients have a very hard time giving them up. Benzodiazepine addiction as a result of medical use (iatrogenic addiction) is a serious problem and accounts for a high percentage of detoxification treatments paid for by insurance companies.

Mood Stabilizers

When I arrived at NIMH in July 1979, I worked for Dr. Robert M. Post, who played an important role in the introduction of mood stabilizing drugs in psychiatric practice. At that time, Bob was primarily studying the effects of carbamazepine (Tegretol) on rapid cycling bipolar patients. Like most of the mood stabilizers that followed, carbamazepine is an anticonvulsant first used to treat epilepsy.

In research studies—such as Christine described in Chapter 3—we would attempt to switch a patient out of depression using sleep deprivation or some other technique that reset bodily rhythms. We would then try to lock in a more normal mood state using one or more stabilizing medications. We were seldom successful with these early treatments. But the knowledge that emerged from the work of Dr. Post and others was that mood stabilizers could dampen the wild mood swings that some people experience.

Mood stabilizers, however, are not as effective at switching patients out of a deep depression, though they can help to end a manic episode. More importantly, once a person enters a better mood state, the drugs can help keep them there. In addition to bipolar disorder, mood stabilizers are often used with borderline personality disorder (see Chapter 6), dissociative disorders (see Chapter 8), and periodic violent behavior such as intermittent explosive disorder. They are also used—so called "off label" prescribing—in patients with non-psychiatric conditions, such as unusual pain syndromes and for certain neurological disorders.

WHAT DO PSYCHIATRIC DRUGS REALLY DO?

When you think about it, no psychiatric medication actually cures the disorder that it is used to treat. These drugs are not like penicillin in that they can eliminate the cause of the problem—they primarily work by altering mental state.

Antipsychotics calm the agitated psychotic patient and impose a mental state characterized by thinking anchored more in logic and reality; they improve emotional control. Antidepressants reverse despair and despondency and restore feelings of hope and pleasure. As they lift the depression, the drugs also change the person's sense of self and relationships. Antianxiety drugs blunt pangs of dread and flashes of panic by submerging them in a slowed-down, detached state of woozy inner tranquility. The mood stabilizers dampen wild gyrations in emotional state and constrict the individual's intensity and range of moods and emotions.

The common price that all psychiatric medications exact is that they limit the range of states—bad and good—that an individual can experience. They shrink the individual's state-space. When we pharmacologically reduce or eliminate access to negative states such as psychosis, mania, depression and anxiety, we also tend to reduce access to joy, creativity, playfulness, sexuality, and spirituality. The worst-case scenario is the emotionally flat, cognitively constricted, energy depleted people who haunt our mental hospitals and clinics.

In my experience, psychiatric medication decisions need to be made and then frequently re-evaluated on a case-by-case basis. The dynamic balance between allowing a person access to a greater range of states of being while at the same time still keeping him functional and out of trouble requires frequent attention. Of course, the time and resources available to do this for our patients is rarely sufficient.

ANESTHESIA

For over 150 years we have used drugs to induce another extreme state of being: unconsciousness. The primary purpose of the modern art and science of anesthesia is to avoid pain. Anesthetists typically use a complementary pair of drugs to create and maintain the precarious state of being known as general anesthesia. Intravenous sedatives, opiates, and anxiolytics such as barbiturates, fentanyl, and Valium induce unconsciousness. Inhaled gases such as nitrous oxide or halothane maintain it.

But what is unconsciousness—and how can we know if someone is truly in that state? That question is difficult to answer, primarily because we do not understand what consciousness is. We do have a few physiological measures; as consciousness fades, the low-voltage, high-frequency, rapidly shifting brain electrical activity on an EEG slows down and locks into a pattern of slow wave brain activity that resembles deep, nondreaming sleep (see Chapter 3). Brain regions that process sensory information decrease metabolic activity. There is evidence that they also become functionally disconnected from each other. The range of brain activity states, both electrical and metabolic, becomes very limited. Indeed, some authorities suggest that it is this extensive constriction of state-space that is the hallmark of unconsciousness (Alkire, Hudetz, & Tononi, 2008).

But experiments with people undergoing surgery suggest that some degree of awareness continues, even when scientific instruments indicate unconsciousness. It is standard practice during most major surgeries to administer a drug that totally paralyzes the patient in order to achieve maximum relaxation of muscle and tissues. So if a person remains conscious during surgery they are unable to speak or move—totally helpless to signal their situation.

If a tourniquet is applied to a patient's forearm and the paralyzing drug is administered above the tourniquet, the patient retains voluntary movement in the hand although the rest of their body is paralyzed. Some patients are then able to carry out commands and signal with their non-paralyzed hand, even though they appear to be completely unconscious. Later, they deny any memory for the surgery. Thus an inability to recall an experience is not proof that the person was not aware of it at the time.

It is estimated that in 1 or 2 out of every 1000 surgeries, the patient may be essentially fully awake but unable to communicate their pain and distress, even with their eyes, which are covered with gauze pads to keep them from drying out (Lang, 2013). As many as 70 percent of these surgical patients develop PTSD—as compared with a rate of about 15 to 20 percent for combat veterans. Hefty court settlements have made anesthesiologists well aware of this problem, but as yet we do not have a definitive measure that absolutely ensures that a surgical patient is unconscious.

While writing this book, I was in an ICU visiting a relative who had just had major heart surgery. The anesthesiologist stopped by the bed and causally asked if he remembered anything from the surgery? "*No, nothing,*" he replied. I noted visible relief in the doctor.

Coming out of anesthesia is different than going under, as we would expect for reciprocal transitions among highly dissimilar states of being. Going under general anesthesia is typically rapid and passes through a stuporous and usually not unpleasant transition that feels like irresistibly falling into a deep sleep. Coming out of general anesthesia, however, can be disorienting and even a bit frightening as the person alternates between groggy semi-aware states and deep sleep-like states. Besides monitoring vital signs, it is important to have someone present to reorient the person as they regain awareness.

VIOLENCE, TRAUMA, AND SUBSTANCE ABUSE

Violence triggered by alcohol is a human failing true across time and culture. Research irrefutably shows that alcohol abuse is a common factor among aggressive youth, between violent couples, and by abusing parents (Wekerle & Wall, 2002). Stimulant drugs, such as methamphetamine and cocaine, are also linked to violent behavior. It is noteworthy that most violence associated with substance abuse (with the exception of drunken driving) occurs among family members and close relationships (Wekerle & Wall, 2002). This reflects more complex psychodynamics than mere proximity.

What do drugs and alcohol "DO" for traumatized people?

The fact that people who had hard and painful childhoods are more likely to develop substance abuse problems is not news to most people. At some basic level, we understand this connection—that their drug and alcohol abuse has something to do with what they had to endure, what they lacked growing up, or what they were forced to do to survive.

So far, however, our attempts to better understand the nature of substance abuse have taken diverse and largely unintegrated approaches. Neuroscience primarily focuses on the overlap of neural circuitry among the brain's pathways for reward, pain, and addiction. Epidemiology seeks to define the scope of the problem and who is at highest risk. It also seeks to understand the relationship between substance abuse and other public health problems such as HIV/AIDS, fetal abnormalities, child developmental problems, and family violence. Behavioral research looks at factors involved in starting and continuing substance abuse as well as what is associated with stopping and relapse. Prevention research seeks to integrate epidemiological and behavioral research into effective public health programs. Economists try to get a handle on the cumulative costs and policy analysts seek to understand how laws, regulations, and enforcement advance or impede social well-being.

But no one seems to be asking the essential question of *"Why do people use and abuse drugs and alcohol?"* The "state" model of PTSD and trauma suggests that one (of several) reason(s) is to suppress the disturbing emotional states and painful memories associated with traumatic life experiences. The belief that people "drink to forget" is widespread. Mental health professionals often conceptualize drug and alcohol abuse as a maladaptive form of self-medication for painful life problems.

Indeed, studies show that substance abusers often seek to manipulate or modulate their mental and physical states. My psychotherapy supervisor, Art Blank (see Chapter 7) first alerted me to this when he told me to take careful histories from Vietnam veterans about their alcohol use. It became clear that most deliberately drank themselves into a stupor at night in an effort to get some sleep by suppressing the traumatic memories, thoughts, images and fears that bubbled up in the quiet darkness.

A STATES OF BEING MODEL OF ADDICTION

Here is another question without an easy answer: What exactly is an addiction? What are the differences between a junkie nodding off in the tenement stairway and a friend who brags about being obsessed by some personal passion or craving such as ballroom dancing, golf, yard sales, chocolate, jelly beans, their smart phone, yoga, or the latest reality show or mini-series?

The drug addict, of course, is physiologically and psychologically dependent on his drugs and when deprived will experience an extremely unpleasant series of states that constitute a given drug's withdrawal syndrome. The drug addict also experiences "tolerance" and needs to progressively increase the dose to get the same effect. The golf "addict" merely needs to spend sufficient time on the links to counterbalance less desirable aspects of life. But when deprived of that playing time, he will become irritable and look for an opportunity to steal away, even if it means calling in sick or lying to a spouse.

Is there something of a continuum here? Is it possible that we all experience some degree of addiction to something that makes us feel good? Brain researchers are finding that some of these behaviors activate the same mesolimbic dopamine brain pleasure system turned on by sex and addictive drugs. Indeed, clinicians and the public increasingly view certain excessive behaviors such as pathological gambling, compulsive viewing of pornography, and obsessive video gaming as forms of addiction. This broadening scope of addiction is in line with the original use of the term, first appearing during the early sixteenth century, to characterize a zealous or immoderate devotion to a person, thing, or behavior.

People consumed by these compulsions exhibit many of the same behaviors and suffer many of the same social, economic and health consequences as drug addicts and alcoholics. They also often mix their addictive behaviors with drugs or alcohol. Combined behavioral and substance abuse "addictions" can be especially difficult to treat.

Effects of Addiction on Personality

Far from everyone who uses addicting drugs, however, becomes an addict in the traditional (and stereotypic) sense. While it is hard to know for certain, studies suggest that only a minority of heroin or cocaine users actually develop significant dependency. For example, the National Institute of Drug Abuse estimates that at the most, only about a quarter of heroin users become addicted (http://www.drugabuse.gov/publications/drugfacts/heroin, 01/30/2016). Many hard drug users seem able to indulge intermittently—just use on weekends for example—and remain comfortably drug free the rest of the time. Likewise, relatively few people who periodically gamble or view pornography become addicted in the sense that these behaviors come to dominate their lives.

So repeatedly getting high is not definitive evidence of an addiction. Rather, it is also all of the other behaviors that surround the act of getting high that prove to be compelling evidence of an addiction's power. It is the lying, cheating, stealing, violence, victimization, self-neglect, self-denigration and degradation. It is the all-consuming total fixation on the drug or behavior to the exclusion of everything and everyone else that defines the addiction. An addict will commit any act or betray anyone to get his fix. The addiction displaces all that was once meaningful, and comes to dominate the person's life.

Thus an addiction involves more than just the drug or the excessively compulsive behavior: it includes all of those behaviors and states associated with feeding and hiding the addiction as well as the intoxicated states per se. This results in a growing accretion of behavioral states surrounding and enabling the intoxicated states that form the nucleus of the individual's addiction. It is this larger set of states of being that underlie and support the intoxicated behaviors that come to constitute an "addictive" region of the person's state-space.

This addictive region of state-space competes for expression with the states and behaviors that constituted the core of the person's normal personality. In full-fledged addiction the addictive region will eventually come to dominate the expression of their former personality. Indeed, we can most clearly see into the state nature of addiction in general when we focus on its effects on personality.

That is because addiction corrupts what most people would consider normal personality. It creates a set of competing states of being that vies for control of a person's behavior. (A similar division of "self" occurs with the anti-gay rights homosexual politician, the embezzling evangelist, and fatherly serial rapist.) In addiction the constellation of states that constitutes addictive behavior comes to form a second—and often secret—life. In many instances, the second "addictive" personality subsumes the person's 'normal' personality and assumes complete control of behavior. People see a pernicious change in the person's demeanor, judgment, values, behavior and relationships— their "personality."

An addiction, whether drug or behavioral, often begins when someone experiences a significant stress or disruption of normal life. If you read the recovery stories of drug addicts, alcoholics, or gamblers, you will find that they typically describe the beginning of their addiction as a coping response to physical pain or psychological distress resulting from a sudden and unexpected injury, loss, or personal setback. For them, they explain, the drug or vice created a state of being that allowed them to ignore, or temporarily forget their overwhelming pain and distress. Initially it was a refuge; eventually they have to seek out that escape to function at all. The need to continually re-activate the intoxicated state comes to dominate their life and displaced family, friends, and work until nothing substantive remains from their past.

Like Another Person

In the early phases of addiction, the individual may periodically alternate between a set of sober or straight states, which we tend to regard as the individual's core personality, and a set of drunken, high, or compulsive behavioral states, which we attribute to their vice. The person may describe a sense of being divided—in conflict with another part of themselves. Significant others begin to draw sharper distinctions between the individual in sober and intoxicated states such, as the little girl who calmly explained to me in great detail how she really had two different fathers: *"good daddy"* and *"mean daddy."* An adult might say something more nuanced such as, *"Doc, he's just not himself when he has been drinking."* Both are commenting on how he now seems like an entirely different person when he drinks.

There is another index of addiction—the pain, anguish, despair and humiliation, social and financial costs it imposes on those who love or are dependent on the addict. Because addiction corrupts personality it is manifest in all of the addict's significant relationships. Unlike the suffering and hardship imposed by a disease, say cancer, which may evoke significant sympathetic distress in one's family and friends, but whose ill effects are largely confined to the sick person, addiction can ruin the lives of innocent others in addition to the addict.

The late stages of an addiction are typically characterized by depression, despair, and destitution. The addict usually has made prior half-hearted attempts at getting help. Usually there is a high rate of failure as the addict repeatedly relapses, often in response to what appear to most people minor stresses in daily life. However, good treatment can be remarkably effective and positive outcomes are not precluded by a history of past treatment failure (see Miller, Walters, & Bennett, 2001).

Addiction Treatment

Treatments for different types of addiction—e.g., alcohol, drugs, and vices—largely resemble each other. In fact, most treatments for behavioral addictions and newer forms of substance abuse are adapted from earlier treatments for alcohol and narcotic drugs. Treatment approaches to addiction typically fall into three basic categories: (1) 12-step type programs; (2) substitutions of another behavior or drug for the addictive drug or behavior; and (3) religious conversion. Often successful treatment involves invoking more than one approach simultaneously. So the 12-step programs explicitly invoke the need for the individual to put their faith in a higher power of some kind. And many alcoholics in AA take prescription medicines to reduce the anxiety and depression that can trigger a drinking binge.

The 12-step approach—exemplified by the original Alcoholics Anonymous 12-step model first published in 1939—involves a group support process coupled with a mental house-cleaning that strips away denial and acknowledges and accepts responsibility for past behavior. The 12-step approach has been applied to scores of different "addictions" from hard drugs, gambling, sexual compulsions and shoplifting to overeating and compulsive hoarding. For many, but certainly not all, addicts, 12-step type programs have proven effective in substantially reducing or eliminating their addictive behaviors—although a central tenet of this model is that the addiction per se never ends.

One of the important aspects of the 12-step approach is that the individual works to create a new identity—that of a recovering addict. The first step in this journey to sobriety is the open acknowledgment of their addictive identity. Hence AA's signature introduction—*"Hi, my name is John and I am an alcoholic."* Indeed in general, changes in identity seem essential to enduring changes in behavior.

Psychiatric and medical substance abuse treatment models rely heavily on using medications to reduce withdrawal and craving during an intense, short-term detoxification process. These drugs are then replaced by longer-term antidepressants, antianxiety or other medications in an effort to reduce the person's experience of stress and to help them to modulate their mood and behavior. Medication is usually supplemented with some sort of supportive psychotherapy or group therapy. The risk is creating a new dependency now to the medication—an iatrogenic (medically caused) addiction.

Religious conversion differs from the slower and more deliberate "spiritual awakening" of Alcoholics Anonymous and other 12-step programs. Religious conversion often occurs in a virtual instant and produces an immediate, global transformation of the individual's identity and belief system. The cessation of alcohol, drugs, or vices is usually total but is only one element of a larger rejection of the person's former life (See Chapter 10). The problem, referred to as the "dry drunk syndrome," is that the person has not dealt with the underlying issues that made him vulnerable to an addiction in the first place. And therefore, many problematic behaviors have not changed.

SYNTHESIS

Since Neolithic times mind-altering drugs have been used to access special states of consciousness. Prescriptions for psychoactive (mind altering) plants and fungi were common in ancient medical texts. Anthropologists document the continued role of mind altering substances in religious rites and healing ceremonies worldwide. Recreational use has probably never been higher.

The modern pharmaceutical industry first arose to meet the sky-rocketing demand for psychoactive drugs such as the barbiturates and chloral hydrate. Mind altering medications continue to be a major source of revenue. The underlying state-based nature of psychoactive medications is implicit in their categorizations, e.g., antidepressant, antianxiety, mood stabilizer etc. On the street, illicit drugs go by slang expressing similar state altering properties, e.g., uppers, downers, ecstasy, crank etc.

Many illicit drugs began as medications, often naively assumed to be free of addictive potential. For some people, however, drug- and alcohol-induced states of being come to dominate their personalities to the exclusion of all else. We speak of them as "addicted." Many have experienced severe trauma, especially as young children. Authorities believe that trauma survivors develop addictions as a result of using drugs and alcohol to "self medicate" PTSD, depression, anxiety, mood swings, sleep problems and other state-related symptoms.

As a society we are broadening the definition of addiction beyond drugs and alcohol to encompass self-destructive compulsive behaviors such as pathological gambling, excessive video gaming, obsession with pornography or other deviant activities that come to dominate an individual's time, energy, and resources displacing more traditional pro social activities. Unchecked these compulsive behaviors can corrode an individual's personality to the same degree as an intoxicating substance. And they can be just as difficult to treat as a drug addiction.

The state model views all of these addiction-related activities—drugs or compulsive behaviors—as responsible for creating systems of states of being that vie for control of an individual's behavior. In an addiction they come to displace more conventional states profoundly altering the individual's sense of self, investment in relationships, interests, and values. At their core, most current addiction treatments attempt to substitute new states of being for the addiction-related ones.

These approaches often involve a profound transformation in the former addict's sense of self, e.g., redefining oneself as a recovering alcoholic or a religious conversion.

Opportunities for Change

CHAPTER 10   EXCEPTIONAL STATES OF BEING

Dwain Weston and Jeb Corliss: Thrill Seeking

Most people would consider BASE jumping an extreme sport. BASE is an acronym for Buildings, Antennas, Spans, and Earth, which are the heights from which BASE jumpers leap in their quest for the ultimate thrill-seeking high. Surreptitiously ascending their platforms, often in violation of the law, BASE jumpers hurl themselves off of tall buildings, cell towers, high bridges, and sheer cliffs. They have just a brief exhilarating moment to enjoy a plummeting fall that would terrify most people before they must pop their parachute or die. The difference between life and death is mere seconds. Any distraction or hesitation can easily cost their life. And many do die. BASE jumping is said to have the highest fatality rate of any sport (approximately 1 death per 60 jumps), although actual numbers are difficult to verify.

It is, of course, this extreme risk, this razor thin margin for error that attracts people to BASE jumping. In that fleeting moment, on the ragged edge of violent death, BASE jumpers feel the most alive. Those who have been in the sport for any length of time will have witnessed the gruesome deaths of fellow jumpers, often close friends, even spouses. Famed BASE jumper Jeb Corliss said that each time he jumps with a group he looks around and thinks, "*Who is it going to be this time?*" Bonds formed in this context, like those on the battlefield, go beyond mere friendship to a sacred trust. (All quotes are from *Fearless: The Jeb Corliss Story*, a five-part documentary by Torstein Heide, available on YouTube.)

A surprising number of men and women who practice extreme sports like BASE jumping say that they never felt that they fit in anywhere until they met other people who also thrive on the extreme nature of their sport. Corliss speaks about being awkward, friendless, lonely, and suicidal most of his childhood and adolescence. His only source of pleasure came from playing with his pets, a collection of tarantulas, scorpions, and rattlesnakes.

When Corliss first tried BASE jumping, he had a win-win attitude in that if he lived he would have done something amazing and if he died he would be released from his suffering. On his sixth jump, from an antenna tower, he almost died, his parachute opening just enough to save him. He slammed into a dirt road. Lying there he experienced the world with an intensity and immediacy he never had felt before. He was a changed person. In chasing death he found a life. He calls it *"the most powerful experience I've ever had."*

Corliss is linked to the legendary BASE jumper, Dwain Weston, by a tragic accident. Weston, an Aussie, introduced platform diving style acrobatics to BASE jumping. When they first met in 1998, Corliss was surprised by Weston's "nerd-like" demeanor, but awed by his jumping style, which he viewed as having no close second. They quickly became a team, performing together at public events as BASE jumping attracted a growing number of adherents and spectators around the world. Led by Weston, they continually pushed the envelope, trying ever more danger-ous and spectacular jumps.

They ranked possibilities on a shared—largely implicit—danger-to-pleasure scale. The introduction of winged suits, which revolutionized the sport by allowing jumpers to briefly soar flying squirrel-like, allowed Weston and Corliss to add aerobatics to their acrobatics as well as to skim along cliff faces and flash over mountain ridges for dramatic video footage.

On October 7, 2003 Weston and Corliss tried a new stunt as the closing act in a three-day BASE jumping festival held at the Royal River Gorge Suspension Bridge in Colorado. Wearing winged suits, they leaped out of an airplane 3,000 feet above the bridge. The plan called for Weston and Corliss to simultaneously fly over and under the spectator-crowded span.

As Corliss emerges from beneath the bridge, he almost collides with Weston's parachute, which unexpectedly pops open in front of him. He is splattered by something and aware of objects flying through the air around him. On the ground he discovers that he is covered in blood. He sees a severed leg lying near him. He can't com-prehend what he is seeing until a spectator tells him that Weston hit the bridge and is dead. The 120 miles per hour impact bends the railings and shatters structural supports. People on the bridge are sprayed in gore.

Yet Corliss, Weston's girlfriend, and many of the BASE jumpers on the bridge that day continue to risk their lives jumping. It is a way of life. It is their life. Corliss says, *"If you die doing something that you love, it is not throwing your life away."*

THE DRIVE TO ALTER OUR STATE OF BEING

Even young children actively seek out altered states of consciousness. This need to experience new ways of being is baked into our nature from the first. They love to be tickled, whirled around, or held upside down—up to a point! Overdoing it, however, can quickly result in a switch in state manifest by distress and tears.

As children gain more control over their own pleasures, they will gravitate to the toys and activities that facilitate the states of being that they most enjoy or that provide refuge from painful reality. From each other they will learn new things to try. And what they learn, they pass on to younger siblings. Alone and together, they will experiment—holding their breath trying to pass out, twirling madly till they are so dizzy they can't walk or stand, or trying to get a buzz by tasting daddy's beer or taking mommy's pills.

One of the most exhilarating youthful altered states is being scared. Playing monsters, telling ghost stories, and ambushing one another in the dark is great fun. The girls practice their ear-piercing screams and everyone laughs nervously afterwards. Older kids flock to horror movies to watch the arrogant jock, the stuck-up cheerleader, the know-it-all-nerd, and other teen stereotypes being relentlessly pursued by living-dead monsters with rotting (acne?) faces that mock futile efforts to hide or fight back by morphing into ever more hideous apparitions. A ghastly death awaits most who must pay for their wanton partying, snobbishness, bullying, and other teen sins.

Adolescent Risk-Taking

Adolescence often leads to an explosion of experimentation with physically exhilarating and often risky altered states of being. Some of the outlets are socially sanctioned: rock concerts, team sports, amusement park rides, skateboarding, dirt biking. By mid-adolescence a new set of state-altering activities becomes available with a driver's license and access to a car. Speeding and reckless driving, coupled with drinking, smoking, huffing household chemicals, taking parental prescriptions, illicit drugs, sex, thrill seeking, and reckless behavior are pursued with little regard for potential consequences. Most of these state-altering activities involve peers, providing an important social context in which to express and to mutually validate experiences and new identities.

An example of risky thrill seeking is the "choking game" (Drake, Price, Kolm-Valdivia, & Wielinski, 2010). These asphyxial games involve squeezing the chest or neck, being strangled, or self-strangulation to restrict the flow of blood and oxygen to the brain. This produces a brief, euphoric high followed by a rush when blood and oxygen flow resumes. Death happens all too often, particularly when the child or adolescent is practicing self-strangulation while masturbating (autoerotic asphyxia). Surveys find that about 10% of high school and 7% of middle school students report playing choking games. Older kids, especially males, with histories of substance abuse problems are most likely to try these practices.

A history of sexual abuse and/or previous suicide attempt also increased likelihood of playing choking games. In general children who are victims, exposed to family violence, or maltreated take many more risks than those who have avoided major trauma. This increased risk taking frequently involves peers who have similar histories and older predatory males. We have documented numerous examples of risky behaviors in sexually abused girls (Trickett et al., 2011).

Better prevention programs, both universal (for all kids) and targeted (for high risk kids), could reduce much of the tragic consequences of adolescent thrill seeking. Thanks to the efforts of Robert Pynoos, MD, the DSM-5 includes risky behavior as one of the symptoms associated with posttraumatic stress disorder in adolescents. People working with adolescents should inquire about risky behaviors, particularly in children believed to have been abused or neglected. This is one area where more upfront attention could save lives and reduce costly lifelong consequences.

Why do teens seem compelled to do this crazy stuff?

In their own way teenagers are seeking growth experiences. These altered, exhilarating, frightening, and intoxicated states of being open up new senses of self and new ways of being. This drive to feel and be "different" than usual is a developmental extension of the young child's impulse to hang upside down on the swing set, spin round and round till they are so dizzy they can't stand, and laugh so hard that they wet their pants.

As parents, we don't think much of this reckless approach to self-awareness. It seems more self-destructive than self-actualizing. We also know and fear that it may shape who our kids become—and what turns them on later in life. We worry about "gateway drugs" and precocious sex. There are, of course, all-too-often tragic consequences. Teens are killed at high rates by their own behavior and by each other. Others are left mentally or physically maimed, addicted, infected, or corrupted by their adolescent search for a new turn-on. There can be a high personal and societal price for such "growth" experiences. However, when seeking to redirect this exploration into more productive channels it is important to accommodate that strong teenage drive to expand their state-space—by trying out new ways of being.

As adults, we often continue the same search ourselves—although hopefully in more discreet, sane, and socially responsible ways. We try new things, set goals of personal change, seek to push ourselves harder, and to expose ourselves to new people and situations in order to grow. We want to be different, to be more than before, to be wiser, kinder, more serene, to see deeper, to feel more, and to live life more fully. Just how far we get on our quest is uncertain—but what is certain is that many industries thrive on our desire for positive personal change and spiritual growth.

PEAK EXPERIENCES

The ultimate personal growth experience is the "peak experience." At least, there is a popular notion of peak experiences as a transformative life event. Afterwards, the person can no longer be the same. They have seen and touched something that has moved them at the very core of their being. Indeed, part of the abstract appeal of a peak experience is that it trumps the individual's will and desires and imposes a change from deep within. The change is total. The person is born again, or forever changed, or an entirely different person.

But, of course, old habits die hard. As the peak experience fades into memory, many people slide back into their former ways of being. But the memory remains and often it fuels a drive to re-experience that peak state. Oscar Wilde observed,

> *We can have in life but one great experience at best, and the secret of life is to reproduce that experience as often as possible* (Wilde, 1891).

Abraham Maslow

Abraham Maslow coined the term "peak experience" in the 1960s, a time of infatuation with altered states of being, chemical and otherwise. Best known for his hierarchy of needs, Maslow was a leader in a movement known as humanistic psychology, which sought to position itself as an alternative to Skinnerian Behaviorism and Freudian Psychoanalysis.

Sometimes referred to as the "Third Force" or the "Third Psychology," Humanistic Psychology is concerned with the "self-actualization" of the individual as a healthy person and as a positive member of society. There is a strong spiritual core to Humanistic Psychology, which Maslow viewed as ultimately leading to yet a

> . . . still "higher" Fourth Psychology, transpersonal, transhuman, centered in the cosmos rather than in human needs and interest, going beyond humanness, identity, self-actualization, and the like (Maslow, 1968 p. iv).

Drawing on personal interviews, essays written by his students, and unsolicited accounts in letters sent to him, Maslow extracted the elements of a peak experience. Among the sources of these experiences were

> " . . . the parental experience, the mystic, or oceanic, or nature experience, the aesthetic perception, the creative moment, the therapeutic or intellectual insight, the orgasmic experience, certain forms of athletic fulfillment, etc. (Maslow, 1968 p. 73).

Interestingly, Maslow felt that no single account described what he called "the full syndrome." Rather, he blended together elements from different reports to describe what he considered the "perfect syndrome."

The basic elements of peak experiences overlap in many respects. They include a sense of wholeness and of unity with a greater power. There is a feeling of perfection, rightness, completion, and fulfillment. There is both simplicity and richness. Goodness, beauty, truth, justice, benevolence and love envelop the person. There is a sense of effortlessness, playfulness, divine grace, and worldly transcendence. All these perceptions are experienced as occurring "out there," rather than existing within the person having the peak experience. Maslow sees these elements as the "facets of Being," which are revealed during a peak experience.

The person having a peak experience is passive. It is happening to them, not something that they are creating or controlling. The individual receives this experience as a divine gift and responds with awe, wonderment, reverence, gratitude, and humility. Moved to tears, laughter, prayer, or struck speechless, they may feel as if it is all "*too much to bear.*" There is a complete surrender to forces far, far greater than oneself. Merging with the universe, they lose their fear of death.

For Maslow, anyone in the midst of a peak experience—no matter how transient—was for that moment "*self-actualized.*" In his words:

"*. . . people in peak-experiences are **most** their identities, closest to their real selves, most idiosyncratic . . .* (Maslow, 1968 p. 103) [emphasis in original].

They are most integrated, least divided, and at the height of their powers. Paralyzing internal contradictions are resolved in a fusion of polar opposites. They exist only in the here-and-now, freed from the past and without fear of the future. This state of being may last only for a few moments, but it leaves an enduring mark.

Some people—very extraordinary people—have recurrent peak experiences and are able to bring the deep feelings and life lessons back into their more prosaic, everyday lives. In Maslow's terms, such people, are self-actualized. They are more than just positive, healthy people; they are pure, creative, independent, and, perhaps, most importantly, integrated people. They have fused the internal mental divisions and psychological splits that sap energy and turn people against themselves.

Out of this resolution of internal contention and contradiction emerges a natural creativity—as opposed to the artistic creativity that may accompany tormented genius—that allows these people to do anything and everything well. Attaining and sustaining this "self-actualized" state of being, individually and collectively, is the goal of Humanistic Psychology.

SEX

Sex is one of the most common ways for people to seek out peak states of being. But sexual experiences can run the gamut from heaven to hell. Few things can evoke the range of emotions and altered states of being that sex is capable of.

Most people will have hundreds to thousands of sexual experiences over the course of a lifetime. Sexual experiences usually begin in childhood as self-stimulation and masturbation. In their many forms, they are increasingly shared with others. With maturation and independence, voluntary sexual experiences will reflect the forms of psychological and physical stimulation that the person finds pleasurable or, at least, tolerable.

Unfortunately for some, formative early sexual experiences are abusive in that caretakers or others victimize them. These experiences can strongly shape an individual's sexual identity, although it is difficult to predict how. While some victims may avoid sex or timidly stick to a limited "safe" repertoire, others aggressively push their sexual behavior beyond socially sanctioned limits. This may take the form of obsessions that evolve over time into complex, highly elaborated, planned sexual experiences with and without partners (or victims), drugs, devices, costumes and settings. Like sex in general, dramatic departures from convention may reflect idiosyncratic quests for intimacy and affection or rampages of demonic desires.

Sex is state altering—or, rather, sex is a series of altered states characterized by a building sense of arousal and physical tension often culminating in explosive release. A few scientists, known as sexologists, study sexual states in the laboratory, hooking up instruments and probes to measure heart rate, blood pressure, brain waves, and markers of genital activation such as erection or vaginal lubrication. Sex researchers and sex therapists also contribute to our knowledge through case studies, surveys, and treatments for dysfunctions and problems.

But mostly, our knowledge of sex and sexual behaviors remains remarkably thin—especially given how common sex is. By social convention, these things aren't talked about in everyday life.

But nonetheless, sex shows up everywhere. Implicit and explicit images, provocative language, double entendres, knowing looks, suggestive gestures, sensual movements, and even selected smells that stimulate the sexual centers of the brain-mind are all around us. Our senses are exquisitely tuned to pick up on sexual signals from others.

Sex appeal comes in many forms, shapes, and sizes. Most people are tuned into smaller subsets of potential partners and possibilities. Exactly what "turns on" someone has a lot to do with formative early sexual experiences although gender, sexual orientation, and culture contribute in complex ways. Until recently, this question was difficult to study. Thus, we largely relied on psychoanalytic case histories and personal accounts to understand how early sexual experiences shape later desires and practices. In this regard there is still a great deal that can be learned from individual sources. Their degree of generalizability, however, always remains an open question.

Richard Rhodes

One of the most open, honest, and explicit personal discussions is Richard Rhodes's account of his sexual life, *Making Love: An Erotic Odyssey* (Rhodes, 1992). Richard Lee Rhodes (b. 1937) is an American journalist, historian, novelist and non-fiction writer, whose best-known work, *The Making of the Atomic Bomb* (1986), won the Pulitzer Prize. His autobiographical account, *A Hole in the World* (1990), relates childhood physical abuse and neglect by his step-mother and his adolescence in a home for orphaned and indigent boys. In *Making Love,* Rhodes narrates an insightful, dispassionate, self-analysis that traces how he came to be sexually aroused by the things that turn him on.

Shortly after arriving at the orphanage, Rhodes learned about masturbation from other boys, although none would publicly admit to it. Being caught in the act led to vicious teasing and continuing humiliation—which served to enforce the socially necessary code of secrecy. Like the other boys, Rhodes sought out places where he could indulge himself with the least chance of discovery. He often hid under a porch, lying on his right side in the dirt, stroking himself for as long as he could prolong the experience:

> *I was a frightened child anyway—bookish, anxious, escapist, desperately lonely. Self-stimulation transported me to an inward place of altered consciousness that I could populate with sensations. Miraculously, my body could generate pleasure out of itself.* (Rhodes, 1992 p. 28)

Masturbation became a state of refuge and his major form of tension reduction. He experimented with ways to sustain this *"sleepy, glowing dominion"* that temporarily freed him from the nagging anxiety that haunted his life.

Opportunities for privacy were rare. When they occurred, Rhodes learned to quickly switch into an erotic mode by visualizing images he found arousing. Pictures of classical sculpture in the *Encyclopedia Britannica* provided one source of voluptuous naked women. The *National Geographic*, which seemingly included at least one bare-breasted native woman in every issue, was a more easily purloined and concealed source of sexual stimulation:

> *Arousing myself with images was a learned skill. Identifying the right detail—a curve in highlight, a prominence of muscle that suggested the body's flesh and weight—incrementally increased arousal. Expression mattered more than physical detail. I always search the model's eyes and face and posture for kindness, openness, warmth. I must already have assembled some inward standard of comparison, some subliminal archetype* (Rhodes, 1992 p. 31).

Still drawn to exotic images, particularly of Asian women, Rhodes continued to frequently masturbate as an adult, now using pornographic videos to initiate the erotic transition:

> *What seems to happen is that I stimulate my penis to build arousal in concert with the images I'm watching until I approach an orgasmic peak. That allows consciousness (and identity) to fade, whereupon through some mental invocation of virtual reality I enter into the images: I become the writhing couple, the ecstatic man and woman, the slick, swollen, feverish genitals themselves: their strokes are my strokes, their cries my cries, their pleasure my pleasure* (Rhodes, 1992 p. 102).

Sexology: The Science of Sex

In recent decades, the scientific study of sexual behavior known as sexology, has become slightly more acceptable. The AIDS epidemic in particular highlighted the need to learn more about teaching people to practice safe sex. Besides finding important differences by gender and sexual orientation, we also learned that people's early sexual histories strongly influence their ability to actually use what they learn about HIV prevention.

Although individuals with histories of childhood sexual abuse score as well as others on tests of HIV prevention knowledge, in real life they frequently fail to practice the safe sex techniques they "know." They know it—but they can't use it. One reason seems to be that sexual situations act as triggers to switch them into a profoundly altered—often dissociative—state of consciousness. They may "blank out," become regressed, passive, or so overwhelmed by flashbacks to childhood abuse that they cannot recall or make use of what they know about practicing safe sex.

The extraordinarily powerful altered states of consciousness associated with sex increase the degree of state-dependence for learning and memory retrieval (SDLM) (see Chapter 5). This increased state-dependency means that sexual behaviors, memories, attitudes, associations and values are more tightly sequestered and compartmentalized from other aspects of the person's life. The mentally walled-off, compartmentalized quality of sexual states of being permits people to avoid close examination of the contradictions in their private sexual behaviors and attitudes with their public positions in everyday life.

SDLM compartmentalization impedes the operation of integrative metacognitive functions such as judgment, moral values, and self-reflection. When the details of sexual escapades by some celebrity or politician become public, we often find ourselves asking, *"How could he be so dumb as to think that he could get away with it?"* SDLM is part of that answer.

The massive commercial success of erectile dysfunction drugs with their obnoxious advertisements has also stimulated interest and funding for sex research. Sexologists seek to understand both the overt physiology of sexual arousal and the secret psychology of sexual desire. The psychobiology of the sex act itself is being examined in ever more sophisticated ways as sexologists take advantages of advances in brain imaging, hormonal assays, and miniaturized sensors. Sexology borrows heavily from research on sleep and dreaming, using a mix of physiological measures and self-reports to link corresponding mental and physical states of being.

In typical experiments, research subjects of varying sexual orientations and preferences are exposed to sexual material in a controlled fashion. As they are shown sexually explicit or neutral "control" videos, for example, subjects signal their emotional response by pressing buttons while an array of sensors tracks their body's response. Penile and clitoral erection, testicular and vaginal vasocongestion, increases in heart rate, respiration and blood pressure, activation of brain affiliation and pleasure centers, and secretion of hormones and potential psycho-sexual substances are correlated with the subject's self-report and observer-rated measures of arousal, pleasure, and distress.

The scientific data indicate that most people are and remain sexual beings. No matter a person's sexual orientation, men tend to have stronger correlations between their psychological and physiological responses. If something turns a man on, his body usually responds corre-spondingly. Men also tend to have smaller ranges of what they find to be sexually simulating—they favor certain "types" of partners and activities.

Women prove far more complex. In the laboratory, they tend to be sexually aroused by a greater range of partners and situations. And they often show physiological arousal even as they report that the material is not arousing—even repugnant. Men, of course, may suffer from the opposite situation, where the mind is aroused but the body doesn't want to perform.

Even if physiological changes do not always line up with psycho-logical experiences, the sex act is still an altered state of being, one that profoundly changes how people feel, think, and act in the moment. The famous (and, to some, infamous) sex researcher Alfred Kinsey observed that *"few persons realize how they behave at orgasm, and they are quite incapable of describing their experiences in any informative way"* (Kinsey, Pomeroy, Martin, & Gebhard, 1953 p. 628).

Voyeurism

People change during sex. They behave in ways that they would never do in other circumstances. Sex is private and hidden, secret and surreptitious. Not just because we are embarrassed to publicly reveal our bodies and genitals, but also because we are reluctant to reveal who we become and what we desire and do in the heat of sexual passion. We depend on intimacy or anonymity to keep our secrets.

Watching sex then is not just about watching feverish genitals in action. It is about watching people become consumed by something that visibly changes them in ways that are exciting. The plentiful pornog-raphy on the Internet demonstrates that vast numbers of people are interested in voyeuristic sexual stimulation. Indeed, many authorities believe that pornography rakes in far more money than any other Internet enterprise. The enormous variety of offerings says something about the range of sexual interests, styles, tastes, fetishes, and perversions people are capable of.

What is it that people are searching for when they consume pornography? Rhodes, for example, searches pornographic videos for evidence of women becoming sexually aroused. For him, signs of female sexual arousal are the ultimate turn-on. It is this transformation that is important. He wants to see them change as they give themselves over to arousal. He describes it thusly:

> *But women performers often also show arousal. They lubricate, sometimes copiously; their nipples erect; their labia open and swell; a rosy flush warms their upper bodies. They register waves of pleasure with curious involuntary flickers of expression, as we all do, baring their teeth, jutting their jaws, curling their lips in ecstatic mammalian snarls. Their eyelids flutter and their eyeballs roll back. They mewl and whimper and moan. They begin kissing, licking and clutching their partners to automatic rhythms, clonicly* (Rhodes, 1992 p. 92).

The admittedly limited evidence suggests that when people consume pornography many are searching for specific signs and sequences, for behaviors and situations, for acts and responses, which are especially sexually arousing for them. They are also searching for elements that they can later incorporate into their sexual fantasies, replay in their mind, or act out during subsequent sexual encounters. Masturbation, for example, is highly organized around sexual fantasies. And most of the pornography on the web is intended for use during masturbation.

But sex with actual partners is also often overlaid with fantasy that serves to mentally remove the person from the actual circumstances of where they are, who their partner is, and what is actually happening. A lot of sexual behavior occurs in the dark and with eyes closed to block distraction and increase the vividness of fantasy. The reality-changing states of arousal contribute to the vividness and compelling nature of sexual fantasy, as compared to run-of-the-mill daydreams.

Why Internet Pornography Is Bad for Kids

Whenever a major sports hero or youth celebrity publicly screws up big time, people come down on him or her because they failed at being a good "role model." As a society, we believe that role models matter. We believe that they influence—for better or for worse—children who identify strongly with them. We want our children to identify with positive role models and we worry when they gravitate towards negative ones. We believe that people in general—especially children—will imitate and emulate the values and behaviors of their role models.

So who and what are the sexual role models available to our kids? As Richard Rhodes openly shared, sexual objects, sexual behaviors, and sexual identities, take form and consolidate in childhood and adolescence. These images, acts, and identities are tightly paired with pleasurable altered states of consciousness usually initially via masturbation. In time these sexual states of being come to form the nucleus of a sexual identity. Just as Rhodes imprinted on the female images in *National Geographic* and the *Encyclopedia Britannica,* today's youth are transfixed on an endless parade of graphic images and sexual acts viewable on the Internet.

The Internet has changed everything with respect to the sexual education of youth. Every sexual act imaginable, no matter how bizarre, is viewable somewhere in cyberspace. The frozen, airbrushed playmate foldouts of yesteryear have long disappeared. Violence, dominance and degradation is embedded or explicit almost everywhere. What kinds of sexual identities are being shaped in children who see this filth?

Technology has outpaced our ability to control what children are exposed to. Parental controls and the family computer have gone the way of the floppy disk and the dial-up Internet. Kids can now access porn virtually anywhere through Internet-connected devices ranging from videogame consoles and music players to tablets and smartphones. It is difficult to scientifically investigate these effects—although the absence of research funding makes it a moot point. But role models do matter. And the sexual role models that children are encountering daily on the Internet do not bode well for healthy adult sexuality and marital harmony.

Identity Alterations during Sex

As with many altered states of consciousness, the individual's sense of self or identity is one of the dimensions that shift in sexual state-space.

Sometimes people use costumes, masks, and props as accessories of transformation; others create scenarios or act out fantasies.

But for some people, this need to be—or at least behave like—someone else to become sexually aroused lands them in big trouble. Consider some of the sex scandals that regularly appear in the media. The mild-mannered individual who is discovered living a salacious secret life; the righteous religious leader who frequents prostitutes; the white-supremacist politician who has children by his African-American maid; the cut-throat businessman who enjoys being humiliated by a dominatrix, and the ardent feminists who engage in sadomasochistic sex. When publicly revealed, it is the apparent duplicity; the seeming hypocrisy in the "who" that they really "are" that is the shocking element, not so much the sexual practices themselves.

Given the powerful and intimate nature of sex, it should not be a surprise that some people develop sexual personalities that veer dramatically from their public selves. The only sign of their latent presence in everyday life may be slips of the tongue, odds twists of speech, taste in dirty jokes, leering looks, or "accidental" bumps, brushes, and touches.

Sexual tension, like the need for sleep, builds over time. At some point, most individuals seek some form of release. People with strong, highly differentiated, "sexual personalities"—particularly ones that deviate from the social norms—will eventually seek out partners and contexts that allow them to express their hidden side. If caught, they may say that they can't help themselves—that they are addicted to their sexual behavior. No matter how hard they try, they can't seem to stop themselves from doing it. Even when they are not doing it—whatever the "it" is—they find themselves thinking and fantasizing about it.

Sexual Addiction

Can sex become an addiction in the same way most people associate with drugs or alcohol? There are some differences, of course, but many of the same brain-reward pathways are involved. And sexual addictions can come to dominate a person's life to the same degree that drug addiction can. People can become as psychologically dependent on their sexual fix as an addict is on his drug of choice. They may have to continually "push the envelope" in the same way a drug addict must continually increase the dose to offset tolerance. Sexual addicts often engage in deceptive and illegal behaviors that come to corrupt the individual's "normal" personality in ways similar to drug addicts. Sexual addictions or perversions are notoriously difficult to treat and many quickly relapse after treatment ends. However, one can argue that sexual addicts are not physiologically dependent on sex in the same way that an addict faces withdrawal symptoms when deprived of an addicting drug.

Peak Sex

The other side of the coin is peak sex—moments of mutually shared sexual ecstasy. Dating back thousands of years, spiritual sexual practices such as Tantric sex techniques, have sought to use sex as an avenue to enlightenment. Known in the West primarily through the *Kama Sutra,* a compendium of Indian texts of sensual and sexual pleasure dating to the second century, Tantric sexual positions and techniques provide the foundation for many peak sex manuals and tapes. In their purest form, Tantric practices are a sexual form of yoga dance between two loving partners using gaze, breath, voice, movement, position, and directed energy to achieve mutual bliss. (More recently, the Tantric positions and practices are marketed as sexual novelties to rekindle interest in bored couples.)

Whether spiritual or commercial, these practices strive to achieve and prolong new and more pleasurable states of being through sex. The many different positions—which are what most people focus on when they first encounter Tantric sex—provide a flowing balance between the genders. Roles of dominance and submission, control and vulnerability, giver and receiver of pleasure, pass back and forth between the partners as they explore together. Slow sensual shared movements punctuated by pauses and gentle touches build arousal. Breath and muscle control seek to prolong pleasure and delay orgasm. When it occurs, orgasm may be prolonged and repeated. The fluidity of roles, deep intimacy, and mutual fulfillment that accompany peak sex in the context of a loving relationship differentiates these practices from the obsessions and compulsions of an addiction.

Sex is one of the most powerful ways for many people to profoundly alter their state of being. Understanding sexual behavior from this perspective helps to explain why, as a society, we are both obsessed with and frightened by sex. It helps us to understand why many people find it difficult to think about or discuss their sexual behaviors and preferences –because they occur in very different states of consciousness and are attached to other senses of self.

Much of the sexual act's mystique is in the losing of oneself as a separate individual and merging with another. We lock ourselves together—intermingling our bodies, our sweat and secretions, and, most importantly, our hearts and souls—in an effort to achieve a divine union. The drive to experience peak sex is about more than just seeking carnal pleasure. It is a quest to connect with the cosmic.

EPIPHANIES AND SPIRITUAL AWAKENINGS

Virtually all religions have mystical traditions growing out of the spiritual revelations of their founders, saints, prophets, or gurus (Geels, 2011). Living religions are continually being reworked by the spiritual experiences of their followers—leading to the splitting off of sects and movements. New religions are continually being born—frequently organized around the apocalyptic visions of a charismatic leader whose followers believe has direct access to the divine. Most of these remain small, patriarchal "cults" that don't outlive their leader and often end badly—not infrequently following the sexual abuse of followers and their children.

Which of these many religious visions and revelations are truly divine and which are the megalomaniac delusions of a paranoid or the sociopathic manipulations of a con artist? In his famous series of lectures on religion, *The Varieties of Religious Experience,* William James sidesteps this question although he opines that no matter how compelling a spiritual revelation may be for a given individual, it holds no authority or power over others who have not had that experience (James, 1901–1902 pp. 323–324).

Rather than grapple with the thorny question of whose spiritual revelations are divine and whose are delusional, James seeks to extract the essence of those mystical experiences that produce profound changes in individuals. For him, the mystical experience of interest "*is that which lives itself out within the private breast*" (James, 1901–1902 p. 262). The ultimate truth of the revelation, James believes, must be found in the degree and longevity of change that it produces within the person who possesses it.

Elements of a Religious or Mystical Experience
Drawing on religious examples from the saints and contemporary accounts of sinners and others who reformed their lives in the psychological aftermath of revelation, James identifies four salient features of

a mystical experience (James, 1901–1902 p. 292ff). The first is the *ineffability* of the experience: words cannot describe it. Those who have not shared a similar experience simply cannot understand it.

The second feature is *noetic* quality, a state of knowledge with *"insight into depths of truth unplumbed by the discursive intellect* (p. 293)." This insight brings an imperative for personal change that remains after the experience has passed.

James also observes that mystical experiences always share a third quality of *transience* and cannot be sustained for long. Most, he notes, last a few hours at most and then fade into the *"light of common day."* And mystical experiences are characterized by the *passivity* of the person seized by revelation. The person feels submerged within a superior power, with no will, only a wish to surrender completely to a greater force.

Bringing the discussion of mysticism (Lecture 6) around to his own experiences with nitrous oxide (see Chapter 1), James declares that his drug-induced altered states of consciousness compelled him to conclude that so-called "rational consciousness" was but one kind of consciousness surrounded by many other, entirely different, forms of consciousness. This insight—for James regards this as one of his most profound and enduring revelations about the nature of the consciousness—leaves him with a sense of deeper harmony.

Looking back at my own experiences, they all converge towards a kind of insight to which I cannot but help ascribing some metaphysical significance. The keynote of it is invariably a reconciliation. It is as if the opposites of the world, whose contradictoriness and conflict make all our difficulties and troubles, were melted into unity (p. 298).

William James is far from alone in having transformational mystical experiences. Indeed, surveys suggest that a significant percentage of people describe a moment in which the world changed for them and they were changed with it. Individual accounts can frequently be found in the lives of spiritual leaders. Yet with a few notable exceptions, such as James and Maslow, such powerfully transformative experiences remain virtually unexamined by mainstream science and are, instead, relegated to the realm of theology.

Marsha Linehan

People who have mystical and religious experiences may be driven to share their transformative insight. In a dramatic public presentation at the Institute of Living in Hartford, CT, Marsha Linehan, the psychologist who developed Dialectic Behavior Therapy (DBT) to treat suicidal women, revealed that she had been one of those self-destructive women (Carey, 2011) (see Chapter 6). At the age of 17 she was hospitalized at the Institute of Living in Hartford, CT, spending more time in seclusion than any of her fellow patients. At her discharge in May 1963, the hospital note read, "*during the 26 months of hospitalization, Miss Linehan was, for a considerable part of this time, one of the most disturbed patients in the hospital*" (Carey, 2011 p. 3).

A short verse Linehan composed during the hospitalization captured her turmoil.

> *They put me in a four-walled room*
> *But left me really out*
> *My soul was tossed somewhere askew*
> *My limbs were tossed here about*
> (Carey, 2011 p. 3)

Burning herself with cigarettes, cutting her arms, legs, and abdomen, banging her head against the wall and floor, Linehan was unrelentingly self-destructive:

> *I was in hell. My experience of these episodes was that someone else was doing it; it was like I know this is coming, I'm out of control, somebody help me; where are you God? I felt empty, like the Tin Man; I had no way to communicate what was going on, no way to understand it.* (Carey, 2011 pp. 2–3)

Diagnosed as schizophrenic, Linehan was aggressively treated with drugs, including Thorazine, and months of Freudian psychoanalysis. According to hospital records, she had at least two courses of electroconvulsive shock treatments.

Linehan vowed that when she got out; she was coming back for others. It was not easy. She was rehospitalized, barely surviving a couple of suicide attempts. She found refuge in her Catholic faith, praying frequently in the chapel at Loyola University where she was taking night classes:

One night I was kneeling in there, looking up at the crosses, and the whole place became gold—and suddenly I felt something coming toward me. It was this shimmering experience and I just ran back to my room and said, "I love myself." It was the first time I remember talking to myself in the first person, I felt transformed (Carey, 2011 p. 4).

This transcendental moment of self-acceptance came to form the core of Linehan's efforts to come back for others. Borrowing from behaviorism for reinforcing new ways of thinking and acting and blending in meditation breathing techniques to increase mindfulness, she tested and refined her approach (Dialectical Behavior Therapy [DBT]) into one of the most effective treatments for borderline personality disorder and related conditions.

Quantum Change

Few scientists are willing to investigate such profound changes in personality, in part because such personal transformation happens outside the laboratory, and in ways that do not permit controlled measurement. William R. Miller, a distinguished psychologist at the University of New Mexico, is an exception to this academic aversion. Miller is well known for his work developing psychological techniques to help people make difficult but necessary changes in unhealthy behaviors. His *Motivational Interviewing* model, codeveloped with Stephen Rollnick, has proven one of the most important advances in the treatment of substance abuse.

Long fascinated by accounts of rapid and enduring personality change often coming at a moment of intense personal crisis, Miller and his colleague, Janet C'de Baca, systematically analyzed transcendental experiences in their book, *Quantum Change* (Miller & C'de Baca, 2001). In many respects, their research confirms James's generalizations and expands Maslow's formulations. Like James, Miller and C'de Baca find that the most compelling feature of such experiences is their long-term transformational power on the individual. Noting that no single definition is sufficient, they describe "quantum change" as "*a vivid, surprising, benevolent, and enduring personal transformation*" (p. 4).

In 1989, they began to interview people who claimed to have a moment of transformation. To their surprise, it was easy to find examples—once a story about their study appeared in the local news, the phone began to ring. For many volunteers, this was the first time that they had ever told anyone about their life-transforming moment. The stories they shared form a profound account of personal narratives about abrupt, and often total, personality change occurring because of a mystical experience.

Miller and C'de Baca are well aware that these narratives are stories and that their truthfulness can never be fully confirmed. Still, they find the stories compelling and respect the reverence that tellers often express as they describe what happened to them:

> *We were personally captivated by the wonder and mystery of the stories themselves, and drawn by a still deeper story that we sensed within and beneath them. It was as if the scientist in us sat side by side at the campfire with a wide-eyed child entranced by a succession of master storytellers. Yet these stories were not make-believe but real, told by the people who lived them.* (Miller & C'de Baca, 2001 p. 9)

This study of mystical change builds upon James and Maslow's work by imposing a greater systematization on cases. This allows a more quantitative overview, although the unavoidable degree of subjectivity will make a hardcore scientist wince. In most respects, however, their ultimate conclusions are remarkably similar to James and Maslow, whom they quote frequently.

They find—as did James—two basic types of personality change. The first occurs gradually, and it's based on a growing awareness of a personal problem or issue. They call this "Type 1 change" and equate it with James's "educational change."

It is "Type 2 change" that most often results in the instantaneous and enduring personal transformation that Miller and C'de Baca identify as a quantum change. Type 2 change is rapid. It is vivid. It takes the individual by surprise. It is emotionally powerful, and it forever changes the person's life.

There are, however, two categories of Type 2 quantum change. The first is an insightful form. But its impact differs from everyday insight in that this flash of understanding profoundly changes the person's worldview such that their sense of self and behavior are forever altered. While powerful, this insightful form of quantum change is understandable in conventional psychological terms. It can be conceptualized as the sudden and now fully conscious consolidation of a growing, but previously unconscious or subconscious, awareness of personal issues.

The second form of quantum change is mystical—it defies conventional theories of personality. The person's sense of inner change is intense and immediate, infused with a *"noetic sense of being acted upon by something outside and greater than oneself* (p. 21)." Life will never be the same again. Unexpected, uninvited, and at first often unwanted, mystical quantum change leaves its recipient with a vivid and awe-filled memory of the moment.

Miller and C'de Baca observe that quantum change experiences are often described in seemingly contradictory terms. They may be simultaneously terrifying and yet peaceful, or both self-affirming and self-annihilating, or joyous but profoundly sad. Often there is an immediate sense of extraordinary emotional and physical relief as if some enormous tension or weight—of which the person had only been partially aware—was suddenly lifted. Only then can the person appreciate how painful and crippling that burden had been.

People who experience a quantum change often express an overwhelming sense of gratitude and humility for what has happened to them. Many describe sensing a loving presence that came to change the direction of their life during its darkest hour. This fleeting vision of an omniscient, omnipresent, benevolence at the center of the universe leaves an enduring sense of peace in its wake. Concerns that used to be greatly upsetting are now viewed as minor annoyances. Fear is replaced by a grateful awareness of being alive and a serene acceptance of death as but reunification with a greater power.

In the afterglow, the person's priorities are dramatically reorganized. Spirituality replaces materialism and qualities of honesty, humility and personal growth supersede desires for physical attractiveness and indulgent pleasure. For Miller and C'de Baca's narrators, the new spirituality was rarely organized around a specific religious doctrine. Rather, more often it encompasses a pervasive sense of the sacred as it infuses all aspects of life. This new awareness and knowledge is sensed as coming from outside of the self. It is the manifestation of a greater and undeniable truth.

In many cases, the quantum change occurs in a moment of deep despair. The person has reached a breaking point. Overwhelmed and hopeless, with nowhere to turn and no longer able to deny or tolerate their misery. The person may be on the verge of suicide when suddenly an outside power steps in and takes over. Not infrequently the outside force takes the form of a voice. Often heard as an internal, "as-if" voice that speaks an undeniable truth about the person's life.

With a new sense of self, the person experiences a new beginning. They are "born again" in religious terms or in Maslow's term have become "self-actualized." The person now knows what life is about and seeks to live accordingly. The answer for most is that life is about an awareness of the presence of the divine in the everyday. This greater awareness may be expressed in religious terms or as a personal philosophy.

It may take some time for a person to fully consolidate this new sense of self and to break free of the demands and habits of their previous life. But there is no turning back. In one way or another, those who undergo quantum change believe that they have seen the truth and they must honor it. But most also recognize that it is a uniquely personal truth that cannot be imposed upon others—it is for them alone. That is why, before meeting Miller and C'de Baca, many volunteers had never told anyone about their experience or had only shared it with a few trusted people. Most were more accepting and forgiving of the foibles of others. And they expressed a new and powerful sense of connectedness with others that often did not exist before their mystical experience.

What Is Happening Here?

Clearly, the mystical moment of quantum change can be seen as an altered state of consciousness. James, Maslow, Miller and C'de Baca, and most others analyzing these kinds of human experience use the language of altered states of consciousness. The trigger for these mystical states may be extreme personal pain, hopelessness, or suicidal despair. For a few, the trigger seems to have been becoming aware of a feature in their environment they had never noticed before, or the sudden strangeness of a familiar activity that turns the world upside down.

This kind of change is an abrupt switch into a profoundly altered state of being. The person's usual level of awareness, thinking patterns, predominant emotions, and prevailing sense of self are instantly replaced by deepened awareness, openness to new ways of being, and an emotional passivity that gives rise to a new and radically different sense of the self and its relationship to the universe. As with similar altered states, the experience is transient and fades quickly. But the mystical moment leaves behind a vivid and compelling memory of the way things looked and felt. The palpable sense of profound relief—as if a great weight has been lifted from the soul—reflects a release of physical and psychological tension that had dominated the person's prior states of being.

In many accounts, life has driven someone into a despairing and hopeless state of mind and the only escape seemed to be death. Instead, the person suddenly encounters a new and harmonious state of being characterized by peace and passivity. It is as if a wormhole had opened in their state-space and the person tumbled into another dimension—a dimension that offers a new perspective from which to view themselves and all of their emotions and dysfunctions. From this new vantage point the troubled person is suddenly able to see himself in full—and begin to consciously change who he is.

While in the throes of quantum change a person visits a new region of state-space. Like other rewarding states of being, a desire often follows to revisit or recreate the experience. But even if it never repeats itself, even if the person never encounters another similar moment, they are forever changed by this trip to a new realm of consciousness.

What changes is not that the person now resides in a new region of state-space. Rather, it is that in that transcendental moment they gained a compelling new self-perspective on the dysfunctional states and reflexive pathways that constituted their personality. They can now deliberately reconfigure this array. They can change who they are. Miller and C'de Baca observe:

> *The result is a new, dramatically reorganized identity. One might draw an analogy here to the development of multiple personality disorder, where early trauma is so great that one's identity is segmented, dissociated into separate parts. In quantum change, it is almost the opposite process. Strained and separate aspects of identity are reordered in one brilliant moment. The deck is reshuffled. The pieces are moved around, and at some level the person suddenly sees how they can be rearranged into a new picture of self.* ***The crisis is resolved by that person becoming someone new*** *[emphasis added] (Miller & C'de Baca, 2001 p. 157).*

It is this process at a metacognitive or higher dimension of state-space that distinguishes quantum change from run-of-the-mill altered states of being. This is the reason why just getting high on drugs or seeking out adrenalin-pumping thrills like skydiving—although they may momentarily reduce tension or increase the sense of "being alive"—seldom change people for the better in enduring ways. It is not the transient exhilarating state alone; it is the higher order self-reflective and self-directed reorganization of mental and emotional states that produces profound change in personality.

MEDITATION

In direct contrast to the spontaneity of epiphany, meditation seeks to achieve a similar result through disciplined, self-directed, and repeated practice. This rigorous, austere regimen aims to push a properly prepared individual through that same transcendental wormhole in state-space to enlightenment. Most schools of meditation stress that repeated and exacting practice of technique is essential to overcome the mind's natural tendency to wander off into thoughts and fantasies.

Mystical states have been deliberately sought, repeatedly induced, and carefully cultivated by many religious traditions for thousands of years (West, 1987). Virtually all major modern religious traditions have mystic sects that practice some form of meditation or seek to induce trance states in which worshipers are filled with the spirit of a divine entity. The cumulative wealth of experiential knowledge encompassed by these ancient traditions must be extraordinary.

Largely the province of Eastern traditions, Western science is now seeking to discern a mechanism or marker that signals a religious or transcendental state. There is an intuitive sense that the knowledge contained within may provide a more enlightened and universal perspective from which to navigate our fragile world. But we in the West still cannot fully translate such a mystical perspective into terms that we readily understand.

The practice of meditation takes on a bewildering array of forms. Staring unblinkingly at a candle, frantically whirling in dizzying circles, endlessly repeating a one-word *mantra*, sitting naked under a freezing waterfall, ruminating on a seemingly irrational *koan*, submitting to starvation, self-inflicting pain, breathing in primal rhythms or just observing oneself breathe naturally—all of these methods can induce mystical states of being. Different techniques often appear wildly contradictory, but those who study them say that all of the techniques follow one of a few broad strategies.

The ultimate goal of meditation is to dwell in a special state of being called *satori or samâdh or enlightenment*. This state is described in words and metaphors a lot like those invoked by individuals who experience quantum change and epiphanies. It is frequently described as being indescribable by mere words. Indeed, when mystics seek to communicate their reality they often use parables and paradoxes in word and deed that challenge a "rational" view of the world.

In this special state of being, the master reports a sense of unity with the universe in which all apparent contradictions are resolved into a harmonious whole. A serene acceptance of mortality arises, with a letting go of cares, regrets, ambitions, passions, and possessions. For the enlightened, these various concerns are of no consequence beside a unifying universal truth.

The meditative path to an enlightened state of being is typically long and arduous. Different groups and traditions have different ways of using these strategies—which leaves an enormous and perplexing assortment of ways to achieve enlightenment. Scholars from different disciplines and traditional meditational practices, however, typically agree on two or three unifying principles.

Unifying Principles of Meditation

The classic discussion of the unifying principles underlying the profusion of meditation techniques is the paired essays of Claudio Naranjo and Robert E. Ornstein, *On the Psychology of Meditation* (1971) (Naranjo & Ornstein, 1971). Both authors draw broadly on a range of religious traditions to extract the essence of meditation from the host of practices that qualify. Later scholarly discussions of the many paths to mystical states prominently cite their essays. The collaboration between Claudio Naranjo, a Chilean psychotherapist interested in meditation and psychedelics, and Robert E. Ornstein, a research psychologist interested in the psychophysiology of mental processes, is another product of the psychedelic era's excitement about the therapeutic potential and spiritual possibilities of altered states of consciousness.

The complementary essays are intended to be a balanced discussion of the Eastern experiential (in Naranjo's case) and the Western experimental (in Ornstein's) approaches to meditation and mystical states of being. Naranjo's essay focuses on identifying common underlying principles in the meditative practices of a broad range of religious traditions. He classifies all meditation techniques into one of three categories: (1) the way of absorption; (2) the way of emptiness; and, (3) the way of surrender.

Attention, Attention, Attention

Ornstein, in turn, sees two basic strategies underlying the diversity of meditation practices; one, a restriction of awareness through the intense focusing of attention; and two, the opening of awareness. Arguing that a focus on the psychophysiology of attention is key to understanding meditation in Western scientific terms, Ornstein recounts the famous story of Zen Master Ikkyu's answer when asked by a disciple for a list of principles to the highest wisdom. In reply, the Master writes "*attention.*" When asked if there was nothing more, he writes "*attention, attention.*" When chastised for his lack of specificity, the Master writes "*attention, attention, attention.*"

Naranjo's way of absorption includes those practices that involve the intense concentration of attention on a single object or source of stimulation. The point of concentration may be visual—a candle flame, an intricate *mandala*, a cross, or the picture of a Master. It can be verbal, such as chanting aloud or silently reciting a *mantra*. It may involve hearing: listening to the rhythmic beating of a drum, the tingling of wind chimes, the ringing of a gong, the murmur of a brook, or the roar of a waterfall. Stylized movements and specific postures such as martial art katas and yoga poses can also be used to concentrate attention. The meditator seeks to become one with the meditative object or activity and to lose awareness of self. The meditative objects or activities chosen by different schools hold religious significance for that tradition.

Ornstein, in turn, draws his explanations from Cold War-funded research on problems encountered by radar operators, pilots, and truckers performing exacting duties under monotonous conditions. These 1960s psychology experiments explored various aberrations in attention and concentration by manipulating sensory input.

Ornstein theorizes that concentrative meditation techniques, no matter what senses they engage, work by narrowing awareness to generate a special mental state that offers at least a context for meditation. He says:

> *So we can say (within our frame of reference) that concentrative meditation is a practical technique which uses an experiential knowledge of the structure of our nervous system to "turn off" awareness of the external world and produce a state of blank-out or darkness, the "void," the cloud of unknowing. The techniques of concentrative meditation are not deliberately mysterious or exotic but are simply a matter of practical applied psychology* (p. 169).

Opening Up Awareness

Ornstein has more difficulty accounting for Naranjo's way of emptiness. He subsumes it under his category of "opening up" meditation techniques. For Naranjo, the essence of the negative or empty way is manifest by "*. . . letting go of habits, preconceptions, and expectations; letting go of control and of the filtering mechanisms of ego* (p. 75)."

As an example of a negative meditation technique, Ornstein offers shikan-taza ("just to sit"). When practicing shikan-taza, the meditator must sit completely still and empty the mind so as to be able to clearly perceive the world. Negative techniques strive to stop all thought in order to create an open blank state of "right mindfulness," "bare attention," and "clear comprehension" from which to view the world. Shikan-taza is extremely difficult. Try it sometime.

For Ornstein, the negative meditation techniques are best explained by Huxley's theory that the brain is a "reducing valve" for the mind (see Chapter 9) that filters out most irrelevant stimuli in order to simplify our perception of the world and to better focus our attention on what matters most. Ornstein notes that the "reducing valve" theory was clearly anticipated by William James in his foundational work, *The Principles of Psychology* (1950):

> *The highest and most celebrated mental products are filtered from the data chosen by the faculty next beneath, out of the mass offered by the faculty below that, which mass was in turn sifted from a still larger amount of yet simpler material, and so on.*
> (James quoted in Naranjo & Ornstein, 1971 p. 190)

Ornstein concludes—as have many before and since—that reality, as we each individually know it, is a personal construct that depends, in part, on the state of the individual. He offers examples from the Islamic meditative tradition of Sufism as evidence that some meditative practices seek to break through this deceptive and filtered version of reality:

> *The Sufis are the clearest precursors of modern psychology's conception of awareness. Sufi teaching stories frequently focus on men who are too preoccupied to hear what is being said, or who misinterpret instructions because of their expectations, or who do not see what is in front of them, because of the limited nature of their constructs. The Sufis emphasize the constantly changing*

biases that constitute our normal awareness. "What a piece of bread looks like depends on whether you are hungry," says a Sufi poet, Juallaudin Rumi (Naranjo & Ornstein, 1971 p. 191).

Naranjo's third way, the way of surrender and self-expression, eludes Ornstein's Western psychology. It is not surrender *from*, but surrender *to*. In essence, it is a form of possession by visionary experiences, automatic movements, release of dominant physical energies, inspired utterance, automatic writing, or spirit possession. The meditator disappears as an individual by becoming the channel through which the possessing spirit speaks and acts:

The aspect of the shamanistic experience is one that the individual expresses either as a separation of the soul from the body (so that it may visit other places and levels of existence), or as a penetration of his soul-free body by other spirits (animal, demonic, or angelic); possibility, by both at the same time (Naranjo & Ornstein, 1971 p. 101).

Naranjo links such possession states with shamanism. Shamanism is a religious vision of the world as influenced by gods, demons, and ancestral spirits that respond only to a shaman's magic. Shamans are active seekers, journeying into the realm of the supernatural to pacify its wrath or influence it on behalf of men. Shamanism was the foundation for humankind's first organized forms of religion in which shamans, priests, and oracles interpreted or interceded with gods and spirits. Human-animal figures believed to be shamans are among the earliest depictions of humans in cave art. Shamanism remains central to a range of religious traditions around the world.

In the Bible, demonic possession is primarily shown by physical signs—contortions, convulsions, deafness, and blindness—and bizarre behavior (Sluhovsky, 2011). Until recently Christianity viewed possession through the medieval lens of demonic possession exemplified by the Devils of Loudon and the Salem Witch Trials. Spiritual possession, however, such as speaking in tongues or glossolalia, is believed to be increasing among modern-day fundamentalist Christians. This socially acceptable form of religious spirit possession allows neuroscientists to probe this unusual state of being and they are finding unique brain activity signatures (McNamara, 2009).

The Neuroscience of Meditation and Religious Experiences

Zen monks, with their legendary prowess in the mental and martial arts, have long fascinated Westerners. Psychologists, psychoanalysts, anthropologists, and others have sought to translate Zen Buddhism into terms comprehensible to our Western frame of mind. As an example of mindful control over attention, Ornstein describes an experiment with Zen monks. Subjected to a repetitive, monotonous clicking noise, the monks did not habituate or "tune it out." Instead they continued to show heightened brain activity for each subsequent click equivalent to their response to the first click.

Control subjects, on the other hand, quickly showed a decrease in brain activity within three or four clicks. After a minute or so, control subjects lost all conscious awareness of the clicking and it failed to elicit detectable brain responses. Ornstein cites this as an example of how certain meditation techniques strive to open awareness, bypassing the habitual filtering or reducing valve function of the brain.

Richard Davidson

Research with Zen monks has continued, most notably in the laboratory of Dr. Richard J. Davidson at the University of Wisconsin-Madison. A friend of the Dalai Lama, Dr. Davidson has studied the brain activity of Zen monks meditating on "pure compassion" or "non-referential compassion" (*dmigs med snying rje* in Tibetan)" (Lutz, Greischar, Rawlings, Matthieu, & Davidson, 2004 p. 16369). This meditational state of unconditional loving-kindness does not focus on any objects, ideas, images, mantras or memories. It is, instead, an opening of oneself to compassion and benevolence as a way of being.

On cue, experienced monks are able to rapidly (within 5–15 seconds) switch into a mental state characterized by a dramatic increase in brain activity in the gamma (25–42 Hz) frequency band of the EEG (see Chapter 3). (This same frequency band shows the largest changes, i.e., the lowest intraclass correlations, across the alter personalities of DID subjects; see Figure 4.1). College students given basic instruction in meditation served as comparison subjects. They were unable to produce similar changes in brain activity. There were also significant differences in types of brain activity between the students and the monks during the baseline resting state before the meditation period. The number of hours of practice was the best predictor of the amplitude and synchronicity of a meditator's gamma brain waves.

In a similar study, Joshua A Grant and colleagues at the University of Montreal measured the ability of Zen meditators to tolerate pain from a heated probe attached to the inner side of the left calf (Grant, Courtemanche, Duncan, Duerden, & Rainville, 2010). Meditators were able to tolerate much higher heat than non-meditating control subjects. MRI brain scans showed that the meditators had thicker areas of the cortex associated with pain perception, including the anterior cingulate cortex (see Chapter 3). The thicker the anterior cingulate cortex in these brain regions, the higher the temperature a meditator could tolerate. Thicker cortexes were correlated with more meditation practice in terms of hours and in years.

The Davidson research group contrasted two common types of Buddhist meditative techniques, focused attention (FA) and open monitoring (OM). Focused attention requires the meditator to concentrate attention on a chosen object such as a sacred image, a rhythmic or natural sound, or a sensation such as breathing. In learning to continually monitor and sustain attention on the chosen object, the meditator acquires the ability to regulate and sustain attention in the midst of external and internal distractions.

Open monitoring, on the other hand, involves watching one's moment-to-moment experiences without reacting or focusing on any particular experience, sensation or object. OM involves taking it all in without becoming distracted by any one part. The practice of OM techniques is believed to enhance metacognitive or executive function capacities as well as to cultivate an awareness of the richness of momentary experience.

Brain imaging studies comparing FA and OM techniques find that each has distinctive patterns of brain activity (Slagter, Davidson, & Lutz, 2011). FA involves greater activation (relative to a control condition) in brain regions associated with attentional processing. OM is associated with increased activity in brain areas involved in somatosensory processing. Both FA and OM uniquely enhance performance on certain kinds of mental tasks testing learning and performance. Intensive practice of FA or OM is also associated with changes in brain structures. Although FA and OM techniques are complementary, novice meditators are frequently first taught FA techniques, which later aid in OM training. The researchers conclude:

Both FA and OM mediation are assumed to induce a predictable and distinctive state (or set of states) whose occurrence is clearly indicated by certain cognitive and emotional features. These states, which arise during practice and are relatively short-term, can allegedly result in enduring changes to mental functions, i.e., in the development of certain traits (Slagter et al., 2011 p. 4).

Are There Degrees of Enlightenment?

The fact that the number of hours of practice was the best predictor of the amplitude and synchronicity of a meditator's gamma brain waves, as well as the relationship between pain tolerance and cortical thickness, implies a process that produces change in increments. And this in turn suggests that attaining and sustaining a compassionate way of being is not an all-or-nothing phenomenon, but may occur over time along a continuum. Commenting on the cortical thickening study, one scientist speculated on the possibility of training our "emotional muscles." The Davidson research group explicitly advocates drawing on meditation practices as tools to systematically enhance brain plasticity and mental function (Slagter et al., 2011).

Do these incremental changes suggest that there are different degrees or levels of enlightenment? Eric Fromm (1900–1980), a psychoanalyst, humanistic philosopher, and vocal critic of Freudian theory, addressed this question in an essay on psychoanalysis and Zen Buddhism (Fromm, 1960). The trio of essays by D.T. Suzuki, Fromm and Richard De Martino is—by the way—yet another of those interesting collaborative efforts from the 1960s to link Eastern and Western visions of the mind.

Using these two disparate bodies of knowledge about consciousness (Zen Buddhism and psychoanalysis), the authors identify a progressive series of parallel mental changes reached by the two different approaches:

The method of Zen is, one might say, that of a frontal attack on the alienated way of perception by means of the "sitting," the koan, and the authority of the master. Of course, all this is not a "technique" which can be isolated from the premise of Buddhist thinking, of the behavior and ethical values which are embodied in the master and in the atmosphere of the monastery. It must also be remembered that it is not a "five hour a week" concern, and that by the very fact of coming for instruction in Zen the student has made a most important decision, a decision which is an important part of what goes on afterwards.

The psychoanalytic method is entirely different from the Zen method. It trains consciousness to get hold of the unconscious in a different way. It directs attention to that perception which is distorted; it leads to a recognition of the fiction within oneself; it widens the range of human experience by lifting repressedness. (Fromm, 1960 p. 139)

Fromm et al. (1960) conclude that both Zen and psychoanalysis achieve their effects in a series of small steps that may stop short of the end goal of *satori* or the proverbial "completed analysis"—and so to reach the ultimate goal one must practice either method over considerable time. Each step or session yields its own incremental benefit. However, it is the first step that is the most important. D.T. Suzuki compares the process to bringing a candle into a totally dark room. The first candle brings light and thus banishes darkness. Successive candles make the room brighter, but the decisive change occurred when light first appeared.

HYPNOSIS

The credibility of hypnosis suffers from its history. Franz Anton Mesmer (1734–1815), the man who put the "mesmer" in *mesmerize*, is often credited with the discovery of hypnosis, which he called *magnétisme animal* (animal magnetism). In fact, he was following an already long tradition with accounts in ancient Middle Eastern and Hindu medical texts.

The Renaissance physician Paracelsus (1493–1541) venerated both as the father of pharmacology and the father of toxicology, first described the use of magnets to induce healing trances. A complex and ultimately tragic figure, Paracelsus challenged the cherished belief, traceable to Hippocrates, that disease was the result of an imbalance in the four humours: blood, phlegm, black bile, and yellow bile. Instead, he believed that disease represented an attack on the body from the outside. He pioneered the medical use of minerals such as zinc and created laudanum, a potent tincture of opium that was a medical mainstay well into the twentieth century.

Paracelsus recognized that the magnets were not directly responsible for his treatment's beneficial effects. As an explanation, he offered a theory of psychosomatic illness, which held that it was the patient's unconscious ideas and beliefs that were responsible for certain conditions. His accounts of magnetic cures, however, led to more than two centuries of "magnetizers," of whom Mesmer was merely the most infamous, but neither the first nor last.

It was James Braid (1795–1860), a Scottish surgeon, who coined the term *hypnosis* in 1841 to describe individuals in a trance state. With this new name Braid sought to locate the phenomenon as living within the patient and to de-emphasize the notion that it was produced by a magnetic field emanating from the therapist. It wasn't until the 1880s, however, that the term hypnosis came into widespread use to describe trance states induced by physicians and other practitioners. Jean-Martin Charcot, Pierre Janet, William James and Sigmund Freud were among the luminaries of the day who studied hypnosis and used it therapeutically.

The Hypnosis Wars

Most authorities recognize Hippolyte Bernheim (1840–1919), founder of the Nancy school of hypnotherapy, as the leading authority on hypnosis of his time. Bernheim and Charcot (see Chapter 8) were bitter enemies. Their vitriolic exchanges about the nature of hypnosis presaged the acrid tone that pervades much of the modern academic debate on the same question. Informally known as the "Hypnosis Wars," the opposing camps stake out positions around the central question of whether or not hypnosis is a special state of consciousness.

The negative position, originally led by Martin Orne (1927–2000), argues that hypnosis is a product of "demand characteristics." Subjects are not really in an altered state of consciousness. Instead, they were merely pretending to please the hypnotist by doing what they think is expected of them. Scientists holding this position construct experiments in which they surreptitiously observe subjects who think that they are alone to see if they stop pretending to be hypnotized—and some do.

Altered-state theorists, argue that hypnosis is a special state of consciousness. Ernest Hilgard (1904–2001) was their leader. His laboratory at Stanford University in California grew from a small house on the edge of campus in 1957 to become an international center for research on hypnosis, attracting noted scientists from around the world. His wife, Josephine, played an important role in the center's research.

Measuring Hypnotic States

With Josephine, Hilgard developed tests for measuring the depth of hypnosis and then used these measures to study its nature. Early tests to measure the depth of hypnosis date to Bernheim. In 1938, Theodore

Sarbin and Joseph Friedlander arranged some of these into a scale based on their increasing difficulty for most subjects. Among the first projects undertaken in the Stanford laboratory was refining hypnosis measures into a series of scales and tests, many of which remain benchmarks against which newer measures are still compared.

Most hypnosis scales include a sequence of motor, sensory, and mental tasks that challenge the subject to perform some act or conversely to inhibit an involuntary act suggested by the experimenter. For example, the experimenter will tell a hypnotized subject that his arm is too heavy to lift and then challenge him to raise it. Subjects may be told that they cannot pull their clasped hands apart and then asked to try. Subjects may be told that they cannot smell anything and then tested with household ammonia or that their hand is numb and then pricked with a pin. Charles Tart recalls such a test:

> *My California postdoc was with Ernest Hilgard, another former American Psychological Association president, and a real gentleman and scholar. His laboratory at Stanford was devoted to doing hypnosis research thoroughly and carefully, systematically exploring one of those dark alleys, as it were, and Hilgard and colleagues' work considerably advanced the field. Some of it was like the bulk of mainstream psychological research, 10 percent changes in, say, hypnotizability with age. Other parts of it were standardized and routine, you got used to them, but really incredible. I spend 10 minutes hypnotizing a talented student with a standard procedure, for example, reading a script really, and a few minutes later I tell him for a minute that he can't smell anything, all sense of smell is gone, and then I tell him, "See, you can't smell, I'll hold a bottle of something with an odor under your nose, you take a good sniff to see that you can't smell anything." What I hold 1 inch under his nostrils is a bottle of household ammonia. He takes a deep sniff and shows no reaction! I ask if he smelled anything, he says no. **Be very careful if you try this at home: The smell is not only powerful, it's quite painful!***
> (Tart, 2011 p. xii; bold is italics in original.)

Over the next two decades Hilgard's laboratory studied a wide range of unusual phenomena that can be summoned under hypnosis. How easy or difficult it is to hypnotize different people was a major focus of their research. Instead of the typical bell-shaped curve that characterizes the distribution of many human traits and capacities such as height or intelligence, the distribution of hypnosis is a curve with two distinct, bell-shaped, humps—a bimodal distribution.

This unusual, two-peaked, curve implies that there are two distinct groups of people with respect to the capacity to be hypnotized: one is large, with low to moderate hypnotizability scores and the other group is smaller but capable of some remarkable feats in a trance state. As far as Hilgard could determine, it was not possible to teach someone in the low to moderate first group to become a member of the second highly hypnotizable, group. Hypnotizability appears to be a relatively fixed trait—at least when evaluated in adults.

From at least the time of the American Civil War, doctors have known that some people could tolerate painful surgery, such as the amputation of a limb, with hypnosis alone. Afterwards the patients would deny memory of the surgery, but relevant details could be elicited by asking the person to recall it while in hypnotic trance. Using measures of brain activation and hemispheric lateralization, the Stanford scientists studied hypnotic anesthesia to different levels of pain induced by electric shock, holding a hand in freezing water, applying heat, and using a tourniquet to block blood flow to the forearm.

Other hypnotic phenomena studied at the Stanford laboratory included posthypnotic amnesia, automatic writing, age regression, and involuntary movements. Alterations in perception, including positive and negative auditory and visual hallucinations, can be induced in some subjects. Positive hallucinations involve seeing something that is not there. A negative hallucination involves not seeing something that is there. It is also possible to create tactile and olfactory hallucinations. For example, feeling an imaginary fly brushing against the face or smelling food that is not present.

The Hidden Observer

The most extraordinary discovery to emerge from the Stanford Hypnosis Laboratory was the "Hidden Observer." During a routine classroom demonstration of hypnosis, a blind student was serving as a subject. The instructor gave the hypnotized student an instruction that he would be completely deaf on the count of three, but that he would regain his hearing when the instructor placed a hand on his shoulder. The hypnotically deaf student now showed no reaction to sudden loud sounds such as the clapping of wooden blocks or shots from a starter's pistol made close behind him.

An observing student wondered if some part of the hypnotized student might be aware. And so the instructor said to the subject, *"Although you are hypnotically deaf, perhaps there is some part of you that is hearing my voice and processing the information. If there is, I should like the index finger of your right hand to rise as a sign that this is the case* (Hilgard, 1986 p. 186). The subject's finger rose.

Out of trance, the subject demanded to know what the instructor had done to make his finger lift. The instructor placed the subject back into a trance and was able to elicit "a part" of the subject that was able to hear during the hypnotic deafness and was responsible for raising the finger. Similar continuously aware "parts" were soon identified in other highly hypnotizable laboratory subjects, including parts that were aware of but not reactive to the pain inflicted during the experiments with hypnotic analgesia.

Hilgard labeled these parts the "Hidden Observer." He cautioned, however:

> *It should be noted that the "hidden observer" is a metaphor for something occurring at an intellectual level but not available to the consciousness of the hypnotized person. It does not mean that there is a secondary personality with a life of its own—a kind of homunculus lurking in the shadows of the consciousness? The "hidden observer" is merely a convenient label for the information source tapped through experiments with automatic writing and automatic talking* (Hilgard, 1986 p. 188).

Hilgard pointed out that hidden observer-type phenomena were identified by earlier investigators of hypnosis, most notably William James. He quotes James from *Principles of Psychology:*

> *It must be admitted, therefore, that in* **certain persons**, *at least,* **the total possible consciousness may be split into parts which coexist but mutually ignore each other**, *and share the objects of knowledge between them. More remarkable still, they are* **complementary**. *Give an object to one of the consciousnesses, and by that fact you remove it from the other or others. Barring a certain common fund of information, like the command of language,*

etc., what the upper self knows the under self is ignorant of, and **vice versa** (quoted by Hilgard, 1986 p. 200; also in James, 1890) (bold emphases are italics in original).

Divided Consciousness

Hidden observers can be found in many, but not all, highly hypnotizable subjects. While researchers elsewhere have replicated many of the Stanford laboratory's findings, a number of critics report experiments that either do not find hidden observers or discounted their presence as a result of demand characteristics or suggestibility. Hilgard responded to these criticisms in his classic book, *Divided Consciousness: Multiple Controls in Human Thought and Action* (1986).

Photographed at the height of his career, a balding and bearded, but youthful appearing Pierre Janet (1859–1947) graces the frontispiece of *Divided Consciousness* setting the stage for Hilgard's neodissociative theory that echoes Janet's ideas from a century earlier. Opening with the statement, *"The unity of consciousness is illusory,* Hilgard organizes his neodissociative theory around the concept that multiple levels of control exist over human thought and action. In every person, there is a set of mental subsystems that people activate differentially depending on the situation at the moment. These subsystems are coordinated and controlled by an executive mental function that continuously monitors the individual's behavior. Certain psychological disorders, such as multiple personality and dissociative symptoms such as amnesias and fugues, are a result of disruptions in a person's executive functions.

Hilgard believes that hypnosis is a special state of consciousness that suspends specific elements of executive function. So while a hypnotized person still retains control over most behaviors, he may give up control to the hypnotist or others—for example, being unable to bend an arm after being told that it is too stiff to bend. Subjects who are instructed to resist a hypnotist's suggestions often still cannot overcome them. Still, they may say that they could have done it if they had wanted to do, but for some reason they just didn't feel like doing it.

When subjects succeed in resisting the hypnotist's suggestions they often report that it took a great deal of concentration and effort. Researchers observing subjects trying to resist hypnotic suggestion often see signs of internal conflict. Hilgard observes:

There were many evidences of behavioral conflict during attempted resistance: hands alternatively being pulled apart and brought back together in resisting, fingerlock broken but clonic movements in the forearms after the hands were separated, and violent expression of anger or disappointment. It is not surprising that under some circumstances the subject preferred not to resist at all (Hilgard, 1986 p. 121).

Proponents of the non-state model, however, see such behavior as simply more evidence that the subjects are just trying really, really hard to please the experimenter. The Hypnosis Wars have outlived Martin Orne, Ernest Hilgard, and other early combatants. They continue today in the guise of disagreement about the existence of dissociative identity disorder, i.e., whether this is a real, naturally occurring, psychiatric condition or is iatrogenically created by therapist suggestion (see Chapter 8).

I favor the altered-states-of-consciousness theory of hypnosis because it best fits the clinical and experimental data. The mental and behavioral elements of a hypnotic state define in many ways the dimensions along which an altered state of consciousness differs from what's considered normal consciousness. These include state-dependent changes in memory such as posthypnotic amnesia or suggested memories.

Changes in identity, including dramatic alter entities such as the hidden observer, reflect state-dependent shifts in the sense and integration of self. Hypnotically suggested changes in sensation and perception reflect state-specific shifts in attention. For example, powerful sensations like pain continue to be registered at some level, but conscious awareness of the pain is either diminished or displaced in a way that it no longer hurts. As described in Chapter 3 (Brain States), brain-imaging studies show that hypnosis activates the same brain regions known to play a role in powerful placebo effects.

For a highly hypnotizable subject, entering into a trance state reflects a significant transition in the person's state-space such that they are now in an altered state of consciousness with respect to their normal pattern of states of consciousness. With practice, a good hypnotic subject can make this non-linear jump in state-space within seconds to a few minutes on cue. This is a "rapid switch" such as described in Chapter 4. Highly hypnotizable people can learn to do this on their own and do not need a "hypnotist" present to quickly achieve a deep trance state.

The ability to self-hypnotize is often taught to dissociative patients as a self-control technique for dealing with overwhelming emotions associated with past traumatic memories. Similarly, many psychotherapy models for PTSD teach patients to enter states of deep relaxation when they are troubled by trauma-related symptoms.

For Hilgard, the essential feature of hypnotic states of consciousness is the nature of the change in the executive functions and self-monitoring capacities of the subject. These functions are subsumed under the construct that I have been calling metacognition/executive functions. The Hidden Observer's calm, objective reporting of the individual's experience also suggests a version of the "observing ego" function that psychotherapists hope to awaken in their neurotic patients.

Among Hilgard's major contributions was the convincing demonstration of the presence of multiple, semi-autonomous controls over human behavior. He did this in part by pitting these internal entities against each other. Some of them are active and others latent, but they all influence behavior. From a states of being perspective, Hilgard's "parts" are highly differentiated states of consciousness that coexist within a highly hypnotizable person's personality system. Mostly latent, their influence on a person's behavior is primarily covert. If directly activated in some fashion—say, by an environmental trigger or hypnotic suggestion—they can emerge and take control of behavior or dispassionately comment on their experience as opposed to the person's experience.

SYNTHESIS

People of all ages seek out exceptional states—to feel more alive, to experience pleasure and excitement, to grow mentally and spiritually. This need is so strong that a few repeatedly risk violent death for fleeting moments of pure exhilaration. The human need to enlarge our personal state-space follows a developmental course. Adolescence is an especially dangerous time, both physically and emotionally, as risky behavior interacts with identity crises and normal adolescent turmoil in the context of a teenager's increasing independence and greater degrees of freedom. Teens with histories of trauma and abuse are at the highest risk, tragically adding to their cumulative toll of trauma.

As adults, many of us continue searching for exceptional states of being that change us in deeply meaningful ways. William James identified four common elements of such moments: *ineffability, noesis, transience* and *passivity*. Maslow believed that while in a peak state, people are most purely "themselves" shedding false identities. For the most part, these are very private experiences—deeply personal moments often involving the self-acknowledgment of painful truths. As such they are difficult to study prospectively. Retrospective accounts, however, share many similarities.

More easily scientifically poked and prodded are the states of being associated with sex and meditation. In the former, scientists sexually arouse their subjects in some fashion and then measure and correlate mental and physical changes in their minds and bodies. In the latter, they observe the exceptional mental and physiological properties associated with deep meditative states of consciousness. Western science can detect that something is happening when experienced meditators meditate. Brain activity patterns change. Perceptions change. Pain threshold, neuroendocrine markers, and other physiological functions differ from non-meditative states. These mental and physical changes, which vary somewhat across types of meditation, are generally experienced as positive and beneficial. Indeed, worldwide enormous numbers of people practice some form of meditation because it makes them feel better and relieves stress.

Perhaps the oldest exceptional state of being, both historical and phylogenetic, is hypnosis. One can even point to passive, trance-like states elicitable in ancient denizens such as sharks and alligators by rolling them onto their backs and gently stroking their bellies. Highly hypnotizable individuals are capable of extraordinary feats including blocking pain sufficient to have a limb amputated. Even strongly motivated people could not sustain this extreme degree of compliance if they were only seeking to please a hypnotist (whom they are likely meeting for the first time). Similar to sleep, meditation and sex, hypnosis research offers an opportunity to discover the human potential associated with exceptional states of being.

WHAT HAVE WE LEARNED
ABOUT STATES OF BEING?

Our understanding that states are distinct—but transient—ways of being is ancient wisdom. There is evidence in myth, in history, and in every-day life of people overcome by powerful emotional and mental states that seize control of thought and action, but which then pass leaving them wondering or regretting what has happened.

More recently, the psychedelic drug culture, personal experiences with meditation, yoga, the martial arts, religious epiphanies, peak experiences, and the recognition of post traumatic flashbacks have expanded general awareness of the existence of powerful states of being lying outside of normal, everyday consciousness. However, the ubiquity of more mundane states of being in our daily lives diminishes appreciation of their ever-present influence on our thoughts, feelings, and actions. Except in extreme circumstances, we largely ignore the influence that the particular state that we are in at the moment has on the "who" that we feel we are at that same moment.

Modern science, especially brain imaging, is developing the hardware, software, and research paradigms to identify specific mental states and correlate them with signature patterns of brain activity. We can take vivid color pictures of Zen meditation or posttraumatic flashbacks. Quantitatively we can identify unique patterns of activation in key brain structures for states of mind such as anxiety, depression, and daydreaming. As yet, we don't understand what those pictures mean at finer levels of analysis, but we can discriminate among certain types of states with fair precision. What we can say with confidence is that something unique is happening in the subject's brain when they are in an altered state of consciousness compared with a control condition.

Principles of States of Being

States of being are transient, organized patterns of mind, body, and brain variables each defining a circumscribed region within a larger multi-dimensional state-space that, for a finite period, influence how a person thinks, feels, and acts. Each state uniquely influences perception, cognition, memory, emotion, motivation, core values, interpersonal interactions, physiology and a host of other domains and functions. The effects of any given state may be minimal or profound depending upon circumstances. They may serve to reinforce an individual's predispositional course or lead to a sudden wild deviation.

Our overview of different types of states allows us to say that they are discrete, repeating constellations of variables defined along dimensions that may include elements of behavior, cognition, emotion, brain and bodily physiology. States exist as discrete regions within a much larger, multidimensional state-space that can be mapped at many scales of scientific analysis. There are isomorphic axes that connect these levels, theoretically allowing descriptions of mechanistic linkages that span the molecular level to gross behavior, although this degree of detail is unlikely to be achieved in the foreseeable future. However, bridges are being built that span at least two levels of analysis, e.g., identification of specific patterns of brain activity characteristic of mental states of anxiety, depression, daydreaming or meditation.

All of the important principles and basic phenomenology of states of being can be identified in healthy newborn infants. Mothers and researchers recognize a repeating cycle of a half-dozen states—depending on the coding system chosen—that captures the majority of healthy newborn infant daily behaviors. Brief transitions or switches lasting seconds to a few minutes link the much longer duration infant states. Switches show directionality both within a state, e.g., falling asleep and waking up, and across states, i.e., switches from state A to state B differ from switches of B to A. As infants mature, they add additional states as well as new pathways among their constellation of states of being. We see this growth reflected in their awareness and responsiveness to the world around them.

From birth on, every state influences perception, emotion, cognition, and action in unique—state-dependent—ways. The variability of an infant's susceptibility to crying when hearing another infant's cry is an early example of such input/output state-dependency. State-dependency of any given state of being only grows more complicated with time as it is increasingly linked to memories, associations and actions.

States form the foundation of interpersonal interactions. A mother's emotional states interact with her infant's behavioral states in powerful ways. The quality and consistency of this complex interaction (which we seek to objectify with measures of attachment and attunement) has powerful mutual effects—for better or worse. Ideally, the child's budding self-awareness together with healthy parenting facilitates a growing self-control over her state. In everyday life, we see this as: "increasing maturity," as a "longer attention span," and as "greater frustration tolerance" together, with an improved ability to self-recover from upsetting experiences.

Discrete states of being undergird our different senses of self—which we are calling "identities" or "identity states" here. People have multiple identities that they activate in specific life contexts, e.g., work, parenting, intimacy, recreation, religious practice etc. Our different identities, with their state-dependent knowledge and skills, are more or less linked together by superordinate mental processes lumped here under the rubric of metacognition/executive functions/observing ego. These processes act to bridge and integrate an individual's different identity states into a larger—and hopefully more coherent—behavioral structure that we commonly refer to as their personality. Personality is the sum and synergy of an individual's different identity states, which are, in turn, a legacy of the individual's life experiences, temperamental and genetic pre-dispositions, and interpersonal history.

Deficits and disruptions in metacognitive functions can occur as a result of traumatic life experiences, intoxication, brain injuries, and disease. Serious metacognitive failures in bridging and integrating state-dependent memories, knowledge, judgment, moral values and global sense of self may result in the same individual behaving on different occasions as if he were two or more separate people. Failures in meta-cognition functions may result in schisms or divisions of personality that set individuals against themselves: people who are their own worst enemies.

The profound influence of mental state on sense of self is most clearly seen in certain psychiatric conditions characterized by precipitous changes in self-states such as bipolar (aka manic-depressive) disorder, dissociative identity (aka multiple personality) disorder, and borderline personality disorder. But it can be found whenever people self-sabotage their own best interest.

Mystical and peak states of being may forever change people's lives for the better, especially the "who" that the person is from that transcendental moment forward. These exceptional states of being may be triggered by overwhelming trauma, by powerful religious experiences, or induced through state-altering tools such as meditation, ritual, or drugs.

In many instances these life-changing altered states of being occur "spontaneously" or are triggered by a unique convergence of internal and external circumstances that could never be foreseen or scripted.

Can We Take Advantage of What We Know?

If we could systematically take advantage of the existing scientific and experiential bodies of knowledge about states of being, we could tap new levels of awareness, expand our skills and abilities, and achieve deeper understandings that would broaden the human experience. We could extend our senses and activate latent abilities. We could improve mental and physical performance and promote self-resilience. We could reduce stress and treat some forms of psychopathology. We could unify our sense of self and facilitate social and inner peace. Or, at least, we could do a bit better than we currently are in terms of quality of life.

We already have many of these abilities available to us in the form of tools and techniques used to induce or activate specific states of consciousness. Consider the range and common usage of the state altering tools and techniques below.

TOOLS AND TECHNIQUES TO MANAGE STATES OF BEING

Imagination and Fantasy

Imagination and fantasy are among the first mental tools that a child can deliberately invoke to create specific states of mind that she can return to again and again. Favorite daydreams are revisited repeatedly and can be elaborated into secret worlds that a child escapes to in times of boredom or serve as a refuge from chaos, pain, and fear. A few become lost in their imaginary worlds, but most children learn to enter and exit more or less at will.

When young children tell you about their secret worlds they usually involve changes in identity and special powers. Having super or magical powers is common—super strength, ability to fly, invisibility, and invulnerability. Hmmm, sounds a bit like Superman and Wonder Woman. But when you think about it, comic book and movie super heroes and heroines often have secret identities that stem from early life traumatic experiences. It is their traumatic back-story that drives the super heroes' and heroines' unwavering determination to right wrongs, oppose injustice, and protect the oppressed, weak, and endangered. Kids get it!

Children share their fantasies with friends and together create joint fantasies in the form of pretend play. Once again, alterations in identity are a central feature of the shared imaginary activity. Now, it takes the form of mutually agreed upon play roles—fireman, princess, ballerina, doctor, soldier, daddy, mommy, Wonder Woman, Superman, pony, robot, machine, monster etc. The appeal of these "pretend selves" may come to form the nucleus of a life dream so that the person grows up to become the pilot, race car driver, scientist, or teacher she played as a child.

Adults use fantasy too—for mental escape and for sex. Imagination and fantasy are used in therapy and to enhance performance in athletics and activities such as public speaking. In therapy, patients may be asked to imagine anxiety-evoking situations as part of gaining mastery over dysfunctional mental states such as panic attacks. Athletes, especially those in individual events (e.g., gymnastics, skiing, skateboarding, platform diving, dance etc.), mentally rehearse their performance practicing a mind-body state necessary to fluidly execute without thought or hesitation. In the minutes prior to their performance, they can be seen isolating themselves, entering meditative-like detached states of concentration. Many favor headphones, isolating them while delivering special music or inspiring messages.

Rites, Rituals, and Ceremonies

Rites, rituals and ceremonies are as old as humankind. The province of anthropologists, an informed discussion is beyond the scope of this book and my expertise. However, let us consider for a brief moment the sheer number of rites, rituals and ceremonies that exist now or that were ever once practiced by ancient societies. There are ceremonies for birth, puberty, marriage, and death. There are numerous rites of passage—sacred and profane. There are purification ceremonies, cleansing rituals, christenings, baptisms, healing rites, blessings, and exorcisms. There are fertility rituals for mother earth and mothers-to-be. There are ceremonies for planting, harvesting, feasting and fasting. All manner of gods and demons as well as ever-present dead ancestors must be appeased with ceremony and sacrifice. There are rituals for acceptance into and banishment from the tribe or social group. All cultures and societies have their collections of rites, rituals and ceremonies that unite—or sometimes divide—members.

Many rites, rituals and ceremonies are about creating shared states of mind in which exceptional, that is, non-ordinary, things can happen. These shared states promote common ways of believing, thinking and acting as well as acceptance of a particular worldview. Ceremonies, rites and rituals may also be used to create emotionally cathartic experiences or change an individual's identity.

Child Soldiers: The Huila Okupiolissa Ritual

Rituals are often used to promote transitional experiences that involve a change in identity or status within a group. Healing rituals, in particular, spring up wherever they are needed to answer pain and suffering and to restore social function. Two recent examples are the healing rituals observed among the street children of earthquake- and cholera-ravished Haiti and the rituals developed in strife-torn African countries to re-integrate child soldiers back into their home villages.

As part of their indoctrination, child soldiers are often forced to commit atrocities on members of their own tribe or family. Anthropological research in Angola and Mozambique found that ceremonies to reintegrate child soldiers into their villages—which they may have pillaged, raped, and killed—consisted primarily of purification and cleansing rituals that purged the child of sin, guilt, and pacified the spirits of those killed (Green & Honwana, 1999). The Huila Okupiolissa ritual in Angola illustrates the shared ritual state of villagers as they collectively absolve a child soldier of his past and bestow a new identity that is permitted to join the community:

> The community and family members are usually excited and pleased at the homecoming. Women prepare themselves for a greeting ceremony (...) Some of the flour used to paint the women's foreheads is thrown at the child and a respected older woman of the village throws a gourd filled with ashes at the child's feet. At the same time, clean water is thrown over him as a means of purification (...) the women of the village dance around the child, gesturing with hands and arms to ward away undesirable spirits or influences. (...). They each touch him with both hands from head to foot to cleanse him of impurities. The dance is known as: Ululando-w-w-w. When the ritual is complete, the child is taken to his village and the villagers celebrate his return. The child must be formally presented to the chiefs by his parents (...) the child sits beside the chiefs, drinking and talking to them, and this act marks his change of status in the village (Green & Honwana, 1999 p. 4) [The "(...)" are as in the original passage].

Through these return-and-reintegration rituals, the child symbolically changes identity from a killer/rapist/pillager to a tribe member who will conform to social norms and civility. Once the ritual has begun, the child is considered to be in a dangerous state, suspended between two identities, until the transformation is complete. While in limbo, he is not allowed in the village and cannot see family nor eat or sleep at home.

When the ceremony is complete, observers report that many of the child's PTSD symptoms disappear (Green & Honwana, 1999). But for just how long is not known. Child soldiers return to impoverished villages ravished by war and economic collapse, without schools, hospitals, or community government, with crime and drugs, and without jobs or opportunities. Accidents, disease, mental health problems, addiction, and disability are rampant. Despite such healing rituals, enduring hatred and impulses for revenge must remain in victims or their families. These needs, deprivations, threats, stresses and strains are likely to reactivate earlier traumatic states with their accompanying violent reflexes and antisocial responses. If these indigenous healing rituals of return are truly able to hold back such forces and impulses in the face of continuing community stress and trauma, they are worthy of more attention than received to date.

Adult Soldiers: The SERE Ceremony

SERE, which stands for Survive, Evade, Resist, Escape, is a set of trainings for U.S. military personnel potentially exposed to combat or terrorism. There are multiple versions determined by branch of service, previous training, and the degree of risk for capture. SERE students learn to evade capture and how to survive and resist if captured and tortured. Trainees are taught mental techniques to withstand hunger, fatigue, and pain. Intensive levels of SERE training are exceedingly stressful as documented by markedly elevated levels of stress hormones such as adrenaline and cortisol. In fact, research on SERE trainees is used to develop tests to identify individuals for elite military units.

The SERE course involves a war game in which trainees are chased through the woods and swamps near Ft. Bragg, North Carolina. Inevitably captured, they are taken to a prisoner of war camp where the food is terrible and sanitation primitive. Sleep deprived and pushed to their physical and mental limits (which are monitored), the average SERE trainee loses about fifteen pounds.

As prisoners of war, trainees are placed in situations in which they are made to feel that they could die and are forced to struggle to stay alive. For example, they may be stripped naked, tied up, blindfolded, and thrown into cold mud. Sandbags are piled on their backs so that in order to breathe they must continuously strain to raise their faces above the filth. I am told that there is always someone there prepared for a rescue if necessary. Nonetheless, in the words of the SERE course instructors the goal is to strip the prisoners of their identities (CNN Presents: Capture: Inside the Army's Secret School, 10 August, 2002: http://www.cnn.com/CNN/Programs/presents/index.captured.new.html).

To help SERE trainees return to the normal world after this ordeal, an emotional graduation ceremony is staged. A CIA psychiatrist who observed multiple SERE exercises described to me witnessing an over-whelming shift in emotional state occurring on command as the haggard and exhausted soldiers take off their blindfolds and turn around to see the American flag raised as the Star Spangled Banner is played. Most burst into tears. There is usually momentary disorien-tation as they flash back and forth between the overwhelmingly brutal reality of their SERE experience and a return to the normal world. An unfortunate few, however, do not make it all the way back. Personal accounts can be found on the Internet of people who were adversely changed by SERE.

Postures and Movement

Highly elaborated movements and poses are used to induce specific mind-body states. In other instances, unique mental states are necessary to successfully perform certain physical actions or sustain specific med-itative poses. Psychologists have investigated the effects of posture on thought. For example, in a review of research on the waking stream of consciousness, Pope and Singer write:

Posture produced consistent effects: when subjects were in a reclining rather than standing or walking posture, they reported fewer shifts of thought, fewer present-centered thoughts, and less cumulative duration of time spent with consciousness focused on the present. Sitting showed an intermediate effect (Pope & Singer, 1980 p. 182).

For purposes of illustration, I will use as examples the two disci-plines with which I am most familiar, Aikido and Yoga. I do not claim expertise in either.

Aikido is one of the newer martial arts, founded by Japanese Master Morihei Uyeshiba in the 1920s. Master Uyeshiba first mastered several martial arts including judo, fencing, and spear fighting as well as studying Zen Buddhism. He blended these arts together with Zen into a unique martial art that is purely defensive in nature. There are no punches or kicks in Aikido. Indeed it is considered unethical to injure an opponent, although it is permissible to inflict temporary pain sufficient to induce submission.

Aikido is taught by a Master or Sensei in a practice hall called a dojo. As students practice the various arts, they alternate between the role of attacker (*uke*) and the defender (*nage*), who uses Aikido arts to defeat the attack. When judged ready, students are promoted by passing exams. Colored belts denote rank. Philosophy, protocol, and etiquette are taught and practiced through ceremony and ritual.

Aikido uses dynamic movement to seize control of an attacker's energy and initiative in order to redirect it back at the attacker. In essence, the attacker defeats himself. Aikido is based on vertical and horizontal circles, spins and spirals that serve to reverse the attacker's direction and momentum. Specific Aikido arts are composed of flowing sequences of parries, throws, holds, and pins that can be recombined into an enormous number of variations.

As an attack develops, the defender responds to the concentration of the opponent's energy and intention, seeking to control the attack by leading it. The defender joins with the attacker, capturing, then leading the attacker's energy and strength back at him. At no point, does the defender seek to completely stop the attacker's blow, as this would deplete the very energy that the Aikido art requires. The process of capturing and leading an attacker's energy can be subtle and often does not require physical contact because the Master is leading the opponent's mind.

An Aikido Master will spin inside an attacker's strike, sweeping up the opponent's concentrated energy with an irresistible suction. The "energy" that is captured is called *Ki* (pronounced key) in Japanese. It is known as *Qi* or *Chi* (pronounced chee as in cheese) in Chinese. It is analogous to *prana* in Yoga and related to the Western concept of *spiritus*. Ki is a universal life force or energy that flows through individuals. It is possible for an accomplished martial artist to control Ki.

Some martial arts favor hard Ki and others emphasize soft Ki. Hard Ki is concentrated at a point or on along an edge. When used either offensively or defensively it cuts through its target. It is predominantly focused in a straight line, although slashing forms are used in sword fighting. Hard Ki is common in martial arts that seek to focus maximum force at a single point of attack, such as Karate punches and kicks.

Aikido emphasizes soft Ki. Soft Ki is diffuse and enveloping. Through sweeps, spins, and spirals an opponent's aggression is deflected and reversed. The Aikido Master's ability to extend an enveloping sphere of Ki is achieved through a state of unified mind and body. Master Koichi Tohei, founder of the Ki Society, one of several schools of Aikido that have emerged over the years, offers four basic principles for achieving this state of unified mind and body (Maruyama & Tohei, 1984):

(1) Keep one point.
(2) Relax completely.
(3) Keep weight underside.
(4) Extend Ki.

The four principles are all statements about the same mind-body state. If one principle is fulfilled, all are satisfied. If one principle is violated, all fail. The student learns these principles through a series of mind-body exercises.

Keeping one point involves mentally and physically centering mind and body at the *hara* or Centre, a point located about two inches below the navel. The Master tests ability to maintain one point by pushing on a student to see if he loses balance. Usually a gentle touch is all that is necessary to determine if the student is centered—because the Sensei is moving the student's mind.

Relaxing completely involves entering a state of relaxed suppleness, a state of mental flexibility and muscular pliability, able to immediately respond in any direction. Balanced between rest and motion, the Aikido Master remains centered. When completely relaxed and centered over the one point, the Master's weight is underside. When weight is underside, the person becomes enormously heavy and difficult to move. Weight underside may be tested by having two people, each holding one of the student's arms, attempt to lift the student straight up off of the mat. When Ki is extended, even an average-sized person becomes almost immovable. I've experienced this both as the lifter and as the liftee many times.

Extending Ki is best demonstrated through the unbendable arm. When relaxed completely, Ki flows through the body and can be extended through the limbs. In the unbendable arm test, the student extends an arm straight out in a relaxed fashion, slightly bent at the elbow. Resting the student's hand on his shoulder, the Master tries to bend it further by pressing down with both hands on the inside of the student's elbow. Even though already slightly bent, when Ki is extended the arm becomes unbendable.

Yoga

Of all of the disciplines focused on achieving an enlightened state of being, Yoga is among the oldest and best-integrated bodies of knowledge. A comprehensive discussion is far beyond the scope of this book (and knowledge of the author), but a number of principles and practices are worth examining as they provide insight into how the physical, mental, and spiritual components of self can be brought together into a harmonious and rejuvenating state of being.

Yoga makes use of movements, poses, and breathing to focus awareness and to gain self-control over mind and body. By assuming certain poses and by controlling and directing the breath, the yogi seeks to consciously alter her state of being. Specific poses and breathing rhythms induce unique but repeatable states of being that are positive and healthful. By sequencing these states through routines, the Yogi seeks to heighten and generalize the beneficial effects so that they transcend the session and flow into daily life.

Yoga, like many non-Western arts and disciplines, such as the martial arts, acupuncture, and various schools of meditation, emphasize controlling the flow of energy through the body. Yoga seeks to direct energy upward from the base of the spine. As yet, Western science is not able to detect and measure this energy flow, although researchers are able to demonstrate that experienced practitioners are often able to exert phenomenal control over their autonomic physiology and patterns of brain activity.

In the West, Yoga is best known for its postures and poses (*Asanas*). The pretzel-limbed, loin-clothed, yogi contemplating his navel is a cartoon stereotype that reinforces the discomfort that many feel when they first see Yoga in person or pictures. It appears to be an exercise in contortionism that can be mastered only by double-jointed freaks or very flexible young women. To the untrained eye, a sequence of Yoga poses may appear to be a bizarre form of calisthenics. Although the poses have intrinsic physical benefits, they are not "exercises" in the conventional Western sense. Rather they embody or provide access to certain states of being.

Assuming an approximation of a specific posture is only the beginning of the process. The key is to relax into that posture. On the face of it, relaxing would appear impossible for many positions. Relaxation must be consciously achieved through a controlled progressive release of tension. Focused attention, rhythmic breathing, silent mantras, extension of energy and other techniques are utilized to move beyond discomfort and incrementally deepen the pose. Progress is measured by how deeply one can sink into a pose, how completely the body relaxes, how long one can hold it, and how much benefit is derived. The practitioner seeks to achieve a sense of lightness or a feeling of floating while in the posture. Routines maintain a symmetrical balance, alternating left- and right-handed forms of a pose and forward and backward bends and stretches.

From a Western scientific perspective Yoga poses seek to induce altered states of consciousness through the manipulation of physical positions. We intuitively recognize that certain postures are associated with a person's mental and physical state. The depressed person's slumped shoulders, bowed head and downcast eyes. The puffed up chest, tightened arms, clenched fists, and glaring expression of an angry man. The flowing, merging touches, smiling faces, and intense eye contact of a couple in love or of a mother holding her baby. In these examples the person's state of mind shapes their posture.

Yoga reverses this process seeking to go from the person's posture to their state of mind. We have a few scientific experiments showing that if you can get a subject to assume certain facial expressions (such as smiling or frowning) you can induce corresponding changes in heart rate, blood pressure, and other salient physiological responses (Ekman, Levenson, & Friesen, 1983). In everyday life, we advise people to stand tall and look straight ahead to evoke a sense of toughness and self-confidence or conversely to bend low and keep gaze downcast to induce humility.

William James prescribed an exercise to test this idea that the bodily position and physiology influences mental processes (Grilley, 2002). He suggested lying on your back, relaxing your muscles, slowing your breathing and calming your mind. Now try to get angry without tensing your muscles, changing your breathing, raising your heart rate or blood pressure. You can't do it!

Breath

Considered the greatest free diver in history by her peers, Natalia Molchanova (53) disappeared August 2, 2015 while diving for fun with friends off the eastern coast of Spain (Skolnick, 2015). A superstar in the elite world of free diving, she was diving untethered in the open ocean when she vanished. Among her many world records, Ms. Molchanova was able to hold her breath for over nine minutes.

Free diving covers a set of extreme breath holding events that are performed in the water. These range from spear fishing tournaments and deep diving competitions in the open ocean to the "apnea disciplines" held in swimming pools. Recreational forms of free diving are also promoted as producing a state of relaxation, exhilaration, and the wonderment of entering into a wholly different mental and physical universe.

An extreme sport (reportedly second in fatalities only to BASE jumping), competitive free diving revolves around world records for breath holding, depth reached, and horizontal distance traveled. There are a variety of events as well as men and women's records. The most extreme is the "No Limits" category, which is the maximum depth reached by a diver riding a weighted sled down a line and then pulled back to the surface by an inflated bag. For the men the world record is over 210 meters (682.5 feet) and for women it is over 160 meters (520 feet).

Breathing is the most urgent of life's bodily functions. We can forgo eating and drinking for days. To be deprived of breath for mere minutes is to die. Awareness and control of breathing occurs at the boundaries between the conscious and the unconscious—along the interleaved edges of mind and body. Driven by physiological reflexes in the brain stem, most breathing occurs outside of our conscious awareness. It happens automatically, whether we are awake or asleep. Yet, with practice, we can take control of our breathing and use it to facilitate some extraordinary feats of mind and body.

Techniques for control of breathing are taught in many schools of martial arts and meditation. In the martial arts, breath may be used to explosively release concentrated Ki as in a Karate kick or punch. In the midst of danger and chaos, steady smooth breathing is used to conserve energy and calm the mind. In meditation and the healing arts breath may be mentally directed through the body to open up regions of tension or pain. Attention to one's breathing, to the exclusion of all else, is used to quiet the mind for meditation. In therapy, deep breathing techniques are often taught to PTSD patents to alleviate anxiety states triggered by traumatic memories.

Only a highly trained few, however, can override the mind-body's screaming alarms and convulsive reflexes long enough to hold their breath for a meaningful duration

> *There are two major obstructions that stand between the free diver and the depths. One is physical and the other is psychological and they are interconnected. Simply put, the deeper the dive the stronger the legs must be to push up through the great weight of water pressing down from above. After a certain point every foot becomes a millstone and sixty feet become a very long way from fifty feet.*
>
> *Experiencing this enormous weight of water for the first time leaves a deep and abiding impression on the breath hold diver. It is a tight, anxious feeling he is not eager to experience again. It creates tension which robs the breath hold, and tempers the will, if not the courage, to dive deeply. Overcoming these strong feelings that drive from our basic instincts for survival is difficult. Initially, the diver must force himself into a relaxed state at the edge of his personal depth level. Then he must carefully monitor his physical condition, which fluctuates due to fatigue and ocean conditions, and adjust his depth limits accordingly.* (Eyles, 1985 p. 140)

Deep physical relaxation and total mental calmness are essential elements of free diving. Before record-setting attempts, free divers enter a meditative state, eyes closed, breathing slowly, inwardly preparing themselves, mind and body. During the dive they move in slow motion, undulating in languid rhythms—each rippling stroke driving them deeper and deeper. After a certain depth, compressed into negative buoyancy, they passively fall into the abyss. Coming up is another exercise in extreme economical motion. Through physical training and mental discipline, they learn to achieve and sustain a mind-body state that allows them to do what is superhuman for the rest of us.

As with other disciplines that seek to push human limits, free diving is about achieving a state of personal and divine unification. In a 2014 interview, Ms. Molchanova said, *"Free diving is not only a sport, it's a way to understand who we are. When we go down, we don't think, we understand. We are whole. We are one with the world"* (Skolnick, 2015).

Music and Rhythm

Music and rhythm are essential to many ceremonies and rituals. Music creates emotional contexts. Rhythm structures time. Music is deeply symbolic. It conveys information and emotion in non-verbal, non-linear modes. Even singing and chanting depend more on harmony, rhythm, and rhyme than on the meaning of the words.

Music can be state altering. Drumming in particular is associated with altered states of consciousness. The low frequencies, repetitive rhythmic patterns, and driving tempos are believed to synchronize bodily and mental processes (Fachner, 2011). People move to the beat. The frenetic drumming of a trance possession ceremony, the rapid syncopation of a college band marching on to the field at halftime, and the looping drum machines and synthesized bass lines at a rave all drive their listeners to move in time.

Certain musical genres are associated with specific drugs. The acid rock of the 1960s and 70s, cannabis and reggae, punk music and inhalants, and, the earlier associations of marijuana and heroin with jazz in the 1920s and 30s are familiar examples. Today, a form of Techno music is called "Trance music," which in turn, subdivides into a half dozen variations such as Acid trance, Euphoric trance, Epic trance, Stadium trance and Uplifting or Anthem trance is associated with "club" drugs.

Trance music is played at warehouse and club "house parties" featuring strobe and black lights and widespread use of club drugs such as MDMA (ecstasy), cocaine, methamphetamine, and ketamine. The combination is intended to propel participants into a hyper-energized, sexually charged, altered state of consciousness. The DJ (Disc Jockey) who selects and sequences the music plays a critical role:

> *The DJ's job is to select music that will lead partygoers into trance states. (. . .) Attending a rave is more than listening to recorded music. DJs adjust the style, pace and volume of the music based on the feeling they get from those dancing to the music, attempting to bring the ravers into trance states* (Becker-Blease, 2004 p. 95).

The opposite process also occurs—drug experiences may inspire musical (and other artistic) creativity. When asked about the sources of inspiration for the Beatle's *Sgt. Pepper's Lonely Hearts Club Band*, Paul McCartney said:

Experience with drugs, mostly. But remember that in 1976 our drug habits followed a long-established tradition among musicians. We knew about Louis Armstrong, Duke Ellington, and Count Basie that they had always taken drugs. Now it was time for our musical scene to make the experience. Drugs found their way into everything we did. They coloured our perspective of things. I believe we realized that there were fewer limitations than we had expected. And we understood that we were able to break through barriers. (quoted in Fachner, 2006 p. 86)

In addition to drugs, music is frequently paired with other state-altering activities such as dancing. The combination of music and movement is a powerful altered state-generating process in which the music is internalized within and simultaneously expressed without by motion and posture.

Music is also complexly associated with sex. Often used to "get into the mood," it is also blamed for inducing sexual frenzy in teens. Of course, such concerns probably date to the bacchanalia of ancient times. Indeed it is a widespread belief in the power of music to induce altered states of consciousness that makes certain kinds of music "dangerous," e.g., the fear that Elvis Presley and rock and roll would lead to social breakdown.

But mere exposure is not sufficient. One may hear all manner of music intended to influence mood and mind—and yet remain unmoved. The listener must identify with the music. The music must resonate within, before it can transport the listener or performer to another state. What and why a given piece of music moves one person but not another is one of those mysterious blends of personal experience embedded within prevailing culture that filters what we can and cannot hear.

Perhaps the most universal example of using music to alter mental state is the lullaby. In all cultures, mothers sing and hum lullabies for the express purpose of getting children to quiet down and go to sleep (i.e., switch states). Indeed, lullabies have been deciphered from 5000-year-old Babylonian clay tablets. In one, the crying child is gently admonished for waking the sleeping house god.

Lullabies are softly sung, repetitive tunes usually alternating between tonic and dominant harmonies and generally accompanied by a gentle rocking. The story lines are simple (e.g., "Twinkle Twinkle Little Star"), if not always comforting (e.g., "Rock-a-bye-Baby"). Regardless of explicit content, they are intended to communicate a relaxing sense of safety and love, to sooth fussiness, and to facilitate the switch into sleep.

Indeed, music is used to evoke a wide variety of mental states. It is also possible to reverse the process and go from mental states to music. In one study brain waves from two subjects in tranquil resting states of consciousness were translated into musical passages by a computer algorithm. *We were surprised*, the researchers write, *that the music created from the two subjects showed similar tempo and rhythm, and both recordings could be described as "peaceful"* (Lu, Wu, & Yao, 2015). They suggest that translating an individual's state of mind into a musical passage may be a better way to characterize a research subject's current emotional state than self-report.

A great deal more could be written about the power of music to alter states of consciousness. David Aldridge and Jörg Fachner have edited a wonderful volume, *Music and Altered States* (2006), that describes the many uses of music across the centuries and diverse cultures to change state of consciousness (Aldridge & Fachner, 2006). A number of the chapters highlight the healing roles of music, especially for psychological trauma.

Sensory Overload

That altered states of consciousness can be induced by sensory manipulations is ancient knowledge. Possession trance, for example, occurs in ceremonies accompanied by overwhelming noise, music, sights, smells, sensations, and whirling frenetic motion—not to mention drugs and drink. In contrast, spiritual ecstasy seeks out empty, unmoving, eternal silence (Fachner, 2006).

Sensory overstimulation can induce an altered state of consciousness. The massive rave house parties of the late 1980s and 90s blended loud, pulsing music, vigorous dancing, powerful drugs, and pulsating darkness streaked by lasers, flickering projected images, and throbbing dancers waving phosphorescent glow sticks. As predicted, in these altered states, ravers, as aficionados are known, frequently assume a dance floor identity with a "rave name" that has a special meaning for them.

The use of deafening noise, screaming music, or other noxious sounds to wear down political prisoners is another example of sensory overstimulation used to alter state. The noise drowns out thought, disrupts attention and concentration, and progressively degrades a detainee's ability to sustain the focused state of mind necessary to resist. And, of course, it leaves no telltale marks, although former detainees remain forever tormented by a deafening ringing in their ears and intrusive noises in their minds.

Sensory Deprivation

John Lilly's life (1915–2001) is said to have inspired two movies, *Day of the Dolphin* (1974, Director Mike Nichols) and *Altered States* (1980, Director Ken Russell). The first used Lilly's research on dolphin communication as a starting point for an improbable conspiracy in which a trained dolphin is to assassinate the President of the United States. In the second, a scientist experimenting with LSD in an isolation tank regresses into a caveman. Not surprisingly, neither won any major awards nor reflected Lilly's actual life's work.

> *When I was eight or nine years old, my father, Frank W. Putnam, Sr., developed an interest in the effects of animal venoms on blood proteins. He was a biochemist, who was the first to decipher the primary structures for three of the five classes of immunoglobulins* (see his National Academy of Sciences biography at: http://www.nasonline.org/publications/biographical-memoirs/memoir-pdfs/putnam-frank.pdf). *It was an exciting time for me as we visited reptile farms and other menageries of deadly creatures to collect samples. One of the places we went on multiple occasions for octopus and fish venoms was the research laboratory at Marineland of Florida. There I struck up a friendship with F.G. Wood, the director, who let me wander freely around the research tanks filled with exotic marine life.*
>
> *On one occasion, John Lilly was there working with a dolphin. Standing on tiptoes to watch through the little window in the door, I was fascinated by their mutual interaction. Later, I listened while Lilly, Wood, and my father talked about Lilly's idea that he could find a way to talk with dolphins. A few years later Lilly would set-up an institute in the Virgin Islands to explore interspecies communication.*

Initially trained in medicine, psychiatry, and physiology and later in psychoanalysis, Lilly researched high altitude physiology during World War II, inventing a number of scientific instruments and developing an electronic system for displaying brain waves. He joined the National

Institute of Mental Health in 1953, directing a small research group known as the "Section on Cortical Integration" focused on understanding the functioning of the mind when it is deprived of all forms of sensory input. Interest in space flight as well as military missions requiring prolonged isolation provided one justification. It is also likely that investigating the effects of sensory deprivation used in the "brain washing" of American POWs by North Korea provided another rationale.

To separate a person from all external forms of sensory input, Lilly created the isolation tank. An isolation tank is a dark, soundproofed, and enclosed pool of hypertonic salt water in which to quietly float. Epsom salt is used to keep from stinging cuts or eyes and the salinity is so high that the person floats on top of the water and does not have to expend any effort to keep from sinking. The temperature is fixed at 93 or 94° F and sound and vibrations are kept to an absolute minimum.

Over the years, Lilly and colleagues experimented with various designs, ultimately setting up a center with five tanks on a ranch near Malibu. Known locally as the "Lilly Pond," he conducted workshops and introduced celebrities and scientists to isolation tanks as part of a mixed research and promotion effort. As a legacy, commercial home models are available and floating centers with hourly tank rentals exist in cities around the world.

Lilly was his own favorite experimental subject pushing the limits of introspective self-exploration to the edge of psychosis—and perhaps beyond. Out of his personal journey emerged Lilly's model of the nature of consciousness:

> In the first 2 years I was offered LSD-25 from my colleagues at NIMH. I refused it without explanation. My reasons were connected with the tank work and what I called "my brain and mind baseline" unmodified by chemicals or the basic belief systems of others. I spent 10 years developing this baseline which read, "**my basic beliefs are unbelievable and incredible.**"
>
> 1964 ended the 10 years. I felt ready to try LSD-25 in the tank of seawater in the Lab of the Communication Research Institute in St. Thomas in the U.S. Virgin Islands (Lilly, 1977 p. viii).

Lilly's thousands of isolation tank trips—some lasting for days—with and without psychedelic drugs, led critics to conclude that he had taken leave of his senses. Nothing that he said should be taken seriously.

Books about his isolation tank and drug experiences describe trips out-of-body, time-travel, and cosmic consciousness (Lilly, 1977). Rather than relying on Lilly's accounts, which—real or not—are too fantastic to be believable to most, it makes sense to hear from someone else who—although eccentric in his own right—is more credible.

Richard P. Feynman (1918–1988) was a theoretical physicist recognized for his brilliant work on quantum mechanics with the Nobel Prize in 1965. The public knows him for his trenchant analysis of the space shuttle *Challenger* disaster. At the televised hearing he demonstrated the simple cause of the catastrophic failure of a joint in the right solid rocket booster by dropping a sample of the O-ring material into ice water. He concluded the commission's report with the observation that *"For a successful technology, reality must take precedence over public relations, for nature cannot be fooled."*

Feynman was fifty-six when he undertook a series of sessions in Lilly's isolation tanks aimed at exploring hallucinations:

> *I became very curious about hallucinations and welcomed the opportunity to use Dr. Lilly's sensory isolation tanks, for they were reputed to produce hallucinations, safely. I have spent at least a dozen sessions, each of over two hours, in the tank. The experience was very pleasant and rewarding. Although nothing happened for the first two sessions (except idle thinking as when one is going to sleep), hallucinations were experienced nearly every time thereafter. After some brief period after entering the tank, they would continue for hours. I was always aware that I was hallucinating and part of my mind was nearly always making observations. There were the usual out-of-body, or out-of-the-right-time hallucinations. I have later had imaginary flights over scenery etcetera* (Feynman quoted in Lilly, 1977 p. 187).

In aggregate, research on monotonous and sensory-deprived environments demonstrated that when the human mind loses the grounding input provided by normal environmental stimulation, it takes off in unexpected directions. Some of which are experienced as crossing into cosmic states of being while others are journeys into the psychotic.

Virtual Media

A great deal could be written about the state-altering/identity-creating capacity of computers, virtual reality and the Internet. The work of Sherry Turkle, a professor of the Social Studies of Science and Technology at MIT, is noteworthy for her prescience on how many Internet users assume multiple identities (Turkle, 1995). A person may create multiple virtual identities to match diverse Internet contexts, for example as a participant in online games, as a member of multiple chat groups, and in email exchanges with a variety of people on a range of topics.

The famous Steinberg New Yorker magazine cartoon of two dogs in front of a computer, one saying to the other, *"Nobody knows you're a dog on the Internet,"* applies to many humans as well. People assume Internet identities of different genders, ages, sexual orientations, personal histories, professions etc.—switching from one to another remarkably easily as they change venues. Again, which one is their "real" self begs the larger question of the contextual plasticity of human identity. The ability to create multiple selves each with unique perspectives on life appears to be a basic human capacity that flourishes in environments that compartmentalize social interaction. In a few instances, a powerful virtual self may come to displace the individual's more conventional self and thus commandeer the person's personality.

My major concern is that many of the Internet settings, particularly for adolescents, conducive to the creation of strong alter identities are often extremely violent. The video games kids play—girls as well as boys—typically involve fighting, shooting, blowing things up, racing, crashing and killing wantonly—all in high definition graphics. In general, kids have free range over the Internet and routinely access many sites that would horrify their parents. Kids usually have far more technical sophistication and can tap into an enormous pool of peer expertise through their social networks. Parental efforts to block access to forbidden zones are largely fruitless given these skills and resources. I find kids contemptuously relish their abilities to outwit parents in this generational arena.

Virtual identities are strengthened by the complexity and uniqueness of the worlds they inhabit. The more possessions, special powers, personal attributes and longer "life history" they acquire, the greater the virtual persona's individuality and durability. The degree to which virtual selves influence the individual's behavior in "real life," i.e., in actual social situations, defies generalization.

That elements of a teenager's virtual identity do carry over to the "real" world, however, is evident both from tragic events and research. Dr. Jennie Noll and colleagues, for example, found that avatars (virtual alter identities) created by adolescent girls in the laboratory were predictive of whether they would be approached sexually while on the Internet and whether they would, in turn, meet the strange men in person (Noll, Shenk, Barnes, & Putnam, 2009). Girls with a history of sexual abuse tended to create avatars with more bare skin, cleavage, tattoos, body piercings, and other indicators of sexual availability. Not surprisingly, they reported being approached more often on the Internet than the non-abused girls and of actually meeting these men in person. Thus, the various "whos" that you are in cyberspace does have real life consequences.

Can we become "addicted" to the videogames? This question will be argued for some time, but preliminary research suggests that the mental states elicited by videogames activate the same brain reward systems associated with drugs and sex. Massively Multiplayer On Line Role Player Games (MMORPG), the genre for games such as the *World of Warcraft*, in which a large number of players interact with each other in a virtual world, require players to assume an identity with unique attributes and actions. The extent to which such videogame identities can displace an individual's real world identity remains to be determined, although it seems likely that certain people would be susceptible to losing themselves in these complex online worlds, especially where their wealth, status, and power greatly exceeds their actual life circumstances.

Places and Spaces
Sacred places have existed as far back as we can trace humankind. They likely existed for our ancestral species, although we may not be able to recognize the residual traces for what they once were. Caves were among the first and the most venerated sites for ritual and religious experiences. Paintings, carvings, offerings and other evidence of religious rituals (including seeds from psychoactive plants) have been found deep in caves and hidden beneath rock overhangs dating back over 30,000 years. Caves appear frequently in early mythology as dwelling places for divinities and spirits. And some ancient caves and grottos remain sacred to major world religions today.

Other natural sacred places exist. Mountains, prominent or unusual stones, springs and waterfalls, and even trees serve to instill religious feelings in worshipers and pilgrims. But caves, with their womb-like qualities, darkness, eerie silence and reverberating echoes, are the most powerful settings for ritual and mystery. It is believed that early tombs and temples sought to replicate the essence of caves including their acoustic properties.

The field of archaeoacoustics investigates the relationship between the resonance properties of caves, burial chambers, and temples and other evidence of the rites and rituals that may have been performed there. It is noted that in many caves, paintings and carvings are located in chambers that display strong resonance with frequencies of the chanting human voice. In these special places, chanting, singing, and drumming would be greatly amplified as well as producing multiple echoes reverberating with different time delays. Coupled with flickering torchlight, dancing shadows, sacred symbols and images, secret rituals and rites, these ceremonies were intended to evoke altered states in the participants.

Today, we build temples, churches, cathedrals, mosques, synagogues, shrines, and other holy places designed and decorated to elicit awe and reverence. Chanting, singing, and inspirational music remain essential elements. Worshipers kneel, bow, prostrate themselves, pray, stand, sing, chant, and assume culturally defined roles in rituals of supplication and blessing. Candles, incense, ethereal images, imposing idols, gold, jewels, stained glass, and other dazzling adornments provide rich multisensory experiences. The total effect is meant to be spiritually mind-altering.

We also build athletic spaces—gyms, stadiums, playing fields, courts, courses, arenas, rings, rinks, tracks and other venues in which to hold and witness passionate matches of skill, strength, endurance, daring, and strategy. Boisterous crowds and loud, aggressive partisanship is an essential part of the fan peak experience. They feed on shared raw emotion, a do-or-die, win-at-all-costs mentality, strong identifications with individual athletes and the team (wearing player jerseys, body painting team colors, etc.) and a tribal sense of belonging in a roaring mob committed to one purpose—kill the other team!

If certain places and spaces evoke powerful and distinct states of being in individuals, we should expect them to also act to compartmentalize identity and memory of these experiences. Perhaps this is one reason why rabid sports fans can go to such extremes with outrageous costumes, make-up, masks and props without being troubled or embarrassed by their public behavior.

There is another place where you can repeatedly test the state-dependent properties of personally meaningful places and spaces—your own home. Notice what is happening when you leave one room on a purposeful errand and yet arrive in the next having forgotten what it was that you just got up to do. Going back to the first room often will trigger recall of what you were thinking of. The rooms and spaces in which we live and work come over time to define personal contexts with distinct states of mind that affect what we think about, what we remember, and how we feel when we are in them.

THE ROLE OF STATES OF BEING IN MENTAL HEALTH TREATMENT

Historically there have been four major approaches to states of being in the treatment of mental and emotional problems. The first is psychotherapy, usually loosely Freudian in nature, conducted with patients who are in an altered state of consciousness, e.g., hypnotherapy or a more extreme example, the WWII drug-induced abreactive therapies for combat neurosis. Most recently research with LSD, psilocybin and Ecstasy (MDMA) for intractable cases of PTSD and improved quality of life in terminal cancer patients has reopened this line of inquiry (Bouso, Doblin, Farre, Alcazar, & Gomez-Jarabo, 2008; Grob, Bossis, & Griffiths, 2013; Mithoefer, Wagner, Mithoefer, Jerome, & Doblin, 2011).

The second is the use of powerful psychotropic medications intended to influence a patient's mental state such as reversing a pathological mental state (e.g., depression or anxiety), stabilizing wildly swinging mood states, or by imposing a tranquilized state (see Chapter 9). Decreasing a rapid cycling bipolar patient's mood swings is a positive example. The zombie-like state of overmedicated chronic mental patients is the other extreme.

A third approach, one that most directly addresses state-related aspects of the patient's problems, has been tried in limited forms. Eric Berne's Transactional Analysis and Mardi Horowitz's Configurational Analysis are two examples of ego state-based psychotherapies with some success (see Chapters 5 and 6). The final approach is the use of biofeedback to help patients increase desirable mental and physical states of being and suppress undesirable states.

Psychedelic Psychotherapy

Drug- and alcohol-facilitated psychotherapy dates at least to the end of World War I, when therapy with soldiers in ether-induced altered states of consciousness proved successful with "shell shock." Between the World Wars, a few British and American psychiatrists experimented with psychotherapy with patients in barbiturate-induced "twilight" states of consciousness. The prevailing theory was that classic Freudian ego defenses were suspended or blocked in the twilight state allowing unconscious conflicts to surface. Although limited, this early experience provided guidance for the rapid, large-scale implementation of narcosynthesis (also called narcohypnosis) for psychiatric combat causalities by the British and American militaries during World War II (see Chapter 7). Since that time, a remarkably wide-range of drugs has been used to facilitate psychotherapy, particularly for conditions that are considered to be the result of neurotic conflicts.

Psychedelic psychotherapy is another example of using drug-induced altered states of consciousness to facilitate treatment. The career of Czech psychiatrist Stanislav Grof spans the gulf between the heady days of LSD-facilitated therapy during the 1950s and early 60s and the current rebirth of interest by a few research groups around the world. Trained as a Freudian psychoanalyst, Grof has conducted more than four thousand psychedelic psychotherapy sessions (Grof, 2009). After a decade of LSD research in Prague, he came to the U.S., initially to Yale in 1965 and later Johns Hopkins and the Maryland Psychiatric Research Center, to continue his work on LSD psychotherapy.

Grof describes a typical LSD-facilitated psychedelic psychotherapy research protocol:

The dosages used in this approach were rather high ranging between 300 and 500 micrograms. Patients were encouraged to stay in a reclining position for most of the session, keep their eyes covered with eyeshades, and listen to selected stereophonic music through headphones. The therapist and a specially trained nurse or co-therapist [of the opposite sex as the therapist] stay with the patient for the entire duration of the drug action, sometimes as many as twelve to sixteen hours. The total number of sessions was limited to three in number because of the research design and other special circumstances. During the drug-free preparation period, which usually lasted between fifteen and twenty-five hours, the therapist explored the patient's life history, helped him understand his symptoms, and discussed his philosophical and spiritual orientation. He gave him basic information about the effects of LSD and explained the rationale of the treatment. There were also several drug-free interviews in the period following the session in which the patient's written account of the LSD experience was discussed in detail. The major purpose of these talks was to help the individual integrate the LSD experience into his everyday life (Grof, 2009 p. 23–24).

Grof emphasizes the critical importance of "setting" in determining the type of experience a patient has:

The setting is an extremely important variable that can have a powerful influence on the nature of the LSD experience. It makes a great difference whether the session takes place in a busy laboratory milieu, in a comfortable homelike environment, in a sterile medical setting with white coats and syringes or in a place of great natural beauty. Each of these settings tends to activate and facilitate the emergence of quite different matrices from the unconscious of the subject (Grof, 2009 p. 223).

In addition to setting, the personality of the therapist, current life situation and past history, childhood and infancy, all play a role in shaping a patient's response.

Having researched LSD on both sides of the Atlantic, Grof notes a key difference in the U.S. and European approaches towards psychedelic psychotherapy. In Europe, therapists conducted more traditional psychotherapies aimed at slowly drawing out and examining the patient's unconscious conflicts. In the U.S. the therapeutic aim was to create a *"deep religious and mystical experience"* with the goal of profoundly changing the patient's personality virtually overnight. In a study of 72 patients, however, Grof found that only three manifested an enduring positive change in their condition after a single LSD session (Grof, 2009). Many others showed transient positive changes that faded within days to weeks. A few experienced a worsening of their condition.

In contrast, Grof observed that when treated with multiple LSD sessions, patients would repeatedly return to specific personal themes that enabled them to process traumatic experiences underlying certain symptoms:

When I studied the material from several consecutive LSD sessions of the same person, it became evident that there was a definite continuity between these sessions. Rather than being unrelated and random, the experiential content seemed to represent a successive unfolding of deeper and deeper levels of the unconscious. It was quite common that identical or very similar clusters of visions, emotions, and physical symptoms occurred in several consecutive LSD sessions. Patients often had the feelings that they were returning again and again to a specific experiential area and each time could get deeper into it. After several sessions, such clusters would then converge into a complex reliving of traumatic memories. When these memories were relived and integrated, the previously recurring phenomena never reappeared in subsequent sessions and were replaced by others (Grof, 2009 p. 19).

Following the criminalization of LSD and related psychedelic drugs officially sanctioned clinical research stopped. Despite jeopardizing their careers, a handful of academics continued to advocate for restarting this line of research. Ultimately several proposals for small clinical trials and studies to assess safety and mode of action were granted exemptions by the Federal government.

To date these drugs have proven medically safe but with some psychological risks (M. W. Johnson, Richards, & Griffiths, 2008). Recent experience suggests that the approach pioneered by Grof and his contemporaries of first preparing the subject, then conducting multiple LSD sessions and finally processing the images, memories, thoughts, feelings and other material in a drug-free state remains the most effective approach to treatment.

At present, a number of small psychedelic psychotherapy research studies are completed or underway. Investigators from major universities in the U.S., Europe, and Israel are involved. Most use standard clinical trials methodology to ensure validity of their results. The studies primarily focus on the treatment of PTSD, alcoholism and drug addiction or with terminally ill cancer patients to decrease anxiety and improve their end-of-life experience (see Epilogue).

Identity or Ego State Psychotherapies

Various identity state or ego state psychotherapies—usually developed and promoted by an individual clinician—have been offered over the years. Two examples, Transactional Analysis by Eric Berne and Mardi Horowitz's *Configurational Analysis,* are briefly described in Chapters 5 and 6. These types of psychotherapies typically focus on an individual's different identity states and how they interact with significant others and the world at large. Classification schemes for identity states range from Berne's simplistic universal trinity of "child, parent, adult" to Horowitz's personalized affect-behavior-demeanor based descriptions unique to each patient. The complexity and necessity to individualize the coding system for each patient has limited the use of state-based psychotherapies in clinical practice.

Conditioned Brain-Body State Therapies

Biofeedback and neurofeedback are examples of therapies that use electrophysiological instruments to provide immediate feedback to subjects seeking to create and sustain specific body and brain states that are associated with positive and stress-reducing effects. Muscle tension, temperature, skin electrical activity, blood flow, heart rate, respiration, carbon dioxide level and blood oxygenation are among the physiological signals that have been used to identify and reinforce desired states. The biological signals are digitized and mathematically transformed to simplify representation of the target state of being that the subject is trying to attain and to sustain. Forms of visual and auditory feedback are frequently combined to increase the subject's ability to detect meaningful changes in performance.

Brain waves are the most common biological signal (usually called neurofeedback) fed back to subjects seeking to experience a desired state of being. The form of the feedback can range from simple graphs to complex swirling psychedelic patterns to animated virtual tasks such as keeping one symbol lined up over another or making a cartoon character perform in a videogame. While theoretical explanations for what the subject is doing vary, most converge on the notion that the person is operantly conditioning (see Chapter 6) a desired state of consciousness or sometimes conversely learning to suppress an undesired state. Others suggest, however, that the therapeutic effects are due to the meditative nature of the conditioned states—so called mental yoga—or to specific patterns of "healing" brain waves.

Neurofeedback is used to treat a variety of problems and disorders including ADHD, depression, anxiety, learning disabilities, PTSD, alcoholism, migraines, epilepsy, chronic pain, sleep problems and brain injuries such as concussions and strokes. Although many practitioners and patients are enthusiastic about their personal results, the evidence for therapeutic efficacy is mixed in controlled studies. Some of this discrepancy is probably just methodological noise given the wide variety of sensory modalities and forms of feedback used by researchers. Other treatment failures may reflect a therapeutic mismatch between the particular state of being that is conditioned and the problem or disorder being treated. A few people may just not be able to do this effectively or are receiving a form of feedback that they cannot use. And biofeedback probably just doesn't work for some conditions, especially if the underlying neurocircuitry is damaged or missing. Again, research is needed to determine for whom biofeedback works best.

WHAT SHOULD A STATE-BASED THERAPY ADDRESS?

To date, no approach has incorporated the many levels on which a state-based treatment model could potentially address psychopathology and support mental health. These include: extreme and dysfunctional states, disruptions and dysregulation of normal state sequences and cycles, switching problems, metacognitive deficits in bridging state-dependencies in knowledge and skills, misuse of drugs and alcohol to manipulate state, and aberrant state-space architectures.

A state model of therapy should seek to coordinate a range of therapeutic interventions designed to stabilize and optimize an individual's state-space and to integrate different identity and emotional states into a coherent and flexible healthy sense of self. It would seek to reduce the time an individual spends in dysfunctional and dysphoric states and eliminate or redirect maladaptive efforts to suppress painful and destructive states of mind. In cases in which an individual is triggered by some internal or external cue such as a traumatic reminder and rapidly switches into an inappropriate state it may be possible to create new pathways that lead to more temperate reactions.

Mental health treatment models based on a comprehensive state-oriented approach to therapy would operate at multiple levels and draw upon a set of procedures and components that influence the dimensions and dynamics of an individual's states of being. Treatment would focus on a series of state-related therapeutic tasks. Altered states of consciousness, either drug- or procedurally induced, might be utilized to generate transformative experiences, change perception, or bypass state-dependent barriers to recall of important memories.

The pathways and architecture of an individual's state-space could conceivably be re-configured to open up alternative, more adaptive responses to emotionally charged, dysfunctional state-triggering stimuli. Theoretically it might be possible to substantially reshape an individual's personality, to eliminate "character flaws" or to unblock latent talents or conflicted abilities—similar to the "quantum change" reorganization of the self described by Miller and C'de Baca (see Chapter 10). Indeed, profound and permanent personality change could happen suddenly and unexpectedly. The possibilities are a little mind-boggling but also ethically disquieting and require careful thinking through.

Levels of Psychopathology

A state-oriented approach to mental health conceptualizes psychopathology as simultaneously occurring on multiple levels. The first is the nature of the dysfunctional, problematic or pathological states per se, e.g., depression, anxiety, panic, intoxication, dissociation, inappropriate anger, unrelenting grief, paranoia, etc. Interventions would be directed at disrupting or destabilizing the pathological states and replacing them with more functional and/or tolerable states of being. Part of this process may involve creating new, more functional and harmonious states to substitute for the dysfunctional or dysphoric states. Deep relaxation, neurofeedback, meditation, virtual reality, hypnosis, guided visualization and other techniques can be used therapeutically to create and refine new states of being to replace problematic ones.

The second level involves the switch process. People can become "stuck" in a particular state of mind to the exclusion of others. Almost everyone has an occasional bout of feeling down or depressed, but usually these events are limited to a few consecutive days at worst. Depression only becomes a psychiatric disorder when it continues unremittingly for at least two weeks. The person has now become "stuck" in a depressed state. If the problematic state were transient and self-limited, then it would not be considered pathological in and of itself. It is the failure to normally cycle out of the state that defines the pathology.

Conversely a person may manifest an inability to sustain a normal cycle of states, instead continually sliding back into dysfunctional or emotionally inappropriate states of mind at the slightest provocation. Minor events, ruminative thoughts, and trivial comments by others, are sufficient to trigger a dysfunctional state of mind that monopolizes the person and crowds out other possibilities. The person *"just can't let go of it"* or *"get over it."*

In examples like the above we might metaphorically describe the switch mechanism as either being too "sticky" or too "slippery." Biological and behavioral interventions directed towards restoring normal temporal progression and natural cycles, e.g., the sleep cycle, daily activity and rest cycles etc., might free individuals stuck in dysfunctional states and stabilize others who are unable to sustain more suitable states of being.

The third level of psychopathology to address therapeutically involves faulty metacognitive or executive functioning—those higher level processes that bridge state-dependent memory and identity. Executive functions integrate state-dependent thoughts, feelings and actions into greater self-awareness and more deliberative behavior over time and across contexts. Mindfulness exercises, perhaps augmented by video sessions or other techniques for providing compelling feedback, can help someone understand how they come across, what triggers set them off, and what kinds of feelings that they need to pay more attention to within themselves. Cognitive Behavioral Therapy (CBT) approaches can address dysfunctional beliefs and cognitive distortions that impede metacognitive functioning locking an individual into a rigid, impoverished, and illogical appraisal of themselves and their options.

Becoming more aware of one's flow of thoughts, feelings and actions as well as their discontinuities will inevitably raise issues regarding the integration of the self. Individuals with a serious fragmentation of the self, e.g., meeting diagnostic criteria for borderline personality or dissociative identity disorder, may need to spend considerable time working at this level. There are therapeutic techniques and approaches to address serious identity fragmentation, although they lack the most rigorous forms of scientific validation (see e.g., the TOP DD study publications (http://www.towson.edu/topddstudy).

And finally, there is the question of addressing all of the dysfunctional and self-destructive ways of coping that the person has been trying for years. In particular, the use and abuse of drugs, alcohol, tobacco, gambling, sex, or thrill-seeking to modulate mood and mental states. There are also the dysfunctional avoidant, phobic and obsessive behaviors that keep emotional triggers and loaded contexts at a safe distance warding off situations that could evoke painful states of being, but, in turn, seriously constrict the person's opportunities and world.

These maladaptive behaviors are ingrained habits, unconsciously activated at the first inkling of trouble. The individual suddenly starts drinking or avoiding social situations without "good reason" because they subliminally perceive a potential threat on the horizon. Possibly, effectively addressing the other levels of state-related pathology will reduce reliance on such maladaptive coping strategies. Unfortunately, their habitual and reflexive nature makes them extremely resistant to change unless a person achieves sufficient self-awareness to detect their impending activation.

A fully state-based therapy would need to address these multiple levels of psychopathology. Based on my experience co-developing evidence-based treatment for maternal depression, child and adolescent trauma, as well the dissociative disorders is that achieving this is not as difficult as it might seem at first. But I don't expect that exclusively state-based psychiatric treatments will be available in the near future. Rather, it is my hope that therapists of all persuasions will consider the relative contributions of these levels of psychopathology as they work with the person in front of them.

IMPLICATIONS FOR RESEARCH

A states of being perspective raises numerous implications for research on human behavior—for research on all animate behavior really. States shape behavior. They influence the mind and body from perception to action. From the propensity of infants to cry at the sound of another's cry (see Chapter 2) to the beatific visions of Aldous Huxley under the influence of mescaline (see Chapter 9), states of being shape how we experience and respond to the world around us. Here, I will limit myself to a few areas in which a states of being viewpoint is relevant to current research on the mind and behavior.

Accounting for Missing Variance

Failure to take into account state-dependent perceptual, cognitive and response biases is a significant source of error in human biobehavioral research today contributing to inconsistent findings across studies of nominally the same behaviors. This is especially pronounced in research involving mind-body interfaces such as functional brain imaging. At present, states are viewed as "noise" and rarely measured or controlled for by investigators seeking to link biological signals (e.g., unique patterns of brain activation) with cognitive or behavioral responses. The typical strategy for reducing "noise" in an experiment is to take repeated measurements with the belief that averaging data points will subtract out the noise, which is random, but reinforce detection of a recurring signal, which is additive. This only works if the "noise" is truly random.

But states of being are not random events. In many respects, they are the signal—not the noise. Two individuals in different states, e.g., mania and depression, or the same individual in different states at two points in time will show dramatically discrepant responses to the same stimulus. Unless we measure or control for a research subject's state of being, we are missing crucial information. But—as the Baby Watchers learned (see Chapter 2)—it can be difficult to get scientists to agree on how to specify states.

Isomorphic Linkage of Knowledge Across Levels of Analysis

The concept of state is "isomorphic" in that is it can be defined at multiple levels of scientific investigation from EEG microstates lasting milliseconds to global emotional states like depression that may span months (see Chapter 3). As such, the concept of "state" offers a bridge— or, rather a series of bridges—that progressively connect the body and brain with the mind. Linking states across multiple levels of analysis helps unify our currently compartmentalized knowledge of the many layers of our body-brain-mind.

Mental Training

States provide a set of tools with which to probe and manipulate the brain-mind. In a seminal paper, Heleen Slagter, Richard Davidson and Antoine Lutz advocate the use of meditative states to study brain plasticity and associated cognitive change (Slagter et al., 2011). They start from the well-established observation that mental training of a motor skill (e.g., imagining the finger movements for a song on the piano or visualizing a gymnastic routine) can produce the same degree of improvement in performance as actual physical practice. Athletes have long appreciated the advantages of mental rehearsal, often conducted in an eyes-closed, meditative-like state.

The brain activity states associated with mental and physical training are, however, unique indicating that the improvements in performance seen with each type of practice (mental or physical) are achieved through different mechanisms. One of the major limitations of physical practice is that it does not generalize well to new tasks. The improvement associated with physical practice tends to be specific to the given task and does not readily transfer to new tasks. For example, practicing just one song on the piano over and over again has limited transferability to playing other songs.

In contrast, mental training generalizes to new tasks. It is suggested, based on brain activation patterns, that mental training of motor skills involves higher cortical processes than does physical training of the same skill. This higher cortical level is more task-independent contributing to increased abstraction and a greater transfer of the learned skill to new tasks and contexts. Slagter et al. believe that these higher processes are essentially metacognitive functions, especially the ability to focus attention and self-monitor one's behavior (see Chapter 6).

By using both types of meditation (focused attention and open monitoring—see Chapter 10), to acquire conscious (i.e., deliberative) control of these metacognitive functions they believe that it is possible to alter both brain structure and function. In proposing meditation to study brain plasticity, Slagter et al. acknowledge the thorny challenge of proving that the observed brain and cognitive changes are uniquely the result of the meditation as opposed to other possible causes. Nonetheless, drawing on their pioneering work with Zen meditation, they offer examples of how scientists could use specific states of being to modify brain structure and activity resulting in improved function and performance.

Attachment, Attunement, and Child Development
States of being are a major channel of human communication. We intuitively read the emotional and mental states of those around us, especially those most important to us. We subconsciously note posture, gestures, tone of voice, facial expression, and affect that all contribute to the "vibes" we get from others. The ability to accurately sense what is going on within other people can be critical to survival in some circumstances.

The most cogent example of states as a common channel of human communication is the attachment relationship between mother and infant (see Chapters 2 & 8). By age six months, normal infants are exquisitely attuned to their mother's state of being. Maternal anger, fear, depression and other negative states register strongly with her infant as evidenced by disrupted biological rhythms. For example, babies show a threefold greater cortisol stress response than their depressed mothers.

The acquisition of self-control over one's emotional states constitutes a critical developmental task that is truly life long. The child must learn to monitor her state. She must learn to recognize which states are contextually appropriate and which are not, and ways to self-recover from disruptions of state. The most visible proxy for this developmental task is a child's ability to sustain attention and to refocus attention after a disruption. In many respects an increasing ability to "stay on task" best reflects the progression of a child's learning self-control over states of being.

Thus a states perspective adds to research on child development and human interactions. In some respects, the concept of state is already well established in child development as a result of research on infant behavior (see Chapter 2) and attachment (see Chapters 2 & 8). It needs to be expanded, however, beyond the first year of life to include other developmental tasks, especially development of metacognitive or executive functions critical to life success (see Chapter 6).

Predicting Violent Behavior

Finally, a states of being approach sheds light on the predictability of human behavior. In legal settings, we often encounter the question of whether a psychiatrist can be expected to predict violence or suicide in a patient. Although there is the widespread assumption that this is—or at least should be—possible, bitter experience has shown that psychiatrists (and everyone else) are not very good at this.

The "speeding car" metaphor is often used to convey the difficulties of predicting future violence in psychiatric patients. Although one may be able to reasonably predict the location of a speeding car a few minutes after it whizzes by, as time passes it becomes increasingly difficult to know where it is or what it is doing. Days, weeks or months later it is impossible to predict precisely where that speeding car might be. This is similarly true for people.

The states of being theory postulates that states behave as non-linear dynamical (chaotic) systems (see Chapter 3). Non-linear dynamical systems are actually rigorously deterministic and precise predictions about any and every future state of the system can be made if you can specify the equations and the starting point in state-space. We cannot supply either. We do not have the equations nor can we precisely measure state in people. Remember Edward Lorenz discovered the "butterfly effect" when he restarted his computerized weather prediction program in the middle of a long run to save time (see Chapter 3). He had rounded off the previous output to three decimal places and that small, only a few tenths of one percent, change in the new starting numbers produced dramatically different results over time. The measurement of human behavior is obviously nowhere nearly as precise.

Thus while the states approach suggests that human behavior is potentially mathematically predictable, it also illustrates the serious limitations of present knowledge. All is not lost, however. We have a few empirical studies that indicate that it may be possible to systematically identify when someone is starting to lose it and at increased risk of harming themselves or others.

One approach to using mathematics to predict violent behavior was conducted by Candice Odgers and colleagues (Odgers et al., 2009). For six months they followed over 100 individuals considered at high risk for violence. Each week they assessed the subjects on a standard measure of psychiatric symptoms as well as one characterizing violent and aggressive acts towards others. Using a single (and relatively simple) dynamical equation they could model each person's symptom trajectory over the six months and see how well it predicted their self-reported acts of violent behavior. Overall their level of prediction was remarkably good in that they accounted for almost three quarters (73%) of the variability across subjects. Most behavioral researchers are pleased if they can account for a third of the variance in their studies.

An interesting pattern emerged. First, it is evident that two factors were critical to the accuracy of the prediction: the frequency with which an individual's psychiatric symptoms waxed and waned (oscillated) and secondly whether the rate of their symptom oscillation increased or decreased with time. Individuals who experienced rapid oscillations of symptoms were more likely to be involved in violent behavior. Likewise individuals who showed an increasing rate of symptom oscillation over time had the greatest number of violent incidents.

The absolute severity of the symptoms was not so important. It was the rate of oscillation of the symptoms and whether this rate was increasing or decreasing with time that predicted violence in the near future. The worst profile was to start with rapid oscillations in symptoms that increased in frequency over six months. About a quarter (28.7%) of subjects initially judged to be at high risk showed this increasingly unstable symptom pattern that proved to be strongly predictive of subsequent violence.

Although "state" was not directly measured in this study, the oscillation of symptoms can be interpreted as reflecting changes in mental state. Individuals rapidly shifting between or among radically different states of being will manifest rapid swings in their psychiatric symptoms (see Chapters 3 & 4). If these switches accelerate over time the person becomes increasing emotionally labile, which, not surprisingly, was associated with a marked increase in risk for violence. Conversely, if the switches slowed down over time, the person would become more stable and less likely to respond violently to perceived stressors or provocations. Thus we don't have to precisely measure a person's "state" to make predictions, but rather, we can glean useful information by looking at the rate of change (frequency of mood/symptom switches) in their states— and the rate of change in the rate of change.

There are other examples of the application of dynamical systems approaches to psychiatric disorders, antisocial behavior and personality change. At present each study stands alone, as there have not been sufficient replications. The larger point is that state-based dynamical systems approaches to analyzing behavior offer opportunities to prospectively identify when someone is at increased risk for violence and quite possibly other adverse outcomes. But that it takes frequent measurements to track that speeding car and determine whether it is driving erratically and speeding up or slowing down. However, the revolution in smartphone Apps and personal tracking devices connected to the Internet makes such repeated measurements readily possible.

THE DARK SIDE OF STATES OF BEING

Mob Psychology and Mass Panic

Certain mental and emotional states are contagious in that they can rapidly spread from one person to another. Two of the most dramatic contagious mental states are mob psychology and mass panic. Pure examples of either are rarer than people might think, but nonetheless their mere possibility demands that authorities plan to prevent or contain them in the face of social unrest or disaster.

Mob psychology was of interest to Freud and early psychoanalysts, some of whom claimed that such group behavior was proof of a collective unconscious. The fact that, as a member of a mob, normally moral people suddenly start behaving in violent and antisocial ways suggested a loss of the individual's ego functions and a submersion of the self into a group identity.

Today, this behavior is the focus of a branch of social psychology known as "crowd psychology." Crowd psychologists seek to understand the psychological mechanisms contributing to "group mentality." In addition to studying violent mobs, they are also interested in examples of passive and obedient group behavior sometimes maintained in the face of extermination.

The key point here is that while in mobs and crowds, people can suddenly start acting in ways that are very different from their normal behavior. Members of a mob may behave as differently from their usual social selves as our hypocritical politician and neighborly serial murderer when they engage in their secret lives.

Mass panic is the other side of the coin in that organized group behavior suddenly breaks down and individuals flee in a disorganized fashion, often increasing their actual danger. In blind panic crowds will trample people to death, pile themselves up against closed doors, and block their only escape routes.

In other situations, enormous numbers of people may suddenly become "hysterically" ill. In the Sarin gas attack on the Tokyo subway in 1995, twelve people were killed and another 50 were seriously injured. But over 5000 people showed up at hospitals seeking medical attention. This is an example of the mass panic that civil authorities must plan for in the event of a terrorist attack with biological, radiological, or toxic weapons, the possibility that huge numbers of people, who are actually unhurt, become "sick" and overwhelm the capacity of medical facilities to triage and care for the seriously injured.

A states of being model would conceptualize mob violence and mass panic as extreme, angry or fearful states of being that are contagiously spread from person to person by primal facial expressions, nonverbal or illogical communication, and frenzied or panicky behavior. Just as a depressed, frightened, angry, intoxicated or psychotic parent communicates her mental state to her child; individuals caught up in mob violence or mass panic broadcast their mental states to others in socially primitive but extraordinarily powerful, largely nonverbal ways.

Extreme states powerfully influence what a person sees and hears—how he thinks and acts. Moral values, logical reasoning, interpersonal skills, reality testing and other normal cognitive processes are bypassed and replace by primitive raw emotions such as rage or fear. Because of SDLM (see Chapter 5) an individual caught up in a mob or mass panic situation is not able to use much of what he knows. If scientists were somehow able to whisk him off to a laboratory and quickly measure his brain, body and mental functions, they would find him grossly abnormal with respect to his normal states of mind.

In fact, we would probably see the fight or flight systems maximally activated; while neural networks associated with logical reasoning, empathy, morality, and judgment are massively inhibited. These extreme states, like all states of being, only last a finite amount of time. Afterwards individuals often have relatively little recall of the events that transpired—and in the case of mob violence they probably are not strongly motivated to examine them either.

Interrogation and Torture

Interrogators and torturers understand states of being. Interrogators seek to create certain states of mind in their subjects that break down willful resistance. Torturers seek to inflict states of terror, pain, degradation and suffering as punishment, to force compliance, or to extract false confessions. The two specialties come together in the form of coercive interrogation that use states-altering techniques to break resistance and extract information from unwilling subjects (Putnam, 2013).

The "KUBARK Counterintelligence Interrogation" manual, dated to July 1963, contains examples of the CIA's approach to coercive interrogation. Now declassified and described as "obsolete" by the U.S. Government, the document was made public through a Freedom of Information Act filing by the *Baltimore Sun* in 1997. A number of versions can be downloaded from the Internet. Among other things, Spanish translations of KUBARK counterintelligence interrogation manuals were used to train large numbers of military personnel from El Salvador, Guatemala, Ecuador, and Peru, and at the School of the Americas between 1987 and 1991.

The manual states:

Coercive procedures are designed not only to exploit the resistant source's internal conflicts and induce him to wrestle with himself but also to bring a superior outside force to bear upon the subject's resistance (KUBARK, 1963 p. 83).

All coercive techniques are designed to induce regression . . . As a result, "most people who are exposed to coercive procedures will talk and usually reveal some information that they might not have revealed otherwise" (KUBARK, 1963 p. 84).

[All quotation marks, brackets, eclipses, bold, spellings etc. in this and the following KUBARK, quotations are retained as in original.]

The manual details a range of techniques designed to induce fatigue, pain, sleep loss, and anxiety that disrupt and destroy an individual's identity and sense of control over their life. Starting with the subject's arrest, which is to be carried out in the early morning hours when capacity for physical and mental resistance is at its lowest ebb, the manual details how to systematically re-shape the prisoner's world so as to undermine the capacity to resist:

Control of the source's environment permits the interrogator to determine his diet, sleep pattern, and other fundamentals. Manipulating these into irregularities so that the subject becomes disoriented is very likely to create feelings of fear and helplessness (KUBARK, 1963 p. 88).

The use of sensory deprivation to deny detainees orienting and organizing sights, sounds, tastes, smells and tactile sensations is standard. Research by John Lilly is quoted at length in the manual, which states that:

The more completely the place of confinement eliminates sensory stimuli, the more rapidly and deeply will the interrogatee be affected. Results produced only after weeks or months of imprisonment in an ordinary cell can be duplicated in hours or days in a cell which has no light (or weak artificial light which never varies), which is sound-proofed, in which odors are eliminated, etc. An environment still more subject to control, such as water-tank or iron lung, is even more effective (KUBARK, 1963 p. 91).

Coercive interrogation techniques also seek to disrupt and disintegrate the person's integral sense of self. The detainee is cut off from all familiar and reassuring objects, interactions and connections that support his usual states of being:

Usually his own clothes are immediately taken away, because familiar clothing reinforces identity and thus the capacity for resistance. (Prisons give close haircuts and issue prison garb for the same reason.) If the interrogatee is especially proud or neat, it may be useful to give him an outfit that is one or two sizes too large and to fail to provide a belt so that he must hold his pants up. The point is that man's sense of identity depends on a conti- nuity in his surroundings, habits, appearance, actions, relations with others, etc. Detention permits the interrogator to cut through these links and throw the interrogatee back upon his own unaided internal resources (KUBARK, 1963 pp. 86–87).

The surprising theme that emerges, however, from the manual's chapter on coercive techniques is that it is the threat of some ter- rible thing, e.g., pain, death, or deprivation, that is actually more effec- tive than the thing itself:

The threat of coercion usually weakens or destroys resistance more effectively than coercion itself. The threat to inflict pain, for example, can trigger fears more damaging than the immedi- ate sensation of pain. In fact, most people underestimate their capacity to withstand pain. The same principle holds for other fears sustained long enough, a strong fear of anything vague or unknown induces regression, whereas the materialization of the fear, the infliction of some form of punishment, is likely to come as a relief. The subject finds that he can hold out, and his resistances are strengthened. "In general, direct physical bru- tality creates only resentment, hostility, and further defiance" (KUBARK, 1963 pp. 90–91).

Thus the black art of coercive interrogation involves not only an ability to create states of extreme distress that undermine resistance, but also the necessity to avoid evoking those states of mind that strengthen a person's resolve and capacity to resist. The manual notes that pain, for example, can actually focus or intensify a subject's resis- tance. More effective is pain that the subject is made to inflict upon himself. In this situation, the manual notes that, *"The motiva- tional strength of the individual is likely to exhaust itself in this internal encounter . . ."* (KUBARK, 1963 p. 95).

The manual discusses the use of altered states of consciousness such as hypnosis and narcosis. In a similar fashion, it notes that the threat of drugging or the subject's mistaken belief that they have been drugged may actually be more effective than any known drug. The detainee can, instead, be given a placebo, sometimes in the form of a dramatic but innocuous injection of ominously-colored saline:

> *In the interrogation situation, moreover the effectiveness of a placebo may be enhanced because of its ability to placate the conscience. The subject's primary source of resistance to confession or divulgence may be pride, patriotism, personal loyalty to superiors, or fear of retribution if he is returned to their hands. Under such circumstances his natural desire to escape from stress by complying with the interrogator's wishes may become decisive if he is provided an acceptable rationalization for compliance. "I was drugged" is one of the best excuses* (KUBARK, 1963 p. 100).

Conversely, when a real "truth serum" is used to facilitate interrogation, it should be administered secretly:

> *The judicious choice of a drug with minimal side effects, its matching to the subject's personality, careful gauging of dosage, and a sense of time . . .[make] silent administration a hard-to-equal ally for the hypnotist intent on producing self-fulfilling and inescapable suggestions . . . the drug effects should prove . . . compelling to the subject since the perceived sensations originate entirely within himself"* (KUBARK, 1963, p. 100).

The cumulative effect of coercive techniques is to disrupt the individual's metacognitive capacities. The person is set against himself. He is cut-off from all manner of social and emotional support that reinforces sense of self. He is subject to deprivation and erratic access to sleep, water, food, hygiene and other necessities. Semi-deafened and mentally numbed by blasting noise, the detainee is made to freeze or swelter without hope of relief. Continually intimated and terrified with threats of impending pain and suffering, the detainee exists in a seemingly unending state of physical, physiological, and psychological misery. As hopelessness sets in, the metacognitive glue that holds the many aspects of self together begins to dissolve.

Driven into a nether region of his state-space the detainee loses touch with the previously compelling cherished values, loyalties, and beliefs. The normal regenerative effects of the sleep-wake-eating-elimination-activity-rest cycle are obliterated. Instead, a myriad of uncertainties and unpredictable access to the anchors of sleep and food prevent re-establishment of a self-stabilizing rhythm or routine. As metacognitive functions and temporal structures crumble the detainee loses his ability to think, to act, and thus, to resist.

In his memoir, *Den of Lions,* journalist Terry Anderson describes his experience as a hostage in Beirut during seven long years of captivity, most of it in solitary confinement (Anderson, 1993). Continuously blindfolded, chained to a bed, unable to sit or even change his position more than a few inches from side-to-side, forced to pee into a bottle while lying down, Anderson feels himself come apart. No longer can he remember the things that he believed, that were central to the "who" that he used to be:

At first, the mind is a blank. Jesus, I always thought I was smart. Where are all the things I learned, the books I read, the poems I memorized? There's nothing there, just a formless gray-black misery. My mind's gone dead. God, Help me (Anderson, 1993 p. 78).

What Anderson can remember, the people he cares most about, his pregnant fiancée and his daughter, now become almost too painful to recall. He is filled with remorse for the way he has lived his life, for the people he has hurt, for the stupid things that he has done. The memories that should sustain him and give him something to live for, now become almost unbearable regrets and self-recriminations. He is being turned against himself.

Thus the coercive interrogator focuses his attacks at many of the same levels of states of being that a therapist seeks to heal. The interrogator creates unbearable states of torment by combining pain and extreme physical misery with feelings of terror, dread, helplessness and hopelessness that anything will change. He disrupts the normal day-night, sleep-wake cycle of states thereby cutting the detainee off from the essential anchors that organize and restore daily mental and bodily functions and rhythms. The interrogator seeks to destroy the detainee's prior identity and integrity of self by disrupting the metacognitive functions that connect him with his core values and beliefs. Indeed, the interrogator pits the detainee against himself further fragmenting personality and destroying the unity of self that undergirds the capacity to resist. In its place, the interrogator imposes another identity, characterized by abject passivity and a humiliating dependency on pleasing the interrogator.

Although we celebrate—mostly in fiction—the heroic resistance of the few who manage to hold out against this concerted destruction of their humanity, many, if not most, people are broken by extended coercive interrogation. Whether they successfully resisted or not, those who survive are forever haunted by disabling posttraumatic symptoms (Putnam, 2013). Ironically, the KUBARK manual notes that coercive interrogation methods are often counterproductive because people will say anything that they think the interrogator wants to hear to make the torture stop. Thus it is difficult for the interrogator to sort fact from desperate fabrication.

Despite the scandalous failure of the American Psychological Association to uphold its own ethical principles of not cooperating with torture (Soldz et al., 2015) most mental health professionals are barred from participating in such activities by professional codes of conduct as well as personal integrity (Putnam, 2013). There are legitimate reasons to work with law enforcement and intelligence agencies. While at the NIMH, I consulted with several of the three-letter agencies around questions of national security, personnel fitness, and criminal behavior. Later in Cincinnati I worked with the FBI around Internet victimization of children. But whatever the justification for such cooperation, we are bound to never use our professional knowledge to inflict physical or mental pain or injury.

Have I Created a Monster?

I may have created a monster! A NIMH colleague, Wayne Rasband, startled me with that spontaneous confession many years ago as he grappled with the implications that his groundbreaking image processing software, *NIH Image,* could be used to falsify research data. Many years later, as the Research Integrity Officer (RIO) at Cincinnati Children's Hospital, I investigated alleged research misconduct cases in which Photoshop was used to deliberately falsify scientific imaging data. Indeed, "Photoshopped" research is an all-to-common occurrence in science in general.

Wayne didn't create a monster. He created an extraordinary (years ahead of its time), open source, image processing software program that is cited in over ten thousand scientific publications. But he worried then, as do I now, about possible abuse of our ideas. By including extensive quotations from pioneers, I have sought to make clear that others before me understood the role of states of mind in human behavior. In this book, however, I pull these sources together into a more integrated, multi-dimensional perspective on the powerful roles that states of being play in an individual's moment-to-moment sense of identity and behavior as well as their larger personality.

If there is any merit to a "states of being" perspective on complex and perplexing human nature, then it is subject to inadvertent and deliberate misuse and abuse. As a simple example I can foresee the application of a states perspective to provide a finer grained analysis of the enormous trove of personal data already collected by commercial, governmental, and political interests. Current sources of personal data, e.g., items purchased, books read, movies watched, trips taken, and causes donated to etc. reflect decisions influenced by complex internal and external factors. While some of the extrinsic factors are knowable, e.g., the individual's bank balance, political party, or health status, a crucial missing piece is the person's gut reactions to the appeal.

Under the rubric of neuropolitics and neuromarketing, a variety of commercial ventures and political entities are collecting psychophysiological data (e.g., facial expressions, heart and respiratory rate, galvanic skin response, attentional focus and gazing patterns) as people respond to emotional and neutral stimuli. This is happening under controlled conditions with volunteers in laboratories and in real life on unwitting people in public settings.

In the laboratory, controlled studies collect essentially the same brain and bodily responses that I measured on the MPD/DID research subjects and that researchers today measure on PTSD, depression, anxiety and other state disorders (see Chapters 3, 4, and 7). In public, hidden miniaturized sensors remotely track many of these same responses without the person's awareness. Digital smart signs, for example, use embedded cameras, infrared eye-tracking and heart rate sensors, and special software to parse a viewer's emotional reaction as they momentarily glance at a political ad.

These kinds of physiological data are believed to reflect a person's unconscious (socially uncensored) motivations, beliefs, and prejudices, and therefore represent their "real" reactions. Indeed, physiological data often proves more predictive of actual behavior than what people are willing to tell you about what they think or how they feel (Bonanno et al., 2002). Smart displays are being widely, if covertly, adopted around the world to test products, politicians, and propaganda.

Here's where it gets even trickier. Once the passerby's photograph is in the system it can be linked to a specific individual through facial recognition software and thereby to enormous amounts of data collected by other means. Over time (and these huge databases contain years of our purchases, searches, downloads, likes, posts, and tweets) dozens of on-the-spot emotional reactions will be included. Mobile devices with their location, travel and connectivity information are another excellent source of data that can be plumbed to monitor an individual's emotional states over time (e.g., is the person recurrently active at 2 AM.)

From brains to beauty to brawn, health apps and fitness devices of all stripes routinely collect mood ratings as they monitor us. For example, over 200 apps are used by millions women and girls in over 180 countries to predict their menstruation cycles as well as to track mood and sexual activity. These data are not protected by the Health Information Privacy and Accountability Act (HIPAA) and may be sold to third parties without the individual's consent. Think of the possibilities for misuse.

Data on an individual's emotional reactions across settings and recurrent emotional state cycles can be used to target them in ways that are more insidious than simply knowing the movies they view or the eBooks they fail to finish. By combining traditional preference data (purchases, entertainment, travel etc.) with real time gut reactions and recurrent mood state cycles (e.g., reads Internet articles on divorce at 2 AM when menstruating) a great deal more can be divined about an individual's moment-to-moment vulnerabilities.

Benignly this information could be used to pop-up ads for divorce lawyers, marriage counselors or menstrual and sleep aids. Maliciously, it could push political ads about organizations, people or ideas that "threaten" the sanctity of marriage and family values. Like the coercive interrogator who chooses the moment of maximum confusion and weakness to press his victim, the telemarketer, the phisher, and the politician may time their strike to take advantage of a person's state-dependent susceptibilities.

In touting a "states of mind" perspective as a powerful approach to mining big data am I giving away the keys to the castle? Of course, they are not my keys to give away. They have been hanging outside the castle door since William James published *The Varieties of Religious Experience: A Study in Human Nature* (James, 1901–1902).

Nonetheless, never before has the capacity been available to continuously gather the kinds of data that allows the large-scale, remote determination of individuals' moment-to-moment states of being as well as their daily rhythms and larger state cycles. We are all plugged into the Internet—some more tightly than others—and spewing forth torrents of personal data, some of which can be readily parsed for our state of being.

Realistically there is nothing that I can do except to flag this Orwellian possibility as one of the foreseeable abuses of the adoption of a states of being perspective on human nature. I leave unrecorded my more serious concerns.

SYNTHESIS

States of consciousness, mind, and being are an essential ordering principle of human behavior. Despite their many and diverse manifestations, all states share common elements that are evident from birth forward. In their more fully developed form, recurrent states become prominent facets of our personality.

Empirically specified as transient but reoccurring patterns of psychological and biological variables and frequently cued by context, states exist within a larger multidimensional state-space that grows or shrinks with age and circumstance. Ever switching one to another, states travel well-worn pathways such that the appearance of one frequently heralds others to follow. Widely shared states define culture on large and small scales.

Acting as strange attractors in state-space, states coalesce our thoughts and actions, rhythms and moods into the "who" that we are at any moment. They become the temporary filters through which we see, hear, and feel and the revolving catalogs that index our associations and memories. From the first mother-infant embrace, states are the subconscious foundation of all social interaction. As such we have many ways to manipulate our states of being and thus the various faces of our persona. Much is instinctive, but others are learned or imposed.

If states are truly an essential ordering principle of human behavior and a fundamental unit of the self, then they hold profound implications for mental health and well-being. Although many therapies—psychological, physiological, and pharmacological—implicitly address limited aspects of states of being, none integrates our many realms of knowledge. This will require working with individual states, the switching mechanisms by which they are exchanged, the metacognitive processes that bridge state-dependent knowledge and unify self, and the maladaptive coping behaviors that seek to avoid or replace intolerable states of being.

Scientifically, states are viewed as mere distracting noise masking genetic traits that are believed to underlie mental illness. For many (but by no means all) disorders, however, states are a key signal. Definable at multiple levels of scientific analysis, states serve as common denominators for organizing our scrambled layers of knowledge of mind and body. Understanding states of being also provides an empirical opening into mystical realms of knowledge that may prove essential to improving the human condition.

Ethically, a deeper understanding of states of being challenges us to respect the sanctity of the mind-body in ourselves and in all others.

EPILOGUE

EPILOGUE

In late December 2012 I am diagnosed with a highly malignant form of prostate cancer. In January, I learn that it has spread to my bones. I have a fatal disease. When I learn my prognosis, I am told that I probably *"still have many months"* to live. This news, together with the physiological shock caused by dropping my testosterone level to zero over a few months as part of treatment, launches me on an emotional roller coaster marked by frequent crying jags triggered by reminders of my impending death.

The most painful of all the emotions is an anguishing grief at losing my wife and sons. It is as if they are the ones dying—not me. I am losing them. There are no words.

But other parts of me continue to function. I supervise therapists, collaborate writing research papers, and work on this book. Close friends are helpful and check on me often. But it is Karen, my wife, who lovingly holds me together during the worst moments.

I struggle to gain control of my emotions and to come to an acceptance of my death. I begin journaling—writing several times a day in a tear-spattered volume. Writing is immensely helpful in expressing the most agonizing feelings. At other times it takes the form of a running blog in my head—only a small part of which is ever transcribed.

During February—March 2013 I realize that I could use some sort of end-of-life therapy. There are things that I want to deal with. Questions I need to ask and answer. Fears to face. I need a therapy that is both deep and quick—which is not typical of psychoanalysis for example. Medication is out. I am not depressed so much as deeply grieving my loved ones and the end of my world. Plus I have more than enough unpleasant side effects from my cancer treatment.

I know that there are a few, small experimental studies using psychedelic drugs to treat resistant PTSD or to help terminal cancer patients deal with end-of-life issues. Through friends, I am referred to a research program, The Psychopharmacology of Psilocybin in Cancer Patients, at Johns Hopkins University in Baltimore, Maryland.

This program has been in existence since 2006 with a good track record of publications (Grob et al., 2013). That is important to me. I want my participation as a research subject to contribute to a greater good. At one point I voice technical concerns about the research design and one of the researchers, Roland Griffiths, kindly suggests that I let him worry about that. Later, Karen, a biostatistician, explains how the study design increases their statistical power.

Psilocybin is a novel psychedelic drug occurring naturally in many species of mushrooms. It has been used for thousands of years in religious ceremonies in the ancient world and the Americas. Thirty times more potent than the Mescaline taken by Aldous Huxley (see Chapter 9), it produces strong visual hallucinations without confusion or increased anxiety. It is known for inducing states of ecstasy associated with a sense of spiritual unification with others and the universe. Many people report a continuing positive effect on their mood and outlook long after the drug effects wear off.

In the 1960s researchers found psilocybin to be especially effective with terminal cancer patients, who reported reduced pain, an improved quality of life, and a greater acceptance of their imminent death. Unfortunately the sociopolitical turmoil of the Vietnam era led to the termination of all legal research with psychedelic drugs.

More recently the hospice movement emphasized the importance of quality of life for terminally ill people. The concept of spiritual well-being, especially finding meaning in one's life, is frequently identified as an essential factor in improving quality of life. Recognizing that psilocybin is one of the few drugs that affect spiritual well-being, the U.S. government is allowing psilocybin research with terminal cancer patients to go forward in small studies at a handful of major universities, Johns Hopkins being one.

I encounter considerable difficulty qualifying as a research subject. The Johns Hopkins Institutional Review Board (IRB) requires participants to meet stringent standards of good physical health—which can be a problem when you are dying. At times, my struggle to qualify for the end of life research protocol seems more of an archetypal quest—with challenge after challenge to overcome.

Once I stagger miles through a blinding tropical rainstorm after my taxi crashes with a metro bus on the way to the research unit. My blood pressure is an abnormally low 90/50—having mistakenly overdosed myself on an unfamiliar anti-hypertensive medication in an effort to meet the IRB's unrealistic blood pressure criteria (increased BP is a side-effect of my chemotherapy). I can barely stand. No race I ever swam or ran drained me more. Ultimately my efforts, aided by the extraordinary understanding and support of the research team, prevail. Finally I qualify.

Although Psilocybin has little toxicity for the body, it has extraordinarily powerful effects on the mind. Thinking about what I am seeking to do, I feel anxious. Here I am about to take a mind-blowing psychedelic drug and then explore the most frightening thing in the world—my own death. But I am driven to do this.

In my journal I record my doubts, "*I've gone too far to pull out—and you never know. My fear is that I'll turn up some incredible psychological hang-up that will blow apart my coping—my hope is that I will have a transformative experience that puts my life and death within some larger context that gives the world meaning*" (6/4/13, 8:50 AM). In their own way—each proves true.

Facing death is a great clarifier. Almost at the very moment that I truly realize that I am really going to die, what is important and what is not important becomes crystal clear. At virtually that same instant—in that examination room in front of the doctors and students—Karen turns to me and says, "*We'll make every day the very best day it can be.*"

A multitude of unresolved questions and "should dos" that occupy or preoccupy my attention—just vanish. They aren't important anymore. Lots of decisions that I hadn't even consciously considered—are made instantly without a second thought. Some life-long interests lose their appeal. But others, long-lost interests, resurface in new ways that echo a changed appreciation of my attachments to the world. It is a time of terrible angst and lucid self-revelation. I know at the deepest level what I truly care about. But, the accompanying anguish seems unbearable.

Sharing with close friends (many of whom are psychologists and psychiatrists) my intention to participate in end-of-life research using psychedelic drugs, some support me saying they would probably do the same. While others question the wisdom of it. In the end, several are crucial in helping me make it happen as well as serving as independent raters of my mental state for the research.

In preparation, one of the more emotionally difficult tasks is choosing important items and photographs to bring to the psilocybin sessions in Baltimore. The project coordinator informs me that research subjects may bring important personal mementos such as stuffed animals, small objects, and lots of photographs. These serve multiple purposes such as personalizing the therapy setting, providing emotional comfort, and stimulating memories. As I will be flying, I choose to bring only photos, which I print in my new digital darkroom. Photography being one of those long-lost interests reactivated by my prognosis. Each photo selected brings tears as I think about what it represents.

One picture is of our small cabin on a remote lake in Maine taken in the dead of winter. Karen and I snow shoed across the frozen lake a couple of Februaries before spending one of the most beautiful weekends of our marriage cocooned in a sleeping bag in front of a roaring fire. It never made it much above 40 degrees in the cabin, but we were warm. I wept inconsolably as I choose that photo—this is where I want my ashes scattered. I am going to spend the rest of forever beneath that ice-blue blanket of snow.

The Hopkins protocol largely follows a standard psychedelic psychotherapy format dating back to the 1960s. Originally developed for treating alcoholics, this approach has been extended to other conditions, notably severe posttraumatic stress disorder and terminal cancer patients (see Chapter Eleven).

Prior to the psychedelic sessions, I spend several sessions—over five total hours in my case—meeting with the two guides who will accompany me during the psilocybin sessions. We discuss my issues and agendas. They carefully and repeatedly prepare me for the drug experience. In addition, I meet separately and together with both of the researchers as part of the initial screening and later before and after each psilocybin session. There are many experienced professionals watching me at every point in the process. They are kind, open, and comfortable with dying.

Traditionally there are two "guides," who provide physical safety and psychological grounding during the psilocybin sessions. The psilocybin sessions are, however, mostly a self-directed, internalized, highly individual process with relatively little input from the guides. At times they reassure me or hold my hand when I am overcome with emotion. Most of the time, however, I am largely unaware of their presence. I trust them and feel safe, comfortable and respected.

In early June 2013 I have my first psilocybin session. But before the pharmacy will release the drug I have to give a urine sample for a drug screen—having been prohibited from taking pain and sleeping meds prior to the session. Once I'm cleared, it begins with a simple ceremony, but one that I sense is very meaningful for the entire research team.

In addition to the guides, the two researchers join us in the small session room. The psilocybin arrives and is placed in a ceremonial earthen cup given to the project by the Mazatec people of Oaxaca in the central Mexican highlands. I receive the cup respectfully in both hands and study the blue capsule. After swallowing it, I am required to drink the whole glass of water—after all this is research. Every possible detail must be controlled.

Psilocybin usually takes about 30–40 minutes to start acting. While waiting, I sit between my two guides on the couch looking at a book on Monet's gardens that I chose from a shelf filled with picture books of the cosmos, Indian mandalas, the Impressionists, modern art and nature. Video cameras look down on the couch and a stack of audio components takes up a shelf of the bookcase. The room is softly lit and decorated with statues of the Buddha, mandalas, flowers, and mystical art.

The research subject lies on a white couch while the guides sit in stuffed armchairs set back about four feet from the couch. A small meditation cushion on the floor next to the couch is used when a guide needs to sit closer to the subject. An oriental rug partially overlays the nondescript gray carpet. Later I learn that this was a storage room until the research team claimed it.

When my guides, Bill and Matt, feel that the time has come. I lie down on the couch covering up with a light blanket. They fit me with a plush purple satin eyeshade held tightly in place by straps above and below my ears. A roomy set of stereo headphones cups my ears. A blood pressure cuff is wrapped around my arm beneath the blanket. The music begins.

For a while nothing unusual seems to happen. Then I begin to see muted, pastel-washed imagery. It is difficult to discern the scene at first—but it resolves into a harbor—brick paved streets, no vehicles, a stone quay with small wooden sailboats moored to heavy iron rings set in the stone. I feel confused about what I am doing there or supposed to do there? The sky is a brilliant blue. Seagulls wheel above me. A nearby rack holds a row of simple black bicycles.

I feel impelled to get into one of the boats—which are riding below the street level. I don't see a way down. The imagery skips back and forth—so that at moments it is as if I am in the boat and other times as if I am standing on the quay watching myself sail away. I feel enormous grief each time I am in the boat. I hear myself saying—*"It means leaving everything behind."*

Eventually I am completely in the boat—sailing out to sea. Looking back, the harbor has disappeared. I am consumed by indescribable grief. There was nothing in sight—just empty sky and sea. This seems to last a very long time. I cry copiously, my eyeshades filling up to the point where I have to keep lifting the bottom edge to let the tears stream out.

I am totally lost. I have no idea of where I am supposed to go or to do—then I see a wavering rosy light, like a sunset or sunrise, on the horizon. I tack the boat heading for the light. This is the first time I feel some control over what is happening. The light flickers for a while, eventually disappearing. In the distance there seems to be land—although it is difficult to see it clearly—as if misty.

The boat runs aground onto a muddy shore—primordial ooze. Stepping out, I walk around. There is no life. No animals, birds, insects or even vegetation. The earth is wet reddish brown. Suddenly I come upon a brilliant green field of grass. In the middle is an enormous stone structure—part castle part cathedral. Walking up I look for a door—but don't find one. I walk around the side—tracing the huge stone blocks of the wall with my fingertips. They are smooth but not polished, dull granite gray. At the back is a massive double door of black wood with enormous wrought iron hinges but no handle or knocker.

Then I am inside (with no memory of going through the door). It is a medieval city with steep, narrow, cobblestone streets. The stone houses are crowded against each other with small lead paned windows and simple wooden doors. There are other people but they are gray shadows—their faces indistinct. They are engaged with each other—no one pays attention to me.

I find myself in front of a small arched door. It opens. My parents are standing there. They look happy. We hug. Nothing is said. (I cry—but these are tears of happiness.) I realize that I am in a city of the dead. I go looking for a former girlfriend, Julie, and find her with Peter, her adult son. Both died the prior year. Then the imagery ends.

At this point I have to get up to pee. Returning, I need to sit for a while because of the pain in my hips and spine. Bill hands me a picture of Karen and me taken at Assateague Island in Virginia on our twenty-sixth anniversary just a few weeks earlier. I cry (wail really) saying, *"I'm going to miss her so much"* and hug the picture tightly against my heart. I hold it there for what seems like hours. The imagery is over. I spend the rest of the session lying there listening to the music cradling Karen's picture. At some point I fall asleep—

waking to the last verse of Louis Armstrong singing, "It's a wonderful world."

Afterwards, I'm exhausted. Following a debriefing with my guides and the researchers, Karen drives me back to the hotel, where I collapse and sleep. But after several hours I feel refreshed. We go out for a late dinner. During dinner we have a deep conversation about our life going forward. I feel more optimistic about the quality of my remaining life.

I am surprised and puzzled by the allegorical nature of my psilocybin trip. I had expected something more classically psychedelic—although my experience with psychedelic drugs is limited to a few trips in college on what was alleged to be LSD (I graduated from Wesleyan in 1969). At times I felt that I was pushing the imagery, making things happen. It was more like a lucid dream—very vivid—but controllable at points. For example, I felt that I made myself walk up to the building in the green field and search for a door. But other things, such as seeing my parents, were complete surprises. I'm unsure what was accomplished—except that I feel reassured that everyone is together with a loved one.

The next day Karen drives us home to the Blue Ridge Mountains. It is late spring; the Shenandoah Valley is extraordinarily beautiful. I feel at peace and truly happy for the first time since learning my prognosis in January. For several days following the session I feel peaceful and happy in an effortless fashion.

But gradually this positive effect lessens—I find myself slipping back into pessimistic trains of thought. After the first session I essentially stop all crying, but a couple of weeks later a few tears are beginning to seep out as I contemplate my future. Much of my thinking centers on how to make my death and its consequences the easiest for Karen and our boys. When thinking about these issues, I note that I sometimes hear in my head—as a separate stream of thought—the voice of one of my guides, Bill, commenting on my options.

For me this is the hallmark of a good therapist. When supervising new therapists, I listen for a stray comment from their patient/client to the effect that at some critical juncture, the client heard the therapist's voice providing guidance or testing reality. That tells me that the person has started to "introject" the therapist who is now becoming part of their "observing ego" (see Chapter 6).

Bill's calm voice is, in turn, replaced by a voice with no identity—I come to call it the "psilocybin voice." It offers me "tough love" advice. Usually after feigning a tad of sympathy it says something like, "*But hey, it's no big deal. Everybody does it. Everyone dies. Why should you be any different? Let it go.*" While I could use a little more empathy, its advice is good, if not exactly uplifting.

By the end of June, however, I've largely lost the psilocybin effect (although the voice continues on occasion). I'm having more pain, together with massive hot flashes often several times an hour (ladies, men really have no clue!) that soak my clothes which then chills my body. Yuck! I'm growing weak and tired.

I also realize (first gradually and then suddenly in a glaringly unde-niable fashion) that there is a major long-standing personal issue that I must face. I realize that a set of past experiences have seriously trauma-tized me—although, for complex reasons, I did not understand that until now. I recognize that reminders are continuing to trigger traumatic states in me.

As a result of painful emotional states elicited with overwhelming hurt feelings, angry thoughts and self-destructive fantasies, I sometimes behave in ways that I am not proud of. Me—a trauma therapist—and I don't recognize that I am being traumatically triggered. Perhaps because my particular set of experiences are not regarded as traumatic in the conventional sense. But then, we all are blind to ourselves at times.

One of my agendas for the second psilocybin session is to privately examine (i.e., it is not shared with my guides) this ongoing situation to see if I can end the repeated triggering that is increasingly tormenting me. Surprisingly, despite my intention, the issue doesn't come up in an identifiable way during the second session. Instead, other things happen. Yet, the session still seems to provide an answer to the hurt from the past.

The last entry in my journal made just before my second session directly raises my hurt, fears and fantasies in the context of a new traumatic reminder occurring that morning. The next entry made in the evening after the session begins, "*So it* [the source of my hurt] *doesn't matter . . . That was made known to me on my second psilocybin trip*" (7/12/13, 9:48 pm).

This psilocybin session is completely unlike the first. Following the blue capsule ceremony, we look at a book of Van Gogh paintings. I notice a mild nausea developing and put on the eyeshades and headphones, and lie down. The psychedelia begins with muted hues but rapidly evolves into a torrent of dazzling colors and startling images. I have the sensation of speeding through a tube or tunnel—later it becomes more canyon-like with a starry sky glittering above me.

There are Escheresque geometric patterns that sparkle and glow as if outlined in radiant jewels. Sections of the tunnel have a predominate color—reds, purples, blues—one section is vivid greens and yellows. In each section there are always other colors—but they are in rainbows around the fringes of the patterns. At times there are identifiable objects—I recall seeing a bat (reminiscent of the red bat in the Van Gogh book) and a couple of skulls. I don't find these images frightening or threatening. They are quickly gone as I am swept along.

It is difficult to recall the sequence of this next part of the experience—but I become aware that I am having a trip through my body. I resolve to search out my cancer and see what it looks like. When I find it, I recall thinking that cancer is aptly named. It is crab-like—sort of like a horseshoe crab with sharp spikes and thorny spines sticking out everywhere. It is a dull-greenish bronze color and looks almost metallic. While it seems alive—there is no intelligence. There is nothing sentient to connect with.

I begin searching for my pain (one of my agendas) and find a bubbling pool of molten lava glowing dull red. I am able to get to the edge of the pool, but unable to dive in despite trying several times. So I stand at the rim and watch for a while.

Then I am in a cathedral looking up at massive beams arching high above me. I realize that I am inside my chest and looking at my curving ribs. I am a small point of light inside an enormous cavern of a body. I begin to make a distinction between my body and myself—they are no longer the same. I am living in my body but I am not my body. Bill asks me what is going on? I reply to the effect that I now understand what people mean when they say that your body is a temple. I resolve to eat healthier in the future.

I'm not sure what comes next—somewhere in here I become deeply involved in the music. I am hearing music the way I have always wanted to hear it. Hearing everything—every voice, every instrument, every note and chord perfectly. Simultaneously listening to each separately, yet appreciating their harmonious interplay. A huge smile grows on my face as I listen to an ethereal soprano solo, while visualizing a glowing sunrise.

I take a bathroom break. When the eyeshades came off, but before I open my eyes everything seems incredibly bright. I am having fascinating "sunny" hallucinations and reluctant to open my eyes. When I do, I see Bill and Matt. They seem larger than life—their faces are huge—both are smiling broadly. I'm happy to see them.

Lots of things are happening in the room with the furniture and objects as I make my way to the bathroom. Urinating is a primal experience. Washing my hands I look in the mirror and am reassured by what I see. My face is familiar and friendly. I look younger. I feel calm, but a little unsteady on my feet.

When I return (Matt always stood outside the bathroom monitoring me on these breaks), Bill places a single rose in a simple vase on the floor in front of me and tells me to look at it. At first, I think it is "pretty." Bill urges me to look again. Then I see that the rose is moving, breathing, pulsating, glowing, living—just as Huxley described (see Chapter 9). It is incredible—I really enjoy watching this.

As I look at the rose, the Oriental rug begins moving. Pulsating in and out in the periphery of my vision, which is centered on the rose. At some point the nondescript gray carpet begins to do tricks, too. Its faint diamond pattern suddenly standing up three dimensionally—as if demanding that I pay attention to it also. As Bill and Matt have me lie back down, I tell them about seeing the rose and rug tricks. Later, they tell me that neither of them had ever noticed the faint diamond pattern in the gray carpet before.

I return to the tear-soaked eyeshades with their inner visions. Convinced that I am having a major psychedelic experience and determined to work on the agendas I brought with me. I will not detail these here—although I shared all but the most personal one with my guides and the research team. One that I will share here is the work with my pain.

Towards the end of the 5-hour session, I again grapple with my pain, which is quite intense at this point. I have gone two days without pain meds in order to maximize it for the session. Lying on my back is especially hard since I have metastases in my hips, spine and shoulder blades. Repeatedly I try to dive into my pain and go through it as Bill suggests that I do with any and all the unpleasant or frightening things I encounter on my trip. *"Remember—it is all in your mind. There is nothing there that can hurt you."*

But these efforts are only briefly successful. At times I am able to transform my pain into a sensation of warmth that wraps my back and hips—but this keeps breaking down. And then it feels worse. I continually struggle against an impulse to sit up to ease the pain. By this time, the psychedelia has ceased. Bill asks me what is happening? I answer, *"It's just me and my pain in here."*

At times it is as intense as any pain I remember (a 10 for me on that nebulous 10-point pain scale every patient gets asked about these days). My lower back goes into spasm—which I attempt to relieve by drawing my heels up tight against my butt and massaging my back. This is only partially successful, but eventually the pain diminishes sufficiently that I can get back into the music. But the music—although pleasant—has lost its magical depth and clarity. The crescendos only seem to heighten my pain—I desperately want them to stop. I keep listening for the final song, "It's a wonderful world." Finally I hear Louie's gravelly voice and flash Bill and Matt two thumbs up.

Afterwards, I'm shaky and have a mild headache, but Bill and Matt look like themselves again. We chat until the researchers arrive to debrief me. Then Karen is brought into the room. I see her relief at seeing me smiling and happy. We hug and kiss. I learned something that I need to tell her, but it is private. I will wait for the right moment.

For almost two weeks following the second session, I again experience an effortless, peaceful feeling similar to the first session, despite undergoing a course of chemotherapy and one of my sons having major surgery for an athletic injury. However, I consider my attempt to work with my pain a failure—since I experienced some of the most intense pain of my life during the session.

But surprisingly, I find that I don't require as much pain medication as before to be comfortable. In part, I'm concerned about the effects on my kidneys of the enormous doses of Tylenol bundled with the opiates. The chemotherapy is already destroying my kidney function. Tylenol adds to that inevitable damage. But, I also find that I can tolerate more pain—although it can still get the better of me from time to time, especially at night. I'm able to cut my pain meds to about half of what I needed before the psilocybin sessions.

But the old emotional hurt starts coming back—in new ways. Now I really understand how often I am being traumatically triggered. But the knowledge that "*it doesn't matter*" brought back from the second session has a noetic quality. I just know—in my heart of hearts—it to be true. Feeling secure in this knowledge, I believe that I can achieve a state of equanimity in which to directly confront the source and presumably stop being triggered. This proves only partially true—as I'm emotionally derailed by new details emerging from the confrontation.

These details generate new triggers that threaten to undermine my coping. I lose my cool multiple times. But after many episodes, the psilocybin voice is still there—reminding me of what is important. What I truly care about which ultimately trumps the aching hurt and runaway fears and fantasies. I work through a series of new triggers—as if my unconscious is throwing everything it has long stored up at me. At times the psilocybin voice is all over me—especially in the morning shower—reminding me of what I learned. Preparing me for the day.

As I write the next three paragraphs, I am roughly 24 months out from the second psilocybin session. About a year afterward, I asked for one additional drug-free psychotherapy session with Bill to examine my personal issue and its effect on my end-of-life preparations. From this temporal distance, much of the psychedelia has faded. What remains as the most powerful memory of the second psilocybin session was an experience that I did not even include in my original immediate post-session written account above. I am not certain why I omitted it except that at that time it was more of an inchoate feeling than an articulable vision.

Somewhere I came to an end of speeding through that long dazzling tunnel and was shot out into the glittering stars overhead, not as a physical body but as mist, dust, smoke. I remain there a long, long time. Not conscious but nonetheless somehow diffusely aware. At a much later time, Karen joins me as smoke that intermingles with mine. This is what I must tell her. As we drive home the following day through the summer ripened Shenandoah Valley, I turn to her with tears in my eyes and say: *We will always be together.* True or not, it is extremely comforting.

It would be misleading to leave the impression that everything is worked out. That I have achieved a state of enlightened acceptance of my demise and detachedly embrace the painful course of dying that lies ahead. But the psilocybin trips—together with the pre- and post-trip preparation and integration—made an enormous positive difference in my attitude as I go forward.

For me, the psilocybin end-of-life sessions were and continue to be extremely valuable. I would do it again in an instant—although the awesome power of the experience is not for everyone. At one point in the second session, I say to Bill and Matt that I am glad that I was never forced to hurt or kill someone (such as being sent for Vietnam), because that could be hell to relive under psilocybin.

One unforeseen benefit is that I can continue to hear music in greater depth and clarity. My attention is no longer captured by one element such as the melody or lyrics. With just a little deliberate attention, I seem to be able to hear it all. The ability to switch into or out of an inclusive mode of listening feels analogous to learning to see an ambiguous figure, e.g., the famous optical illusion, "vanity," in which a woman primping in front of a dressing table mirror can be turned into a skull by changing one's mental frame of reference. In retrospect, I realize that I have always had an ability to hear it all, but I just didn't know how to access it.

As a result of my psilocybin experiences, I believe that psychedelic-assisted end-of-life therapy should be available to those who want it. I would urge that it be considered early in the terminal course—as it can be emotionally and physically exhausting. (I would have great physical difficulty qualifying for and completing the research protocol today.) It also requires time to integrate the insights gained into a new perspective on life and death. But ultimately research such as this study will tell us whether it is a wise, safe and effective way to improve the quality of life remaining to the terminally ill. And—as my psilocybin voice keeps reminding me—*"Hey everybody does it. Everyone dies."*

REFERENCES

REFERENCES

Alderidge, D., & Fachner, J.C. (Eds.). (2006). *Music and Altered States.* London: Jessica Kingsley Publishers.

Alkire, M.T., Hudetz, A.G., & Tononi, G. (2008). Consciousness and anesthesia. *Science, 322* (7 November), 876–880.

American Psychiatric Association. (1980). *Diagnostic and Statistical Manual of Mental Disorders (DSM-III)* (3 ed.). Washington DC: American Psychiatric Press.

——— (1994). *Diagnostic and Statistical Manual of Mental Disorders (DSM-IV).* Washington, DC: American Psychiatric Press.

——— (2013). *Diagnostic and Statistical Manual of Mental Disorders (DSM-5).* Washington, DC: American Psychiatric Press.

Ammerman, R.T., Putnam, F.W., Altaye, M., Chen, L., Holleb, L.J., Stevens, J., . . . Van Ginkel, J.B. (2009). Changes in depressive symptoms in first time mothers in home visitation. *Child Abuse & Neglect, 33*, 127–138.

Anderson, T. (1993). *Den of Lions: Memories of Seven Years.* New York: Ballatine.

Armstrong, J.A., Putnam, F.W., & Carlson, E.B. (1997). Development and validation of a measure of adolescent dissociation: The Adolescent Dissociative Experiences Scale. *Journal of Nervous and Mental Disease, 185*, 1–7.

Babloyantz, A., Salazar, J.M., & Micolis, C. (1985). Evidence of chaotic dynamics of brain activity during the sleep cycle. *Physics Letters, 111A*(3), 152–156.

Balon, R. (2008). The dawn of anxiolytics: Frank M. Berger, 1913–2008. *American Journal of Psychiatry, 165*, 1531.

Barach, P.M. (1991). Multiple personality disorder as an attachment disorder. *Dissociation, 4*, 117–123.

Becker-Blease, K.A. (2004). Dissociative states through new age and electronic trance music. *Journal of Trauma and Dissociation, 5*, 89–100.

Berlin, L.J., Ziv, Y., Amaya-Jackson, L., & Greenberg, M.T. (2005). *Enhancing Early Attachments: Theory, Research, Intervention and Policy.* New York: Guilford Press.

Berne, E. (1964). *Games people play.* New York: Grove Press.

Berthoz, A., Israel, I., Georges-Francois, P., Grasso, R., and Tsuzuku, T. (1995). Spatial memory for body linear displacement: What is being stored? *Science, 269*, 95–98.

Blank, A.S. (1985). The unconscous flashback to the war in Viet Name veterans: clinical mystery, legal defense and community problem. In SM Sonnenberg, AS Blank & JA Talbott (Eds.), *The Trauma of War: Stress and Recovery in Viet Nam Veterans* (pp. 295–319). Washington, DC: American Psychiatric Press, Inc.

Boly, M., Garrido, M.I., Gosseries, O., Bruno, M.A., Boveroux, P., Schnakers, C., . . . Friston, K. (2011). Preserved feedforward but impaired top-down processes in the vegetative state. *Science, 332,* 858–862.

Bonanno, G.A. , Keltner, D. , Noll, J.G., Putnam, F.W., Trickett, P.K., LeJune, J., & Anderson, C. . (2002). When the face reveals what words do not: Facial expressions of emotion, smiling, and willingness to disclose childhood sexual abuse. *Journal of Personality and Social Psychology, 83,* 94–110.

Bouso, J.C., Doblin, R., Farre, M., Alcazar, M.A., & Gomez-Jarabo, G. (2008). MDMA-assisted psychotherapy using low doses in a small sample of women with chronic posttraumatic stress disorder. *Journal of Psychoactive Drugs, 40,* 225–236.

Bower, G. H. (1981). Mood and memory. *American Psychologist, 36,* 129–148.

Brand, B., Classen, C., Lanius, R.A., Loewenstein, R.J., McNary, S., Pain, C., & Putnam, F.W. (2009). A naturalistic study of dissociative identity disorder and dissociative disorder not otherwise specified patients treated by community Clinicians. *Psychological Trauma: Theory, Research, Practice and Policy, 1,* 153–171.

———— ———— McNary, S., & Zaveri, P. (2009). A review of dissociative disorder treatment studies. *Journal of Nervous and Mental Disease, 197,* 646–654.

———— McNary, S.W., Myrick, A.C., Loewenstein, R.J., Classen, C.C., Lanius, R.A., . . . Putnam, F.W. . (2013). A longitudinal, naturalistic study of dissociative disorder patients treated by community clinicians. *Psychological Trauma: Theory, Research, Practice, & Policy, 5,* 301–308.

Breuer, J., & Freud, S. (1957). *Studies on hysteria* (J Strachey, Trans.). New York: Basic Books.

Broughton, R.J. (1968). Sleep Disorders: Disorders of arousal. *Science, 159,* 1070–1078.

Bunney, W.E., & Murphy, D.L. (1974). Switch processes in psychiatric illness. In NS Kline (Ed.), *Factors in depression* (pp. 139–158). New York: Raven Press.

———— ———— Goodwin, F.K., & Borge, G.F. (1972). The "switch process" in manic-depressive illness. *Archives of General Psychiatry, 27,* 295–302.

Byck, R. (Ed.). (1974). *Cocaine Papers (of Sigmund Freud).* New York: Stonehill.

Cahill, S.P., Rothbaum, B.O., Resick, P.A., & Follette, V.M. (2009). Cognitive-behavioral therapy for adults. In E.B. Foa, T.M. Keane, M.J. Friedman

& J.A Cohen (Eds.), *Effective Treatments for PTSD, 2nd Edition* (pp. 139–222). New York: Guilford Press.

Carey, B. (2011, June 23, 2011). Expert on mental illness reveals her own fight. *New York Times*.

Carlson, E.A. (1998). A prospective longitudinal study of attachment disorganization/disorientation. *Child Development, 69,* 1107–1128.

Carlson, E.B., & Putnam, F.W. (1993). An update on the Dissociative Experiences Scale. *Dissociation, 6,* 16–27.

Childs, N.L., & Mercer, W.N. (1996). Brief report: Late improvement in consciousness after post-traumatic vegetative state. *New England Journal of Medicine, 334,* 24–25.

Cicchetti, D., & Barnett, D. (1991). Attachment organization in maltreated *Development and Psychopathology, 3,* 397–411.

Custers, R., & Aarts, H. (2010). The unconscious will: How the pursuit of goals operates outside of conscious awareness. *Science, 329*(2 July), 47–50.

Cyr, C., Euser, E.M., Bakermans-Kranenburg, M.J., & Van IJzendororn, M.H. (2010). Attachment security and disorganization in maltreating and high-risk families: A series of meta-analyses. *Development and Psychopathology, 22,* 87–108.

Darwin, C. (1872). *The Expression of the Emotions in Man and Animals.* London: John Murray.

Davis, D.H., & Thoman, E.B. (1987). Behavioral states of premature infants: Implications for neural and behavioral developmental. *Developmental Psychoology, 20,* 25–38.

De Quincey, T. (1821). Confessions of an English Opium-Eater: Being an Extract from the Life of a Scholar. *London Magazine, 4,* 293–312, 358–379.

Deikman, A. (1977). The missing centre. In N.E. Zinberg (Ed.), *Alternative States of Consciousness* (pp. 230–241). New York: The Free Press.

Deptula, D., Singh, R., & Pomara, N. (1993). Aging, emotional states and memory. *American Journal of Psychiatry, 150,* 429–434.

Donovan, W.L., & Leavitt, L.A. (1985). Physiologic assessment of mother-infant attachment. *Journal of the American Academy of Child Psychiatry, 24,* 65–70.

Doria, V., Beckmann, C.F., Arichi, T., Merchant, N., Groppo, M., Turkheimer, F.E., . . . Edwards, A.D. (2010). Emergence of resting state networks in the preterm human brain. *Proceedings of the National Academy of Sciences, 107*(46), 20015–20020.

Drake, J.A., Price, J.H., Kolm-Valdivia, N., & Wielinski, M. (2010). Association of adolescent choking game activity with selected risk behaviors. *Academic Pediatrics, 10,* 410–416.

Dutra, L., Bureau, J.F., Holmes, B., Lyubchik, A., & Lyons-Ruth, K. (2009).

Quality of early childhood care and childhood trauma. *Journal of Nervous and Mental Disease, 197*, 383–390.

Ebern-Priemer, U.W., Kuo, J., Kleindienst, N., Welch, S.S., Reisch, T., Reinhard, I., . . . Bohus, M. (2007). State affective instability in borderline personality disorder assessed by ambulatory monitoring. *Psychological Medicine, 37*, 961–970.

Egeland, B., & Susman-Stillman, A. (1996). Dissociation as a mediator of child abuse across generations. *Child Abuse & Neglect, 8*, 544–548.

Eiser, A.S., & Schenck, C.H. (2005). Dreaming: a psychiatric view and insights from the study of parasomnias. *Schweizer Archive fur Neurologie und Psychiatre, 156*, 440–470.

Ekman, P.R., Levenson, W., & Friesen, W.V. (1983). Autonomic nervous system activity distinguishes among emotions. *Science, 221*, 1208–1210.

Elkes, J. (1977). Subjective and objective observation in psychiatry: A note toward discussion. In N.E. Zinberg (Ed.), *Alternate states of consciousness* (pp. 242–263). New York: The Free Press.

Ellenberger, H.F. (1970). *The Discovery of the Unconscious*. New York: Basic Books.

Erikson, E.H. (1975). "Identity crisis" in perspective. In E.H. Erikson (Ed.), *Life History and the Historical Moment*. New York: Norton.

Eyles, C. (1985). *The Last of the Blue Water Hunters*. San Diego: Watersport Publishing.

Fachner, J.C. (2006). Music and drug-induced altered states of consciousness. In D. Alderidge & J.C. Fachner (Eds.), *Music and Altered States* (pp. 82–96). London: Jessica Kingsley Publishers.

——— (2011). Time is the key: Music and altered states of consciousness. In E. Cardena & M. Winkelman (Eds.), *Altering Consciousness: Multidisciplinary Perspectives, Volume 1: History, Culture and the Humanities* (Vol. 1, pp. 355–376). Santa Barbara: Praeger.

Felitti, V.J., Anda, R.F., Nordenberg, D., Williamson, D.F., Spitz, A.M, Edwards, V., . . . Marks, J.S. (1998). Relationship of childhood abuse and household dysfunction to many of the leading causes of death in adults: The Adverse Childhood Experiences (ACE) Study. *American Journal of Preventive Medicine, 14*(4), 245–258.

Field, T. (1985). Attachment as psychobiological attunement: being on the same wavelength. In M. Reite (Ed.), *The Psychobiology of Attachment and Separation* (pp. 415–454). New York City, New York: Academic Press.

——— Greenwald, P., Morrow, C., Healy, B., Foster, T., Guthertz, M., & Frost, P. (1992). Behavior state matching during interactions of preadolescent friends versus acquaintances. *Developmental Psychology, 28*, 242–250.

——— Healy, B., Goldstein, S., & Guthertz, M. (1990). Behavior-state matching and synchrony in mother-infant interactions of nondepressed versus depressed dyads. *Developmental Psychology, 26*, 7–14.

Fink, M., & Taylor, M.A. (2003). *Catatonia: a Clinician's Guide to Diagnosis and Treatment*. Cambridge: Cambridge University Press.

Freud, S. (1897/1954). Letter to Wilhelm Fliess Sept 21, 1897. In M. Bonaparte, A. Freud & E. Kris (Eds.), *The origins of psycho-analysis: Letters to Wilhelm Fliess, Drafts and Notes: 1887–1902* (pp. 215–218). New York: Basic Books.

———— (1955). *The Origin and Development of Psychoanalysis*. Chicago: Henry Regnery Company.

———— (1913). *The Interpretation of Dreams* (A. A. Brill, Trans. Third Edition ed.). New York: The Macmillan Company.

Frohlich, F., Sejnowski, T.J., & Bazhenov, M. (2010). Network bistability mediates spontaneous transitions between normal and pathological brain states. *Journal of Neuroscience, 30*, 10734–10743.

Fromm, E. (1960). Psychoanalysis and Zen Buddhism. In D.T. Suzuki, E. Fromm & R. De Martino (Eds.), *Zen Buddhism and Psychoanalysis* (pp. 77–141). New York: Grove Press.

Fulbright, R.K., Troche, C.J., Skudlarski, P., Gore, J.C., & Wexler, B.E. (2001). Functional MR imaging of regional brain activation associated with affective experience of pain. *American Journal of Radiology, 177*, 1205–1210.

Gazzaniga, M.S. (2011). Neuroscience in the court room. *Scientific American, April*, 54–59.

Geels, A. (2011). Altered consciousness in religion. In E. Cardena & M. Winkelman (Eds.), *Altering Consciousness* (Vol. 1, pp. 255–276). Santa Barbara, CA: Praeger.

Gerhardstein, P., Adler, S.A., & Rovee-Collier, C. (2000). A dissociation in infants' memory for stimulus size: evidence for the early development of multiple memory systems. *Developmental Psychobiology, 36*, 123–135.

Gil, M.M. (1996). In Memoriam: David Rapaport, 1911-1960. In M.M. Gil (Ed.), *the Collected Papers of David Rapaport*. Northvale, NJ: Jason Aronson Inc.

Goldstein, S., Field, T., & Healy, B. (1989). Concordance of play behavior and physiology in preschool friends. *Journal of applied developmental psychology, 10*, 337–351.

Gottschalk, A., Bauer, M.S., & Whybrow, P.C. (1995). Evidence of chaotic mood variation in bipolar disorder. *Archives of General Psychiatry, 52*, 947–959.

Grant, J.A., Courtemanche, J., Duncan, G.H., Duerden, E.G., & Rainville, P. (2010). Cortical thickness and pain sensitivity in Zen mediators. *Emotion, 10*, 43–53.

Green, E.C., & Honwana, A. (1999). Indigenous healing of war-affected children in Africa. *IK Notes, 1999,* 1–4.

Grilley, P. (2002). *Yin Yoga: Outline of a Quiet Practice.* Ashland, OR: White Cloud Press.

Grob, C.S., Bossis, A.P., & Griffiths, R.R. (2013). Use of the classic hallucinogen psilocybin for treatment of existential distress associated with cancer. In B.I. Carr & J. Steel (Eds.), *Psychological Aspects of Cancer* (pp. 291–308): Springer.

Grof, S. (2009). *LSD: Doorway to the Numinous.* Rochester, VT: Park Street Press.

Hammon, K.W., Ben-Ari, A.Y., Laundry, R.J., Boyko, E.J., & Samore, M.H. (2015). The feasibility of using large-scale text mining to detect adverse childhood experiences in a VA-treated population. *Journal of Traumatic Stress, 28,* 505–514.

Harter, S., Bresnick, S., Bouchey, H.A., & Whitesell, N.R. (1997). The development of multiple role-related selves during adolescence. *Development and Psychopathology, 9,* 835–853.

Haynes, J.D., & Rees, G. (2006). Decoding mental states from brain activity in humans. *Nature Reviews: Neuroscience, 7,* 523–534.

Herman, J. (1997). *Trauma and recovery.* New York: Basic Books.

Hilgard, E.R. (1986). *Divided consciousness: Multiple controls in human thought and action.* New York: John Wiley & Sons.

Hofstadter, D.R. (1979). *Gödel, Escher, Bach: An Eternal Golden Braid.* New York: Basic Books.

Horowitz, M. (1979). *States of Mind.* New York: Plenum Press.

———Milbrath, C., Ewert, M., Sonneborn, D., & Stinson, C. (1994). Cyclical patterns of states of mind in psychotherapy. *American Journal of Psychiatry, 151,* 1767–1770.

Hustvedt, A. (2011). *Medical Muses: Hysteria in Nineteenth Century Paris.* New York: W.W. Norton & Company.

Huxley, A. (1954). *The Doors of Perception.* New York: Harper & Row.

——— (2004). *The Perennial Philosophy.* New York: Harper Perennial.

James, W. (1882). Subjective effects of nitrous oxide. *Mind, 7,* 186–208.

——— (1890). *Principles of Psychology, Vol 2.* New York: Henry Hold & Company.

——— (1901–1902). *The Varieties of Religious Experience: a Study in Human Nature (Gifford Lectures at Edinburgh in 1901–1902).* New York: Signet.

——— (1950). *The Principles of Psychology, Volume 1.* Mineola, NY: Dover Publications, Inc.

——— (1987). A pluralistic mystic. In B Kuklick (Ed.), *William James: Writings 1902–1910.* New York: The Library of America.

Johnson, J.L., & Leff, M. (1999). Children of substance abusers: overview of research findings. *Pediatrics, 103,* 1085–1099.

Johnson, M.W., Richards, W.A., & Griffiths, R.R. (2008). Human hallucinogen research: guidelines for safety. *Journal of Psychopharmacology, 22*, 603–620.

Jurad, M.B., & Rosselli, M. (2007). The elusive nature of executive functions: a review of our current understanding. *Neuropsychology Reviews, 17*, 213–233.

Killingsworth, M.A., & Gilbert, D.T. (2010). A wandering mind is an unhappy mind. *Science, 330* (12 November), 932.

Kim, K., Trickett, P.K., & Putnam, F.W. (2010). Childhood experiences of sexual abuse and later parenting practices among non-offending mothers of sexually abused and comparison girls. *Child Abuse & Neglect, 34*, 610–622.

Kinsey, A.C., Pomeroy, W.B., Martin, C.E., & Gebhard, P.H. (1953). *Sexual Behavior in the Human Female*. Philadelphia: W.B. Saunders.

Koch, C., & Greenfield, S. (2007). How does consciousness happen? *Scientific American, Oct 2007*, 76–83.

Koenig, T., Prichep, L., Lehmann, D., Sosa, P.V., Braeker, E., Klienlogel, H., ...John, E.R. (2002). Millisecond by millisecond, year by year: Normative EEG microstates and developmental stages. *NeuroImage, 16*, 41–48.

Kolb, L.C. (1985). The place of narcosynthesis in the treatment of chronic and delayed stress reactions of war. In SM Sonnenberg, AS Blank & JA Talbott (Eds.), *The Trauma of War: Stress and Recovery in Viet Nam Veterans* (pp. 211–226). Washington, DC: American Psychiatric Press, Inc.

KUBARK. (1963). *KUBARK Counterintelligence Interrogation*. Washington, DC: The National Security Archive - The George Washington University.

Lang, J. (2013). Awakening. *The Atlantic, Jan/Feb*, 49–58.

Lanius, R.A., Hopper, J.W., & Menom, R.S. (2003). Individual differences in a husband and wife who developed PTSD after a motor vehicle accident: a functional MRI study. *American Journal of Psychiatry, 160*, 667–669.

———— Vermetten, E., Loewenstein, R.J., Brand, B., Schmahl, C., Bremner, J.D., & Spiegel, D. (2010). Emotion modulation in PTSD: Clinical and neurobiological evidence for a dissociative subtype. *American Journal of Psychiatry, 167*, 640–647.

Laureys, S. (2007). Eyes open, brain shut. *Scientific American, May*, 82–89.

———— Faymonville, M.E., Degueldre, C., Del Fiore, G., Damas, P., Lambermont, B., . . . Maquet, P. (2000). Auditory processing in the vegetative state. *Brain, 123*, 1589–1601.

Layne, C.M., Strand, V., Popescu, M., Kaplow, J.B., Abramovitz, R., Stuber, M., . . . Pynoos, R. (2014). Using the core curriculum on childhood trauma to strengthen clinical knowledge in evidence-based practitioners. *Journal of Clinical Child and Adolescent Psychology, 20*, 286–300.

Lee, M.A., & Shalin, B. (1985). *Acid Dreams: The Complete Social History of LSD: The CIA, the Sixites, and Beyond*. New York: Grove Press.

Lehmann, D., Strik, W.K., Henggeler, B., Koenig, T., & Koukkou, M. (1998). Brain electrical microstates and momentary conscious mind states as building blocks of spontaneous thinking: I visual imagery and abstract thoughts. *International Journal of Psychophysiology, 29*, 1–11.

Lezak, M.D. (1983). *Neuropsychological Assessment* (2nd ed.). New York & Oxford: Oxford University Press.

Lilly, J.C. (1977). *The Deep Self: Consciousness Exploration in the Isolation Tank*. New York: Simon and Schuster.

Liotti, G. (1992). Disorganized/disoriented attachment in the etiology of dissociative disorders. *Dissociation, 5*, 196–204.

—— (2004). Trauma, dissociation, and disorganized attachment: Three strands of a single braid. *Psychotherapy: Theory, Research, Practice, Training, 41*, 472–486.

Lu, J., Wu, D., & Yao, D. (2015). Using a scale-free method to convert brain activity into music. *Advances in Computational Psychophysiology, 1*, 48–49.

Lutz, A., Greischar, L.L., Rawlings, N.B., Matthieu, R., & Davidson, R.J. (2004). Long-term meditators self-induce high amplitude gamma synchrony during mental practice. *Proceedings of the National Academy of Sciences, 101*, 16369–16373.

Lydic, R. (Ed.). (1998). *Molecular regulation of arousal states*. Boca Raton: CRC Press.

Lydic, R., & Baghdoyan, H.A. (Eds.). (1999). *Handbook of Behavioral State Control*. Boca Raton, FL: CRC Press.

Lyons-Ruth, K. (2008). Contributions of the mother-infant relationship to dissociative, borderline, and conduct symptoms in young adulthood. *Infant Mental Health Journal, 29*, 203–218.

—— Brofman, E., & Parson, E. (1999). Maternal frightened, frightening, or atypical behavior and disorganized infant attachment patterns. *Monographs of the Society for Research in Child Development, 64*, 67–97.

—— Yellin, S.M., & Atwood, G. (2003). Childhood experiences of trauma and loss have different relations to maternal unresolved and Hostile-Helpless states of mind on the AAI. *Attachment & Human Development, 5*, 330–352.

Main, M., & Hesse, E. (1990). Parent's unresolved traumatic experiences are related to infant disorganized attachment status: Is frightened and/or frightening behavior the linking mechanism? In M.T. Greenberg, D Cicchettic & E.M. Cummings (Eds.), *Attachment in the Preschool Years* (pp. 161–181). Chicago: University of Chicago Press.

—— & Solomon, J. (1986). Discovery of a new, insecure-disorganized/disoriented attachment pattern. In T. B. Brazelton & M Yogman (Eds.), *Affective Development in Infancy* (pp. 95–124). Norwood: Ablex.

Maruyama, K., & Tohei, K. (1984). *Aikido with Ki.* Tokyo: Ki No Kenkyukai H.Q.

Maslow, A.H. (1968). *Toward a Psychology of Being.* New York: Van Nostrand Reinhold.

Masson, J.H. (1984). Freud and the seduction theory: A challenge to psychoanalysis. *Atlantic Monthly, Feb.,* 4–71.

Max, D.T. (2010). The Secrets of Sleep. *National Geographic, May,* 76–91.

Mayberg, H.S. (2006). Defining neurocircuits in depression. *Psychiatric Annals, 36,* 259–268.

McHugh, P.R., & Putnam, F.W. (1995). Resolved: Multiple personality disorder is an individually and socially created artifact. *Journal of the American Academy of Child and Adolescent Psychiatry 34,* 957–963.

McNally, R.J. (2003). *Remembering Trauma.* Cambridge, MA: Belknap.

McNamara, P. (2009). *The Neuroscience of Religious Experience.* Cambridge: Cambridge University Press.

Mellman, T.A., Pigeon, W.R., Nowell, P.D., & Nolan, B. (2007). Relationships between REM sleep findings and PTSD symptoms during the early aftermath of trauma. *Journal of Traumatic Stress, 20* (893–901).

Menninger, W.C. (1945). Psychiatry and the war. *The Atlantic, 176,* 107–114.

Metcalfe, J., & Shimamura, A.P. (Eds.). (1994). *Metacognition.* Cambridge, MA: MIT press.

Michal, M., Roder, C., Mayer, J., Lengler, U., & Krakow, K. (2007). Spontaneous dissociation during functional MRI experiments. *Journal of Psychiatric Research, 41,* 69–73.

Middlebrooks, J.S., & Audage, N.C. (2008). The effects of childhood stress on health across the lifespan (pp. 18). Atlanta: Centers for Disease Control and Prevention, National Center for Injury Prevention and Control.

Miller, W.R., & C' de Baca, J. (2001). *Quantum Change.* New York: The Guilford Press.

——— Walters, S.T., & Bennett, M.E. (2001). How effective is alcoholism treatment in the United States. *Journal of Studies in Alcohol, 62,* 211–220.

Mithoefer, M.C., Wagner, M.T., Mithoefer, A.T., Jerome, L., & Doblin, R. (2011). The safety and efficacy of {+/–} 3,4-methylenedioxymethamphetamine-assisted psychotherapy in subjects with chronic, treatment-resistant posttraumatic stress disorder: the first randomized controlled pilot study. *Journal of Psychopharmacology 25*(4), 439–452.

Miyashita, Y. (2004). Cognitive memory: cellular and network machineries and their top-down control. *Science, 306*(15 October), 435–440.

Morey, L.C., Hopwood, C.J., Gunderson, J.G., Skodol, A.E., Shea, M.T., Yen, S., . . . McGlashan, T.H. (2007). Comparison of alternative models for personality disorders. *Psychological Medicine, 37,* 983–994.

Naranjo, C., & Ornstein, R.E. (1971). *On the Psychology of Meditation* New York: The Viking Press.

Nardi, A.E., Lopes, F.L., Valenca, A.M., Nascimento, I., Mezzasalma, M.A., & Zin, W.A. (2004). Psychopathological description of hyperventilatin-induced panic attacks: A comparison with spontaneous panic attacks. *Psychopathology, 37*, 29–35.

Nijdam, M.J., Baas, M.A.M., Olff, M., & Gerson, B.P.R. (2013). Hotspots in trauma memories and their relationship to successful trauma-focused psychotherapy: A pilot study. *Journal of Traumatic Stress, 26*, 38–44.

Noll, J.G., Shenk, C.E., Barnes, J.E., & Putnam, F.W. (2009). Child abuse, avatar choices, and other risk factors associated with internet-initiated victimization. *Pediatrics, 123*, e1078–e1083.

———— Trickett, P.K., Harris, W.W., & Putnam, F.W. (2009). The cumulative burden borne by offspring whose mothers were sexually abused as children: Descriptive results from a multigenerational study. *Journal of Interpersonal Violence, 24*, 424–449.

Odgers, C.L., Mulvey, E.P., Skeem, J.L., Gardner, W., Lidz, C.W., & Schubert, C. (2009). Capturing the ebb and flow of psychiatric symptoms with dynamical models. *American Journal of Psychiatry, 166*, 575–582.

Ogawa, J.R., Sroufe, L.A., Weinfield, N.S., Carlson, E.A., & Egeland, B. (1997). Development and the fragmentation of self: Longitudinal study of dissociative symptomatology in a non-clinical sample. *Development and Psychopathology, 9*, 855–879.

Oosterman, M., De Schipper, J. C, Fisher, P., Dozier, M., & Schuengel, C. (2010). Autonomic reactivity in relation to attachment and early adversity among foster children. *Development and Psychopathology, 22*, 109–118.

Overton, D.A. (1984). State dependent learning and drug discriminations. In L.L. Iversen, S.D. Iversen & S.H. Snyder (Eds.), *Handbook of Psychopharmacology, Vol 18* (pp. 59–127): Plenum.

Owen, A.M., Coleman, M.R., Boly, M., Davis, M.H., Laureys, S., & Pickard, J.D. (2006). Detecting awareness in the vegetative state. *Science, 313*(8 September), 1402.

Papolos, D.F. (2003). Switching, cycling, and antidepressant-induced effects on cycle frequency and course of illness in adult bipolar disorder: a brief review and Commentary. *Journal of Child and Adolescent Psychopharmacology, 13*, 165–171.

Peyron, R., Laurent, B., Garcia-Larrea, L. (2000). Functional imaging of brain responses to pain: a review and meta-analysis. *Neurophysiology Clinics, 30*, 263–288.

Pieron, H. (1913). *Le Problème Physiologique du Sommeil*. Masson (Paris).

Plato. (1961). Phaedrus (L. Cooper, Trans.) *The Collected Dialogues of Plato*. Princeton, NJ: Princeton University Press.

Pope, K.S., & Singer, J.L. (1980). The waking stream of consciousness. In J.M. Davidson & R.J. Davidson (Eds.), *The Psychobiology of*

Consciousness. New York: Plenum Press.

Prechtl, H.F.R., & O'Brian, M.J. (1982). Behavioral states of the full-term newborn. The emergence of a concept. In P. Stratton (Ed.), *Psychobiology of the human newborn* (pp. 53–74). New York: John Wiley & Sons.

——— Theorell, K., & Blair, A.W. (1973). Behavioral state cycles in abnormal infants. *Developmental Medicine and Child Neurology, 15*, 606–615.

Putnam, F.W. (1982, October 1982). Traces of Eve's Faces. *Psychology Today, 16,* 88.

——— (1984a). The psychophysiological investigation of multiple personality disorder: A review. *Psychiatric Clinics of North America, 7*, 31–39.

——— (1984b). The study of multiple personality disorder: General strategies and practical considerations. *Psychiatric Annals, 14*, 58–61.

——— (1989). *The Diagnosis and Treatment of Multiple Personality Disorder*. New York: Guildford Press.

——— (1991). The satanic ritual abuse controversy. *Child Abuse & Neglect, 15*, 175–179.

——— (1994). The switch process in multiple personality disorder and other state-change disorders. In R.M. Klein & B.K. Doane (Eds.), *Psychological Concepts and Dissociative Disorders* (pp. 283–304). New York: Erlbaum.

——— (1997). *Dissociation in Children and Adolescents: a Developmental Perspective*. New York: Guilford Press.

——— (2003). Cherish your exceptions. *Journal of Child Sexual Abuse, 12*, 133–135.

——— (2013). The role of abusive states of being in interrogation. *Journal of Trauma and Dissociation, 14*, 1–12.

——— Carlson, E.B., Ross, C.A., Anderson, G., Clark, P., Torem, M., . . . Coons, P.M. (1996). Patterns of dissociation in clinical and non-clinical samples. *Journal of Nervous and Mental Disease, 184*, 673–679.

——— Helmers, K. , & Trickett, P.K. (1993). Development, reliability and validity of a child dissociation scale. *Child Abuse & Neglect, 17*, 731–740.

——— Loewenstein, R.J., Silberman, E.K., & Post, R.M. (1984). Multiple personality disorder in a hospital setting. *Journal of Clinical Psychiatry, 45*, 172–175.

——— Zahn, T.P., & Post, R.M. (1989). Differential autonomic nervous system activity in multiple personality disorder. *Psychiatry Research, 31*, 251–260.

Putnam, K.T., Harris, W., & Putnam, F.W. (2013). Synergistic Childhood Adversities and Complex Adult Psychopathology. *Journal of Traumatic Stress, August 2013*(26), 435–442. doi: 10.1002

Putnam-Hornstein, E., Cederbaum, J.A., King, B., Eastman, A.L., & Trickett, P.K. (2015). A population-level and longitudinal study of adolescent mother and intergenerational maltreatment. *American Journal of Epidemiology, 181*(7), 496–503. doi: DOI:10.1093/aje/kwu321

Raichle, ME. (2006). The brain's dark energy. *Science, 314*, 1249–1250.

Rapaport, D. (1996). States of consciousness: A psychopathological and psychodynamic view. In MM Gil (Ed.), *The Collected Papers of David Rapaport* (pp. 385–404). Northvale, NJ: Jason Aronson.

Rhodes, R. (1992). *Making Love: an Erotic Odyssey*. New York: Touchstone.

Rosenbaum, M. (1980). The role of the term schizophrenia in the decline of multiple personality. *Archives of General Psychiatry, 37*, 1383–1385.

Sacks, Oliver. (2012, August 27). Altered States: Self-experiments in chemistry. *The New Yorker,* 40–47.

Schenck, CH, Milner, DM, Hurwitz, TD, Bundlie, SR, & Mahowald, MW. (1989). Dissociative disorders presenting as somnambulism: Polysomnographic, video and clinical documentation (8 cases). *Dissociation, 2*, 194–204.

Schulz, P, & Curtin, F. (2004). An early description of REM sleep behavior disorder. *Sleep, 27*, 1216–1217.

Shane, S. (2011, March 24, 2011). Panel of psychiatrists backs F.B.I.'s finding that scientist sent anthrax letters. *New York Times,* p. A19.

Shay, Jonathan. (1994). *Achilles in Vietnam: Combat Trauma and the Undoing of Character*. New York: Scribner.

Shirataki, S, & Prechtl, HFR. (1977). Sleep state transitions in newborn infants: preliminary study. *Developmental Medicine and Child Neurology, 19*, 316–325.

Shulgin, A, & Shulgin, A. (1991). *PiHKAL*. Berkeley, CA: Transform Press.

————— & ————— (1997). *TiHKAL*. Berkeley, CA: Transform Press.

Siclari, F., Khatami, R., Urbanick, F., Nobili, L., Mahowald, MW, Schenck, CH, . . . Bassetti, CL. (2010). Violence in sleep. *Brain, 133*, 3494–3509.

Silberman, E.K., Putnam, F.W., Weingartner, H., & Post, R.M. (1985). Dissociative states in multiple personality disorder: A quantitative study. *Psychiatry Research, 15*, 253–260.

Skolnick, A. (2015, August 4). Free Diver Natalia Nolchanova descends for fun, then vanishes. *New York Times*.

Slagter, H.A., Davidson, RJ, & Lutz, A. (2011). Mental training as a tool in the neuroscientific study of the brain and cognitive plasticity. *Frontiers in Human Neuroscience, 5*, 1–12.

Slevin, M. (2000). Altering the NICU and measuring infant's responses. *Acta Paediatrica, 89*, 577–581.

Sluhovsky, M. (2011). Spirit possession and other alterations of consciousness in the Christian Western tradition. In E Cardena & M Winkelman (Eds.), *Altering Consciousness: Multidisciplinary Perspectives* (Vol. 1: History, culture, and the humanities). Santa Barbara, CA: Praeger.

Sneader, W. (2005). *Drug discovery: A history*. West Sussex, England: John Wiley & Sons.

Soldz, J., Raymond, N. , Reisner, S., Allen, S.A., Baker, I.L., & Keller, A.S.

(2015). All the president's psychologists: The American Psychological Associations secret complicity with the White House and U.S. intelligence community in support of the CIA's "Enhanced" Interrogation program. Washington, DC: American Psychological Association.

Spiegel, D. (2010). Dissociation in the DSM-5. *Journal of Trauma and Dissociation, 11*, 261–265.

Tart, C. (1970). Marijuana intoxication: common experiences. *Nature, 226*, 701–704.

——— (1971/2000). *On being stoned: a Psychological Study of Marijuana Intoxication.* Lincoln, NE: iUniverse.com, Inc.

——— (1983). *States of Consciousness.* El Cerrito, CA: Psychological Processes, Inc.

——— (2001). *Mind science: Meditation Training for Practical People.* Novato, CA: Wisdom Editions.

——— (2011). Preface: Extending our knowledge of consciousness. In E. Cardena & M. Winkelman (Eds.), *Altering Consciousness: Multidisciplinary Perspectives, Volume 1: History, Culture and the Humanities* (Vol. Vol 1, pp. IX–XX). Santa Barbara: Praeger.

Taylor, E. (1982). *William James on Exceptional Mental States: the 1986 Lowell Lectures.* New York: Charles Scribner's Sons.

Thigpen C.H., & Cleckley, H. (1957). *The Three Faces of Eve.* New York, McGraw-Hill.

Thoman, EB. (1990). Sleeping and waking states in infants: a functional perspective. *Neuroscience and Biobehavioral Reviews, 14*, 93–107.

Trickett, P.K., McBride-Chang, C., & Putnam, F.W. (1994). The classroom performance and behavior of sexually abused females. . *Development and Psychopathology, 6*, 183–194.

——— Noll, J.G., & Putnam, F.W. (2011). The impact of sexual abuse on female development: Lessons from a multigenerational, longitudinal research study. *Development and Psychopathology, 23*, 453–476.

Tronick, E.Z., Als, H., Adamson, L., Wise, S., & Brazelton, T. B. (1978). The infants' response to entrapment between contradictory messages in face-to-face interactions. *Journal of the American Academy of Child Psychiatry, 17*, 1–13.

——— & Weinberg, M.K. (1997). Depressed mothers and infants: the failure to form dyadic states of consciousness. In L. Murray & P. Cooper (Eds.), *Postpartum Depression and Child Development* (Vol. 1, pp. 54–81). New York: Guilford.

Turkle, Sherry (1995). *Life on the Screen: Identity in the Age of the Internet.* New York: Simon & Schuster.

Tymoczko, D. (1996, May). The nitrous oxide philosopher. *Atlantic Monthly,* 93–101.

United States Department of Justice. (2010). Amerithrax Investigative

Summary. Washington, DC: U.S. Department of Justice.

Van De Ville, D., Britz, J., & Michel, C.M. (2010). EEG microstate sequences in healthy humans at rest reveal scale-free dynamics. *Proceedings of the National Academy of Sciences, 107*, 18179–18184.

van der Kolk, B.A. (1987). *Psychological Trauma*. Washington DC: American Psychiatric Press.

——— (1996). The complexity of adaptation to trauma: Self-regulation, stimulus discrimination, and characteriological development. In B.A. van der Kolk, A.C. McFarlane & L Weisaeth (Eds.), *Traumatic Stress: The Effects Overwhelming Experience on Mind, Body, and Society* (pp. 182–213). New York: Guilford Press.

——— (2015). *The body keeps score*. New York: Penguin Books.

Weingartner, H. (1978). Human state dependent learning. In B.T. Ho, D.W. Richards & D.C. Chute (Eds.), *Drug Discrimination and State Dependent Learning* (pp. 361–382). New York: Academic Press.

——— Miller, H., & Murphy, D.L. (1977). Mood-state-dependent retrieval of verbal associations. *Journal of Abnormal Psychology, 86*, 276–284.

Wekerle, C, & Wall, A (Eds.). (2002). *The Violence and Addiction Equation*. New York, NY: Brunner-Routledge.

West, M.A. (1987). *The Psychology of Meditation*. Oxford: Clarendon Press.

Whitfield, C. (1995). *Memory and Abuse*. Deerfield Beach, FL: Health Communications, Inc.

Widom, C.S., Czaja, S.J., & DuMont, K.A. (2015). Intergenerational transmission of child abuse and neglect: Real or detection bias? *Science, 347*, 1480–1485.

Wilde, Oscar. (1891). *The Picture of Dorian Gray*: Ward, Lock, and Company.

Windt, J.M. (2011). Altered consciousness in philosophy. In E. Cardena & M. Winkelman (Eds.), *Altering Consciousness: Multidisciplinary Perspectives, Volume 1: History, Culture and the Humanities* (Vol. 1, pp. 229–254). Santa Barbara: Praeger.

Wolff, P.H. (1987). *The Development of Behavioral States and the Expression of Emotions in Early Infancy: New Proposals for Investigation*. Chicago: University of Chicago Press.

INDEX

A

abreactive therapy, 205–206, 239, 356
abuse. *See* child abuse; sexual abuse
Achilles in Vietnam (Shay), 195
Adamovicz, Jeffrey, 147–148
addiction, 107. *See also* alcoholism; substance abuse
    barbituate, 257
    cocaine, 258
    methamphetamine, 259
    opiate, 260
    to psychiatric drugs, 272
    sedatives and hypnotics, 277
    sexual, 21, 305–306
    in states of being model, 281–285, 286–287
    susceptibility to, 20, 99, 286
    treatments for, 284–285, 359
Adolescent Dissociative Experiences Scale (A-DES), 212–213
adolescents
    alternate identities on Internet, 353–354
    dissociation in, 212–213
    identity crisis of, 178–180
    risky behaviors of, 214, 293–295, 330
Adverse Childhood Experiences (ACEs), 214–215, 218–219, 248.
    See also child abuse; sexual abuse
Aikido, influence on state of mind, 340–343
Ainsworth, Mary, 43–44, 221
alcohol
    effects of, 270–271, 280
    in family violence, 280
    uses of, 99, 356–357
    wide use of, 253, 255–256
alcoholism, 131. *See also* addiction; substance abuse
    treatments for, 9, 359
Aldridge, David, 349
Alles, Gordon, 259
Allison, Ralph, 244
Altered States of Consciousness Consortium, 71
American Psychological Association, 376
Ammerman, Robert, 45

amnesia
    anterograde, 131
    dissociative, 125–128, 173
    posthypnotic, 6, 326, 329
    of trauma, 204
Anderson, Terry, 375
anesthesia, 278–280
anger
    influence on mother-child attunement, 14, 28
    in PTSD symptoms, 202–203
Anna O., case study of, 7, 19, 234–235, 244
anthrax attacks, 147–152
anxiety, 10, 98–99
    treatments for, 276–278, 337, 345
appearance and demeanor, alter personalities, 112
Aserinsky, Eugene, 53
attachment, 45–47
    children's focus on maintaining, 221, 227
    classifications of, 43–44, 156, 221
    in developmental model of personality, 155–157
    effects of disturbed, 14, 19, 42, 49, 224–225
    effects of healthy, 42, 49
    importance of, 161, 219–221, 224–225
    shared states of being in, 248, 366–367
    type D, 221–226, 248
attention deficit hyperactivity disorder (ADHD), 219
attunement, 220
    of mother and infant, 26–27, 37, 40–42
    shared states of being in, 14, 248, 366–367
Augustine, Saint, 175
autobiographical memory, 16, 132-133, 136, 145, 174

B
Babinski, Joseph, 241–242
Barach, Peter, 222
barbituates. *See* sedatives and hypnotics
BASE jumping, 291–292
Baudelaire, Charles, 261
Bayfield, Robert, 100–101
behavior, 178, 319

abnormal sleep, 51–52, 54, 56–58
    in bipolar disorder, 95–97
    changes in, 166, 167–169
    complexity of, 140–141, 143
    contradictory, 17, 139, 165–166, 177, 301
    contradictory in secret lives, 152–153, 283, 305
    control of, 19, 283, 328–330
    in dissociative identity disorder, 19, 106
    increasing complexity of infants', 27, 33, 40, 143
    infants', 26, 28–31, 30, 39
    influences on, 23, 129–130, 171, 328–330
    instability of in, 185–186
    maladaptive, 363–364
    observing ego of own, 181–182
    predicting, 367–369, 377–379
    problems with addiction, 282–283
    of type D attachment children, 221–222
behavioral states, infants', 13–14, 31–33, 160
    regulation of, 17–18
    switches among, 15, 34–38, 106
Berger, Frank, 276
Berger, Hans, 60–61
Berne, Eric, 8, 140, 356, 360
Bernheim, Hippolyte, 324
biofeedback, 356, 360–361
biological psychiatry. challenging psychoanalysis, 94, 170–171
bipolar disorder, 244
    medications used with, 8, 277–278, 356
    states as strange attractors in, 81–82
    switches among states in, 15, 89–98, 101–102, 121, 145
Blank, Arthur, 193, 197–199, 201, 281
Blood, Benjamin Paul, 3–4, 176
body, 41, 69, 343. *See also* heart rate; mind-body interfaces; physiology
    biofeedback monitoring, 360–361
    effects of depression on, 63–64
    effects of drugs on, 255–257, 259–261
    mental states' influence on, 14, 343
    paralysis of, 57, 279
    sexual responses in, 301–303
    states of being reflected in, 30–38, *36*
    synchrony of, 46–47
borderline personality disorder, 185–186

treatments for, 187–188, 277–278, 310
Bourne, Ansel, case study of, 126–129
Bower, Gordon, 135
Bowlby, John, 43
Braid, James, 324
brain, 74, 169, 354
    development of, 168–169
    effects of conditioning on, 167–168
    effects of drugs on, 259–260, 271–272, 279–281
    effects of meditation on, 321–322, 365–366
    microstates of, 70–74, *72*
    other influences on, 48, 206
    plasticity of, 169–170, 322, 365
    pleasure centers of, 167–168, 259–260, 271–272, 282
brain activity, 52, 171
    in altered states of consciousness, 319–320, 329
    of alternate personalities in DID, 109–110
    measuring and monitoring, 60–63, 86 (*See also* brain imaging tech-
            nologies)
    in mental and physical training, 365–366
    mental states' relation to, 75–76, 333
    in sleep, 53–55, *54,* 69
    states of, 63–70
brain imaging technologies, 10, 60–63, 71, 171, 321
    advances in, 86–87
    in mindreading, 75–78
    during pain, 65–66
    uses of, 15, 67–70, 108–110, 206–209
brain states, 84
    hyperaroused PTSD *vs.* dissociative PTSD, 207–209, *208*
    mental states and, 12, 14
    resting, 73–74
    study of, 15, 78–83
brain waves, 60–61, 72, 349
    of alternate personalities, 109–110, 113–116
    neurofeedback and, 360–361
Brand, Bethany, 246–247
Brazelton, T. Berry, 41–42
breath, 98, 306
    influence on states of being, 210, 310, 315, 343–346
    in sleep, 32, 53–54
    varying in states of being, 30, 34–35, 38

Breuer, Joseph, 7, 232, 234–235
Buchsbaum, Monte, 105, 108
Bunney, William, 94
butterfly effect, 80–81, 367–368

C
caregivers. *See* mothers
catatonia
    periodic, 15, 93–94, 121
    switches into, 99–101
C'de Baca, Janet, 22, 310–315, 362
ceremonies, 347
    to create states of mind, 337–340
    sacred places and spaces in, 354–355
chaos theory, 39, 80. *See also* dynamical systems, non-linear
Charcot, Jean-Martin, 228–230, 241–242, 324
child abuse, 248. *See also* sexual abuse
    Adverse Childhood Experiences study of, 214–215
    in causation of DID, 206, 211–215, 227–228, 239
    effects of, 186–187, 199–200, 218–221, 226–227, 247, 330
    effects on attachment, 220–222
    multigenerational effects of, 213–215, 225–226
    treatment for, 225–226, 247
Child Dissociative Checklist (CDC), 212–213
Child Parent Psychotherapy (CPP), 225–226
child soldiers, 338-339
children, 72, 145, 294, 304. *See also* child abuse; infants
    development of, 161, 183–184
    dissociation in, 212–213, 217–218, 223–226
    effects of caretakers' emotional and mental states on, 14, 42, 44–47,
        217–218
    Huila Okupiolissa ritual for, 338–339
    identity alters as, 112–113, 243
    personality of, 17, 154–155
    seeking altered states of consciousness, 293, 336
    trauma's effects on, 186, 204, 211–215
    type D attachment of, 221–226
chloral hydrate, 256–257, 276
choking game, adolescents', 294
Christine, case study of, 82, 89–92

Cicchetti, Dante, 222
cocaine, 282
    effects of, 257–258, 260, 272, 280
    Freud on, 7, 258
coding systems
    for infants' states of being, 13–14, 29–30
    for mental states, 14, 140, 143
cognition. *See* thinking
cognitive associations, in state dependent learning and memory, 136
cognitive behavioral therapy (CBT), 64, 99, 181, 209–210
Collins, Wilkie, 137
Combe, George, 137
communication
    parent-child, 222–223, 370
    through states of being, 366–367, 370
Complex PTSD, 186
conditioning,
    classical and operant, 166–170
    fear, 167, 208
Confessions of an English Opium Eater (De Quincey), 260–261
configurational analysis, 8, 139, 146, 356, 360
conflict. *See also* psychological conflict
    unconscious, 357–359
consciousness, 107, 171. *See also* states of consciousness
    divided, 327–330
    state of being as organizing function of, 163–164
Corliss, Jeb, 291–292
Cormack, Allan McLeod, 61
cortisol, 41-42, 46, 64, 222, 339, 367
crowd psychology, 369–371

D
Dandy, Walter, 60
Daniels, Jeff, 120–121
Darwin, Charles, 29
Davidson, Richard J., 320, 365–366
Davy, Humphrey, 5–6
De Martino, Richard, 322
De Quincey, Thomas, 260–261
Default Mode Network (DMN), 74

Deikman, Arthur, 10, 107
Dement, William, 53
Den of Lions (Anderson), 375
depersonalization, of trauma victims, 18, 186, 188, 204, 208
depression, 136
    antidepressants for, 275–276, 278
    brain activity in, 10, 63–64
    effects of mothers' on children, 14, 28, 42, 44–47, 366–367
derealization, by trauma victims, 204, 208
Descartes, René, 85–86, 182
Diagnostic and Statistical Manual (DSM), 11
    DSM-5, 199, 208
    DSM-III, 195–196, 199, 215
    personality disorders in, 158, 238–239
    PTSD in, 195, 199, 208, 215, 294
Dialectical Behavior Therapy, 187–188, 309–310
Diamond, Bernard, 137–138
diseases, 214, 323
dissociation
    causes of, 249, 301
    effects of, 136, 212, 225
    hysteria and, 228–233, 241
    studies on, 206–209, 212–213
    treatments for, 240, 242, 330
dissociative amnesia, 125–128, 173
Dissociative Experiences Scale (DES-II), 213, 224
dissociative identity disorder (DID), 159. *See also* personalities, alter
    cases of, 126, 238
    child abuse in causation of, 206, 211–215, 227–228, 239
    children with, 211–215, 223–228
    diagnoses of, 118, 198, 241–244, 249
    disbelief in, 103–105, 127–128, 198, 238, 241–243, 249, 329
    in DSM, 238–239
    in history of psychiatry, 228–240
    mother's and child's complementary, 217–218
    relation to PTSD, 239–240
    relationship of alternate personalities in, 16, 115–116
    research on, 107–110, 239, 245–247, 249
    switches among states in, 15, 19, 93–94, 101–116, 121, 145
    treatment outcomes for, 245, 247, 249
    treatments for, 105, 206, 245–249, 278
Divided Consciousness: Multiple Controls in Human Thought and Action

(Hilgard), 328
domestic violence, 47, 213–215, 223, 225, 280, 294. *See also* child abuse
The Doors of Perception (Huxley), 251–252
dreams, 14, 51–52
    as flashbacks, 202
    in disturbed sleep, 51–52, 57–58
    multiple personalities in, 174–175
    in sleep stages, 53–55
drugs. *See also* medications; specific classes of drugs; specific drugs
    effects of, 7, 135–136, 251–252, 268
    historical use of, 19, 286
    links to music, 347–348
    psychoactive, 19, 73
    uses of, 99, 356–357, 373–374
dualism. *See* mind-body interface
dynamical systems, non-linear, 9, 15, 78–83, 367–368

E
Eastwood, Clint, 120–121
ego psychology, 140
ego state-based psychotherapies, 356, 359–360
ego states, 8, 140
Eich, Eric, 135
Elkes, Joel, 10
emotional states. *See also* moods
    as contagious, 369–371
    data collection on, 377–379
    development of control over, 161, 367
    effects of, 135–136, 206
    inability to regulate, 188, 216
    influence of caretakers' on children, 14, 27–28, 40–42, 46
    switches in, 106, 171
emotions, 16, 29
    brain activity and, 65–66
    conflicting, 116, 143–145, 177
    effects of drugs on, 278
    in mental disorders, 185–186, 207–209, 210
    regulation of, 220, 226–227
    therapies releasing, 205–206, 210
    of traumatized children, 204, 220, 222, 226–227

in wandering *vs.* task-focused mind, 74–75
empathy, development of, 46
enlightenment, degrees of, 322–323
epiphanies and spiritual awakenings, 22, 307–315
Erikson, Erik, 178
erotic state, in Plato's *manias,* 5
ethics, of life support efforts, 70
executive function, 18, 183, 248
    dysfunctions of, 184–188, 363
    effects of hypnosis on, 328, 330
The Expression of Emotions in Animals and Men (Darwin), 29

F
Fachner, Jörg, 349
False Memory Syndrome Foundation, 241, 245
fantasy, 237
    to create states of mind, 226, 336
    sexual, 21, 303
Father-Daughter Incest (Herman), 186
FBI, terrorism investigations by, 147–152
fear, 28, 167, 293
Ferenczi, Sandor, 238
Feynman, Richard P., 352
Field, Tiffany, 40, 220
Fleiss, Wilhelm, 236–238
Fraulein Anna O. (Freud), 7
free association, Janet's experiments with, 231
Freud, Anna, 237–238
Freud, Sigmund, 8, 231, 235
    cocaine and, 7, 258
    hypnosis and, 206, 324
    on hysteria, 228–229, 232–233, 236
    on incest, 236–238
    model of personality by, 154–155
    on multiple personality disorder, 238–239
Freyd, Peter and Pamela, 241
Friedlander, Joseph, 325
Friedman, Matt, 199
Fröhlich, Flavio, 121–122
Fromm, Eric, 322–323

Fromm-Reichmann, Frieda, 101
fugue. *See* dissociative amnesia

G
Games People Play (Berne), 8
gaze, infants', 41
genes, 73, 161
Gil, Merton, 172
Ginsburg, Allen, 267
Goodwin, Frederick, 94
government, mind-control research by, 263, 273
Grant, Joshua A., 321
Grof, Stanislav, 357–359
Gross, Terry, 120

H
hallucinations, 234
     from drugs, 258, 261–262, 272
     in flashbacks, 201–202
     induction of, 326, 352
     primary process in, 172–173
     psychotic, 274–275
Harris, Andrew, 126
Harter, Susan, 179–180
Hartman, Heinz, 8
Harvard Family Pathways Study, 224
Hatfill, Steven J., 147–148
heart rate, 41, 45–47, 54
Herman, Judith, 186–187
Hesse, E., 222–223
"hidden observer," in hypnosis experiments, 326–328, 330
Hilgard, Ernest, 23, 268, 324–325, 327–330
Hilgard, Josephine, 324
Hofmann, Albert, 263
Hofstadter, Douglas, 83
Horowitz, Mardi, 8, 116, 139–144, 176–177, 356, 360
Hounsfield, Godfrey Newbold, 61
Huble, David, 168

Huila Okupiolissa ritual, 338–339
Humanistic Psychology, 296–297
Hustvedt, Asti, 229
Huxley, Aldous, 251–252, 267, 318
hypnosis
    effects of, 6, 73, 137–138
    history of, 206, 230, 323–324
    other therapeutic uses of, 23, 52, 66–67, 125, 206, 233, 356
    research on, 324–326
    used in treatment of hysteria, 7, 18–19
    used to recover missing memories, 127, 151
hypocrisy, 17, 139, 153, 305
hysteria, 205
    in case studies, 102, 234–235
    dissociation and, 228–233, 241
    seduction in, 236–238
    treatments for, 7, 18–19

I
identity
    changes in, 138, 139–144, 314, 338–339, 349
    changing in fantasies, 21, 226, 336–337
    continuity of, 128–129, 180–184
    crises of, 16, 178–180
    establishing John and Jane Does', 125–126
    group, 369–370
    memory and, 16, 145, 173
    multiple, 151–153, 188–189, 283, 284, 353–354
    recovering addicts creating new, 20, 285, 287
    sexual, 21, 298, 304–305
    state-dependent qualities of, 107, 138–145
    states of being's influence on, 16, 335
identity, sense of, 6, 186, 270–271, 372–376
identity state psychotherapies. *See* ego state-based psychotherapies
identity states, 105, 160
    coding of, 145–146
    personality made up of, 15–16, 161, 335
    switches among, 142–143
    traumatic, 226–227, 248
    working with in therapy, 141–142

identity states, alter. *See* personalities, alter
imagination. *See* fantasy
infants
    attachment of, 42–47, 155–157, 219–222
    attunement with mothers, 26–27, 37, 40–42, 220, 366–367
    behavioral states of, 30–39, 106, 160
    classifications of states of being of, 35
    coding system for states of being of, 29–30, 142
    cycles of states of being of, 36–40, 142
    development of, 45–46, 335
    effects of caretakers' emotional and mental states on, 14, 27–28,
        334–335
    infectious crying by, 25–26
    mothers' influence on, 45, 222–223, 334–335
    observations of, 28–31
    personality of, 17, 154
    sleep and waking cycles of, 47–48, 56
    states of being of, 13–14, 30–33, 39, 334
    switches among states by, 34–38, *36,* 106, 348–349
infectious crying, 25–26
information processing. *See* state dependent learning and memory
initiatory state, in Plato's *manias,* 5
insomnia, 58–59
Internet, 353–354, 377–379
Interpersonal Psychotherapy, 64
The Interpretation of Dreams (Freud), 237
interrogation and torture, use of states of being in, 371–376
intersubjectivity, in development of empathy, 46
intoxication, infants' sensitivity to mothers', 28
Irish Workman, SDLM of, 137
ISH (internal self-helper in DID), 244
isomorphism, 83–87, 334, 365
Ivins, Bruce, 148–152

J
James, William, 26, 74, 182, 269, 311, 318
    on case study of Ansel Bourne, 126–128
    on divided self, 159–160, 327–328
    on identity, 129–130, 179
    on mystical and peak experiences, 22, 307–308, 331

nitrous oxide and, 3–5, 9, 308
    on states of being, 171, 343
    on states of consciousness, 79, 176, 327–328
    therapy by, 233, 324
Janet, Pierre, 7, 228–232, 239, 324, 328
Janice, case study of, 141–142, 177
Joan, case study of, 101–104

K
Kennedy, Robert, 137–138
Kinsey, Alfred, 302
Klietman, Nathaniel, 53
Kluft, Richard, 218
Koenig, Thomas, 71
Kolb, Lawrence, 206
Koller, Carl, 258
Korsakoff's syndrome, 131–133, 174, 185
Krafft-Ebing, Baron, 236
"KUBARK Counterintelligence Interrogation" manual, 371–376

L
Lanius, Ruth, 110, 207, 216
Larry, case study of, 197–199
Lauterburg, Paul, 61
learning, 182. *See also* state dependent learning and memory (SDLM)
    effects of abuse on, 226–227
    sensitive periods in, 168–169
Leary, Timothy, 9
Lehmann, Dietrich, 71
Les paradis artificiels (Artificial Paradises, Baudelaire), 261
Levine, Ira, 83–84
Liebig, Justus, 256
Liebriech, Oskar, 256
Lifton, Robert J., 199
Lilly, John, 10, 350–352
Linehan, Marsha, 187–188, 309–310
Liotti, Giovanni, 223–224
Lister, Joseph, 256

Liveing, Edward, 261
Loewenstein, Richard, 104
Lorenz, Edward, 80–81, 367–368
Lorenz, Konrad, 29
LSD, 271, 351–352, 356–359
Ludlow, Christie, 112
Ludwig, Arnold, 106, 238
Lutz, Antoine, 365–366
Lyons-Ruth, Karlen, 222, 224

M
Main, Mary, 44, 221, 222–223
Making Love: An Erotic Odyssey (Rhodes), 299–300
Mandell, Arnold, 82
mania, 5, 136. *See also* bipolar disorder
Mansfield, Peter, 61
MAPS (Multidisciplinary Association for Psychedelic Studies), 9
marijuana, 268–272
Maslow, Abraham, 21, 296–297, 331
Masson, Jeffery, 237–238
masturbation, 298–300, 303
McCartney, Paul, 347–348
McHugh, Paul, 241–243
medications, 52, 263, 286
    in abreactive therapy, 19, 205–206, 356
    anesthesia as, 278–280
    for bipolar disorder, 97–98
    for borderline personality, 188
    for catatonia, 101
    for depression, 63–64, 97–98, 121
    effects of, 8, 20, 58, 97–98
    for panic attacks, 99
    psychiatric drugs, 272–278
    psychoactive drugs used as, 252–253, 256–259, 272–278
    for PTSD, 19, 209–210
    side effects of, 97–98, 121, 254–255
    in treatments for addiction, 285
meditation, 10, 272
    effects of, 22–23, 315–323
    in mental and physical training, 365–366

memory, 107, 185, 295, 329. *See also* amnesia; state dependent learning and memory (SDLM)
    of alternate personalities, 111, 115, 129, 244
    identity and, 129, 145, 173
    influences on, 16, 63–64, 234, 241, 255–256, 270, 279–280
    loss of, 125–128, 151, 173
    metacognition and, 182–183
    in PTSD, 209–210
    systems of, 131–138, *132*
    of trauma, 193–195, 204, 231, 244
    types of, 136, 145
mental disorders, 73. *See also* specific disorders
    causes of, 213–214
    symptoms of, 93–94, 184–188
mental processes, psychoactive drugs altering, 19–20
mental states. *See* states of mind
Mesmer, Franz Anton, 6, 323–324
metacognition, 18, 182–183, 330
    dysfunctions of, 184–188, 248, 363, 374–375
microstates
    brain, 70–74
    moods and, 84–85
    to personality, *84*
Miller, William R., 22, 310–315, 362
Milner, Peter, 167–168
mind
    control over, 74–75, 343
    unconscious, 170–177
mind-body interfaces, 22, 83–84, 318, 320
    bridging, 85–87
    influence of meditation on, 22–23
    research biases in, 364–365
    uncoupling of, 69
mindfulness, 188. *See also* meditation; self-awareness
mindreading, brain imaging technologies in, 75–78
Minnesota Mother-Child Project, 224–225
mob psychology, 369–371
Molchanova, Natalia, 343–344, 346
mood stabilizers, 277–278, 356
moods. *See also* emotional states
    microstates and, 84–85
    as strange attractors, 81–82

switches among, 95, 106, 121, 186, 227
mothers
    attunement with infants, 13–14, 26–27, 37, 40–42, 220
    children's attachment to, 42–47, 155–157, 221–222
    compromised, 46, 222, 225–226, 248
    depression's effects on children, 44–47
    dissociation of, 217–218, 225
    effects of disturbed communication with infants, 222–223
    influence of states on children, 27–28, 42, 45, 334–335
    learning how to interact with compromised infants, 48–49
movement, 348
    of alternate personalities, 112–113
    in bipolar disorder, 95–97
    to create states of mind, 340–344
    differing among identity states, 142–143
Ms. D, case study of, 194
multi-voxel pattern analysis (MVPA), 75–76
multiple personality disorder. *See* dissociative identity disorder (DID)
Murdock, William, 256
Murphy, Dennis, 94
music, 355
    influence on mental state, 347–349
Music and Altered States (Aldridge and Fachner), 349
mystical experiences, 22–23, 307–315, 358
mysticism, 22–23

N
Naranjo, Claudio, 315–319
National Institutes of Mental Health (NIMH)
    other research at, 213, 351, 376
    research on multiple personalities and, 104, 107–108, 245
    research on switches between states at, 94–98, 101
neodissociative theory, 328
neurofeedback, 360–361
neuromarketing and neuropolitics, 377
neuroplasticity. *See under* brains
neurosis, psychotherapies for, 357
Niemann, Albert, 257
nitrous oxide, 3–6, 9, 176, 308
Noll, Jennie, 43, 213, 354

O
observing ego, 18, 181–182, 184–186, 248, 330
Odgers, Candice, 368
Olds, James, 167–168
On Being Stoned (Tart), 268–272
On the Psychology of Meditation (Naranjo and Ornstein), 315–319
opiates, 260–263
Orne, Martin, 324
Ornstein, Robert E., 315–320
Osmond, Humphrey, 251

P
pain, 283, 321
    anesthesia to avoid, 279–280
    effects of drugs on, 260, 269
    effects of psychoactive drugs on, 19, 254
    hypnosis blocking, 326, 329
    mental states' influence on perception of, 64–67
    threats of, 373–374
panic, mass, 369–371
panic attacks
    medications for, 276–277
    switches among states in, 15, 93–94, 98–99, 121
Pappenhiem, Bertha. *See* Anna O., case study of
Paracelsus, 323
paralysis, hysterical, 102
paranormal research, 118–120
parapsychology, 272
Parent-Child Interaction Therapy (PCIT), 225–226
parents. *See* mothers
Pavlov, Ivan, 167
peak experiences, 21–22, 295–297, 306–307, 331, 355
perception, 64–67, 74, 251–252, 269
Perennial Philosophy (Huxley), 252
personalities, alter, 108, 227–228, 243. *See also* dissociative identity disorder (DID)
    differences among, 110–116, 239
    relations among, 16, 115–116, 239, 244–245
personality
    Big Five Factors in, 157–158, 161–162

changes in, 20, 22, 166, 310–315
childish parts of remaining, 243–244
components of, 15–16, 161
definitions of, 153, 159, 189
development of, 17–18
developmental model of, 155–157, 161
dimensional model of, 157–158, 161
effects of addiction on, 20, 282–284
identity states in makeup of, 105, 161, 335
influences on, 215, 258, 362
microstates to, *84*
psychodynamic model of, 154–155, 161
state models of, 17, 159–166, 180, 189
state-space in mapping of, 162–165, *163*
traits in, 166–169
personality disorders, 158–159. *See also* specific disorders
Phaedrus (Plato), 5
phobias, medications for, 276
physiology
differences among alternate personalities in DID, 110–116, 239
differences among identity states, 142–143
possible misuse of monitoring of, 377–379
Pieron, Henri, 53
PiHKAL: A Chemical Love Story (Shulgin and Shulgin), 264–265
Pinel, Philippe, 229
Plato, 5
poetic state, in Plato's *manias,* 5
Polly, case study of, 125–126
Pope, K. S., 340
pornography, 302–304
possession, demonic *vs.* spiritual, 319
Post, Robert, 89, 94, 101, 104, 277
posttraumatic stress disorder (PTSD), 8
altered states of consciousness in, 18, 139–140, 216
brain imaging technologies to study, 206–209
diagnoses of, 198–200, 208, 211, 215
DID and, 239–240, 245
drugs in treatments for, 9, 356, 359,
effects of, 65–66, 136, 139–140, 207
flashbacks in, 193–195, 200–201
state model of, 202–204, 281
symptoms of, 202–203, 294, 339

treatments for, 200, 209–211, 330, 339, 345
types of, 9, 186, 207–209, *208,* 239–240
from Vietnam War, 195, 206
postures, to create states of mind, 340–344
Prechtl, Heinz, 29–31, 35
Pribram, Karl, 10
Prince, Morton, 105
The Principles of Psychology (James), 126, 128, 318, 327–328
prophetic state, in Plato's four *manias,* 5
psilocybin, 210, 356,
psychedelic drugs, 263–267. *See also* specific drugs
    therapeutic uses of, 9, 210–211, 251,
psychiatric drugs. *See* medications; psychoactive drugs
psychiatry, 6. *See also* psychoanalysis
    biological, 8–10, 94, 170–171
    diagnoses in, 196, 242
    history of multiple personalities in, 228–240
psychoactive drugs, 252–255, 286, 356. *See also* specific drug classifications; specific drugs
psychoanalysis, 101, 172, 206
    biological psychiatry challenging, 8–10, 94, 170–171
    history of, 7–8, 19, 238
    model of personality in, 154–155
    Zen meditation compared to, 322–323
psychological conflict, 144–145, 177–180, 188
    as competition among states of being, 116, 189
    contradictory behaviors and, 17, 152–153, 165–166
    sources of, 16, 221–222, 328–329
Psychological Trauma (van der Kolk), 194
psychologists, banned from inflicting pain, 376
psychology, states theories in, 6, 8
psychopathology. *See also* mental disorders; specific disorders
    levels of, 362–364
psychosis, 259, 274–275, 278
psychotherapy, 16, 19. *See also* specific therapies
    for PTSD, 209–210
    states of being and, 101–102, 140, 356
public health problems
    childhood trauma as, 215
    substance abuse and, 280–281
Pynoos, Robert, 294

Q

Quantum Change (Miller and C'de Baca), 310–315

R

Rae, Hazel, 213
Raichle, Marcus, 73–74
Ramon, case study of, 51–53, 56–57
Rapaport, David, 8, 172–175
rape, 193, 199–201. *See also* sexual abuse
Rasband, Wayne, 376
Read, Louis H., 126
Reasoner, Harry, 118–120
Reinders, A. A., 110
reinforcement, in operant conditioning, 167–168
relationships, 284
    in borderline personality disorder, 185–186
    development of, 37, 46–47
    effects of childhood maltreatment on, 220–221, 226–227
religion, 285. *See also* ceremonies
    mystical experiences and, 307–315
    sacred places in, 354–355
    use of psychoactive drugs in, 19, 252
    Zen Buddhism, 320–322
responsibility, 138, 175, 200
Rhodes, Richard, 299–300, 303–304
Ribot, Théodule, 137
rituals. *See* ceremonies
Rollnick, Stephen, 310
Rosen, Ira, 119–120
Rubinow, David, 103

S

Sacks, Oliver, 261–262
sacred places and spaces, 354–356
Sar, Vedet, 110
Sarbin, Theodore, 324–325
satanic ritual abuse, 240–241
Savarin, Anthelme Brillat, 57–58

Schenck, Carlos, 52, 58
schizophrenia, 244, 258, 309
sedatives and hypnotics, 256–257, 272–277
self, 15–16, 22–23, 363
self, sense of
    of borderline personality patients, 185–186, 188
    changes in, 139–144, 165, 313
    conflicting, 144–145, 179–180
    development of, 20, 45–46
    disruption of, 248, 372–376
    effects of states of consciousness on, 174, 335
    fragmentation of, 18, 226–227
    unification of, 180–184, 248
self-actualization, 297
self-analysis, Freud's, 237
self-awareness
    development of, 181–182, 188
    influences on, 227, 266
    states of consciousness and, 173, 175
    through risky behavior, 294–295
self-destructiveness, 189, 239, 368
    addictions and, 20, 259, 286
    of borderline personality patients, 185–189
    coping mechanisms in, 216, 363
    risky behavior and, 260, 294–295
    treatments for, 187–188, 309–310
self-esteem, effects of child abuse on, 227
Selz, Karen, 82
sensory deprivation, 23, 350–352, 372, 374
sensory information, 6, 74, 98–99
sensory overload, 349–350, 374
SERE ceremony, 339–340
sex, 22, 96, 201, 363
    by adolescents, 178, 186, 214, 291, 295
    altered states of being in, 21, 298–307
    compulsions, 285, 296, 305–306
    drugs and, 260, 269, 275, 278
    effects on brain, 259–260, 271, 282, 354
    mind-brain interfaces and, 22, 168, 282, 298–299, 331
    music and, 347–348
    peak, 306–307
    psychosexual development, 154–155, 238, 247

sleep, 56, 58
    in state model of personality, 164–165
sexology, 22, 298, 300–302
sexual abuse, 213, 241
    effects of, 43, 45, 248–249, 294, 298, 301, 354
    seduction fantasies *vs.,* 236–238
sexual arousal, 20, 168, 299–303, 331, 347
shamanism, 319
Shay, Jonathan, 195
Shen-nung Pentshao Ching (Phamacopoeia of the Heavenly Cultivator),
    253
shimmering states, mixed emotions in, 116, 143–145
Shulgin, Alexander, 9, 264–266
Silberman, Edward, 103
Singer, J. L., 340
Sirhan, Sirhan, 137–138
Skinner, B. F., 167
Slagter, Heleen, 365–366
sleep, 32, 65
    in bipolar disorder, 95–97
    brain activity in, 22, 69, 73
    in case study of Ramon, 51–53
    disorders of, 56–59, 202, 219
    in infants' cycles of states, 36–38, 47–48
    need for, 58–59
    research into, 14, 53, 55, 59–60, 86
    stages of, 53–56, 81
    switches between states in, 89–91, 97, 117
    switches between waking and, 34–35, 92–93, 348–349
social relationships. *See* relationships
sodium amytal (narcosynthesis), 125, 173, 205–206
soldiers and veterans, 281
    diagnoses for Vietnam, 196–197, 199
    healing rituals for returned, 338–340
    psychotherapy for, 356–357
    PTSD of, 195–200, 203, 206
Solomon, J., 221
Spaces and places, 354–355, 358
speech
    in bipolar disorder, 95–97
    differing among identity states, 142–143
    in dissociative identity disorder, 106, 111–112

spiritual awakenings. *See* epiphanies and spiritual awakenings
Spitzer, Robert, 11
state dependent learning and memory (SDLM), 16, 130–131, 134–138, 145,
  244, 301
 bridging of, 180–181, 363
 influence of, 335, 370
 state dependent identities and, 138–145
state models
 on addiction, 20
 implications of, 24
 of personality, 17, 159–166, 180, 189
 of trauma and PTSD, 281
state-space, 55, 71, 80, 219, 221
 blurry boundaries of, 38–40
 butterfly effect in, *81*
 infants', 13–14, 30, *36*
 influences on, 278, 283, 294–295, 361–364
 mapping of, *36,* 38, 162–165, *163*
 sexual, 304–305
states, 92, 335
 alternate displacement of, 116, 177
 becoming traits, 166–169
 concept of, 11–12, 84–85, 87
 PTSD as state disorder, 202–204
 sharing, 37, 40–42, 45
states of being, 10–11, 73. *See also under* switches
 altered, 298–307, 331
 changes among, 121, 313–314
 children's sensitivity to caregivers', 218, 221
 classifications of infants', 30–33, 35, 47, 142
 cycles of, 142, 163–164, 375
 dark sides of, 369–379
 definitions of, 333–334
 developmental changes in, 56, 165–166
 extreme, 218–219, 335–336
 functions of, 18, 163–164, 366–367
 infants', 13–14, 29–30, 39, 47–49, 160, 334
 infants' cycles of, 13–14, 36–40, 142
 influence of, 16, 333–335, 364–365
 making up personality, 161, 189
 in model of addiction, 281–287
 of parents and children, 42, 48–49, 223, 248

psychoactive drugs altering, 20, 254
    regulation of, 13–14, 23, 336–356
    stability *vs.* transience of, 161, 333
states of being perspective, 336, 370, 377–379
    research based on, 364–369
    uses of, 47–49, 356–361, 367–369, 371–376
states of consciousness, 62, 130, 271, 308
    awareness *vs.* wakefulness in, 69, *70*
    dyadic, 219–221
    hypnosis and, 234, 324–330
    James on, 4–5, 79
    properties of, 5, 9, 79
    quality of thinking and, 172, 174–175
    self-awareness and, 173, 175
    switching among, 8, 125–126, 313, 329–330
    traumatic, 139–140
    vegetative states *vs.,* 67–70
states of consciousness, altered, 202, 248, 313
    drive to explore, 21, 291–295
    interest in, 6–7
    knowledge uniquely accessed in, 9–10, 176
    methods of achieving, 23, 286, 315–323, 357
    by psychedelic drugs, 9, 263, 266–267
    in PTSD, 18, 216
States of Consciousness (Tart), 175–176
states of mind, 10–11, 146, 178. *See also* switches among states
    appropriateness of, 92
    brain activity and, 75–76, 333
    brain states and, 12, 14
    coding systems for, 14, 140, 143
    control of, 317, 363–364
    dysfunctional, 47, 363–364
    effects of caretakers' on infants and children, 14, 46–47, 222–223
    effects of frequency of oscillations of, 368–369
    influence of, 64–67, 176–177, 335, 343
    influences on, 278, 355–356
    music and, 348–349
    in personality's Big Five Factors, 161–162
    relation to movements and postures, 340–344
    shared, 337–338
States of Mind (Horowitz), 141, 176–177
Stern, Daniel, 40

still face paradigm, 41–42, 44, 220
stimulants, 257–261, 280
strange attractors, 81–82, *See also* dynamical non-linear
Strange Situation protocol, and attachment classifications, 43–44, 221
stress
    children affected by mothers', 28, 44
    effects of, 58, 65, 161–162
    responses to, 43, 222, 283
Studies on Hysteria (Freud and Breuer), 7, 232–233, 235
subconscious. *See also* unconscious
substance abuse. *See also* addiction; alcoholism; specific drugs
    effects of parents' on children, 14, 47
    in states of being model, 281–285
    of trauma survivors, 214, 227, 280–281, 286
suggestion, susceptibility to, 6
Suzuki, D. T., 322–323
switches among behavioral states, 13–14, 17–18, 34–38
switches among identity states, 142–143
switches among mental states, 121–122
switches among states, 35, *36,* 202, 218, 320
    in dissociative identity disorder, 101–116
    effects of frequency of, 368–369
    influences on, 39, 89–91, 348–349, 362–363
    process of, 94–113, 117
    into screen personas, 118–121
    speed of, 113–115, *114,* 116, 143–145, 202–203
    types of, 92–94, 116–117, *117*
switches among states of being, 15, 82–83, 121, 280, 334
switches among states of consciousness, 8, 125–126, 313, 329–330
Sybil (Wilbur), 238
systems approach. *See* dynamical systems approach, non-linear

T
Tart, Charles, 9, 175–176, 268–272, 325
Taylor, Edward, 212
terrorism, investigations of, 147–149
Thelen, Ester, 82
therapeutic relationship, 140–141, 240–242
therapies, 144, 196. *See also* treatments; specific therapies
    end-of-life, 9

Freud in development of, 154–155, 234–235
goals of, 156–157, 184
observing ego of own behavior in, 181–182
techniques in, 23, 324, 337, 345
use of psychedelic drugs in, 9, 210–211, 251, 356–359
using states in, 117, 141–143, 145–146, 361–364
therapists, 246–247
Thigpen and Cleckley, 105–106
thinking, 15, 136, 365
influences on quality of, 226, 254, 270
states of consciousness and, 172, 174–175
Thoman, Evelyn, 30–32
Thorndike, Edward, 167
thrill-seeking behaviors, 291–292
tip-of-the-tongue (ToT) moments, 185
Tohei, Koichi, 342
traits, states becoming, 166–169
transactional analysis, 8, 140, 356, 360
transcendental experiences, 22–23, 307–315, 358
transference, Janet discovering, 231
trauma, 281, 349
childhood, 152, 186, 215–216 (*See also* child abuse)
effects of, 18–19, 43, 187, 211–215, 219, 231, 249, 294
effects of substance abuse on survivors of, 280–281, 286
effects of unresolved, 223, 225
flashbacks of, 193–195, 201, 219
hysteria and, 18–19, 233
importance of talking about, 225, 233–234
reactions to, 216, 218–219
reliving *vs.* trying to avoid, 198, 203–204, 206–209
sources of, 279–280, 376
from wars, 195–199, 205–206, 239, 356–357
Treatment of Patients with Dissociative Disorders (TOP DD), 246–247
treatments. *See also* therapies
for addictions, 284–285, 306, 359
for anxiety, 276–278, 337, 345
becoming focused on diagnoses *vs.* symptoms, 195–196
for bipolar disorder, 8, 277–278, 356
for borderline personality disorder, 187–188, 277–278, 310
for depression, 63–64, 275–276, 278
for dissociation, 240, 242, 330
for dissociative identity disorder, 105, 239–240, 244–247, 249

in early psychotherapy, 231, 233–234
healing rituals as, 338–340
for hysteria, 7, 18–19
for insomnia, 58
neurofeedback in, 360–361
for panic attacks, 99, 276–277
to prevent intergenerational maltreatment, 225–226
psychedelic drugs used in, 251, 263, 266
for PTSD, 200, 207, 209–211, 216, 239–240, 330, 339, 345
for schizophrenia, 309
states of being in, 356–361
for war trauma symptoms, 205–206
Trickett, Penelope, 43, 213
Tronick, Edward, 41–42, 45–46, 219–220
truth/deception, 4, 76–77
Turkle, Sherry, 353

U
unconscious, collective, 369–370
unconsciousness, anesthesia to induce, 278–280
Uyeshiba, Morihei, 341

V
Vaitl, Dieter, 71
van der Kolk, Bessel, 186–187, 194
The Varieties of Religious Experience (James), 4–5, 129, 171, 307–308
vegetative states, 67–70
Vermetten, Eric, 110
veterans. *See* soldiers and veterans
Vietnam War, 195–197, 199, 206, 281
violence, 282
    alcohol and, 271, 280–281
    domestic, 47, 213–215, 223, 225, 280, 294
    efforts to predict, 367–369
    gender, 304 (*See also* rape; sexual abuse)
    Internet, 304, 353–354
    in interrogation and torture, 371–376
    in mob psychology, 369–371

virtual media, altering states of being, 353–354
von Fleischl-Marxow, Ernst, 258
voyeurism, 302–303

W
Wakermann, Jiri, 71
Wallace, Mike, 120
wars
    therapy for trauma from, 239, 356–357
    trauma from, 195–199, 205–206
Watkins, John, 8
Wehr, Thomas, 94
Weil, Andrew, 10
Weingartner, Herbert, 105, 111, 135
Weston, Dwain, 292
Wiesel, Torsten, 168
Wilbur, Cornelia, 103, 106, 238
Wilde, Oscar, 295
Wolff, Peter, 25–26, 29–33, 35, 39, 82
Wyatt, Richard, 94

Y
yoga, effects on state of mind, 343–344

Z
Zahn, Theodore, 105, 110–111, 115
Zen
  brain activity of monks, 320
  Master Ikkyu, 317
  psychoanalysis and, 332

CPSIA information can be obtained
at www.ICGtesting.com
Printed in the USA
BVHW061935140119
537774BV00005B/28/P

9 780998 083308